Orchid Biology—Reviews and Perspectives, I

Orchid Biology

REVIEWS AND PERSPECTIVES, I

EDITED BY

JOSEPH ARDITTI

Department of Developmental and Cell Biology
University of California, Irvine

COMSTOCK PUBLISHING ASSOCIATES a division of
CORNELL UNIVERSITY PRESS | Ithaca and London

First published 1977 by Cornell University Press.
Published in the United Kingdom by Cornell University Press Ltd., London.

Second printing 1983.

International Standard Book Number 0-8014-1040-1
Library of Congress Catalog Card Number 76-25648
Printed in the United States of America
*Librarians: Library of Congress cataloging information
appears on the last page of the book.*

The paper in this book is acid-free and meets the guidelines for permanence and durability of the Committee on Production Guidelines for Book Longevity of the Council on Library Resources.

CONTENTS

ILLUSTRATIONS

BOARD OF EDITORS

AUTHORS

JOSEPH ARDITTI is a Professor in the Department of Developmental and Cell Biology, University of California, Irvine. He joined the Department in 1966, having received his Ph.D. at the University of Southern California. His research has centered on orchid physiology and phytochemistry.

HENDRIK C. D. DE WIT followed classical education and studied biology at the University of Amsterdam. He went to South Africa in 1937 and specialized in grasses. In 1940, he received his doctorate. Following his stay in South Africa, he went to the Bogor (then known as Buitenzorg) Botanical Gardens (now called Kebun Raya), in Indonesia, and was employed there until 1946, when he was appointed Senior Lecturer at the University of Leiden and joined the Flora Malesiana Project. In 1953 he moved to the University of Wageningen as Senior Lecturer. He was appointed Professor Ordinarius in Plant Systematics in 1959 and heads the Laboratorium voor Plantensystematiek en -Geographie. Since his appointment as Professor, de Wit has specialized in the flora of Tropical Africa.

MICHAEL H. FISCH is group leader of New Venture Projects at Witco Chemical Corporation's Central Research Laboratories. He was educated at Columbia and the California Institute of Technology, receiving his A.B. in 1960 and Ph.D. in 1965. Following postdoctoral years as a NATO fellow at the Institut de Chimie (Strasbourg) and an NIH fellowship at MIT, he joined the faculty at the University of California, Irvine, in 1966 as Assistant Professor of Chemistry. He remained there until 1972, when he moved to his present position. Fisch became interested in orchids after studying their phytoalexins.

CHARLES R. HARRISON received his Ph.D. at the University of California, Irvine. His interest in orchids grew from his association with Joseph Arditti and research work at the UCI Orchid Laboratory. Currently, Harrison is an Instructor in Horticulture and Biology at Saddleback College, Mission Viejo, California.

RICHARD ERIC HOLTTUM was Director of the Singapore Botanic Gardens and Professor of Botany at the University of Singapore. He is the author of several books, including the definitive volume on the orchids of Malaya (volume 1 of *Flora of Malaysia*).

RUDOLF SCHMID and MARVIN J. SCHMID were educated at the University of Michigan, where he received a Ph.D. in 1971 and she an M.S. in 1969. Rudolf Schmid is an Assistant Professor of Botany at the University of California, Berkeley. His research centers on the reproductive anatomy and morphology of vascular plants, particularly evolutionary and functional (including ecological) aspects of flowers. Ancillary interests include paleobotany and pollination and dispersal ecology.

Marvin J. Schmid is interested in economic botany in the broad sense, that is, in the role of plants in the evolving fabric of human society, with special emphasis on herbs and spices. Her other interests include plant ecology and conservation.

MICHAEL B. SLAYTOR is a Senior Lecturer at the University of Sydney. On completing his Ph.D. studies at the University of Sydney, he did postdoctoral work at Imperial College, London, and at Harvard, returning to Sydney in 1963. He is a chemist by training, with special interest in the functions and uses of alkaloids. Of his article he writes, "My interest in orchid alkaloids began when I was invited by the New Guinea Biological Foundation in 1968 to screen the orchids in their large collection at Arawa in Bougainville for alkaloids." He is currently assisting the expanded plant program of the Human Reproduction Unit at the World Health Organization in Geneva.

THAVORN VAJRABHAYA is Professor of Botany at Chulalongkorn University, Bangkok, Thailand. Born in Bangkok, he attended Cornell University from 1952 to 1960, receiving his B.S. in Floriculture in 1955. He worked on cytogenetics of orchids, and received his Ph.D. in 1960. After returning home to Bangkok, he joined the staff of Chulalongkorn University (Thailand's oldest university) and continued his work in various aspects of orchidology.

PREFACE

Numerous scientific papers have been published dealing with orchids, the largest plant family. Written in many languages, appearing internationally in journals over a long period of time, the scattered articles are not easily available, and integrated surveys are relatively rare. Two volumes of review articles have already been published (both edited by Carl L. Withner), but there is an increasing need for a series of reviews to bring into perspective all that has been learned to date. This volume (and, it is hoped, future ones) will endeavor to cover additional topics and points of view.

As in any other field of scientific endeavor, some investigators have had major impact not only on their contemporaries but also on future work. Lindley, Reichenbach, Fitting, Rolfe, Schlechter, F. Müller, Knudson, Bernard, Burgeff, Hoehne, Bateman, and Darwin are examples. Their books and articles are well known and easy to find, but personal glimpses of these men and their work are rarer. Richard Eric Holttum, in his chapter, allows the reader to enjoy this close personal experience.

For many years there was no adequate review on the fossil record of orchids. Fortunately, Rudolf Schmid and Marvin J. Schmid scoured the literature, and wrote the chapter on paleoorchidology (if I may be allowed to coin a new term).

Rumphius, the blind seer of Ambon (Amboina), is both a fascinating and a tragic Job-like figure. He described the plants on the island of Ambon and many of its orchids. His unique and delightful style is preserved well by Hendrik C. D. de Wit, his biographer. When Professor de Wit and I met at the Bogor Botanical Gardens in Indonesia (a country which now includes the island of Ambon), we spent a very pleasant evening discussing Rumphius. As a result, I asked him to write a chapter. He has produced an admirable account of Rumphius and his orchids.

Anthocyanins are clearly visible as the coloring matter of orchid flowers, leaves, roots, stems, and fruits. Alkaloids are not visible, but like the anthocyanins they are important chemical constituents of the Orchidaceae. Both groups are reviewed in this volume, together with a report on vitamin requirements and metabolism, to provide new insights into orchid phytochemistry and physiology.

Tissue culture has assumed an exceedingly important role in the clonal propagation of orchids. However, variations occur during tissue culture. Thavorn Vajrabhaya's review of the subject will be of interest to hobbyists, commercial growers, somatic cell geneticists, and others who engage in tissue culture. The Appendix on tissue culture is a practical manual intended for all those who would like to apply the available methods.

All chapters in this volume were subjected to prepublication review by two experts (one who specializes in orchids and another who works in the general field covered by each chapter but with other plants) and myself to ensure accepted scientific standards.

Orchid nomenclature is in a constant state of flux. Name changes, transfers, and establishment of taxa are all too common and, of course, are matters of opinion. The adoption of one "correct" set of names and a single "proper" classification system could thus be expected to displease as many experts as it pleased. Further, there are advantages to retaining in a review the nomenclature employed in the literature being surveyed. Therefore, as editor, I have allowed each author a wide latitude in the choice of names and classification systems. As an author, I have retained the names used in the original literature.

In editing this volume, I have enjoyed the help of friends and colleagues. Robert Ernst gave freely of his wisdom and scientific acumen and offered advice, collaboration, and sound criticism. Elaine D. Etingoff, my secretary, corrected my spelling, improved my English, did much of the typing, and regularly made sense out of poorly scribbled notes on odd pieces of paper mailed home from all corners of the globe. Brigitta H. Flick, my former laboratory associate, commented on the tissue-culture appendix and helped with illustrations. Michael S. Strauss (at that time a graduate student) read several of the manuscripts and made many valuable suggestions. The staff of Cornell University Press was very helpful. My thanks to all of them. Most of all, I thank the authors, who had early faith in the project.

JOSEPH ARDITTI

Irvine, California

1

A Personal View
of Orchids

RICHARD ERIC HOLTTUM

Plate 1-1. Professor Richard Eric Holttum (1948)

Orchids have never been my primary interest, though I have been concerned with them intermittently, in one way or another, almost throughout my life. My early years were spent in the countryside of East Anglia, where I acquired a knowledge of local plants, including the native orchids which grow on the chalk. But though I felt a strong aesthetic enjoyment in the contemplation of plants, both native and cultivated, I never studied them critically and had no formal biological teaching at school, where however my interest was fostered by the natural history society and a teacher of wide knowledge who was an ecologist before ecology became a subject for formal study. So that when I entered the University of Cambridge and had to choose three subjects to study I chose chemistry and physics (on which I had concentrated during my last two years at school) and botany. I had an inspiring introduction to the whole subject in the first-year lectures given by A. C. Seward, and an illuminating short course on plant physiology from F. F. Blackman. I heard little about tropical orchids apart from some general information on the biology of epiphytes. World War I caused an interruption in my studies; afterwards I continued by taking the courses in botany for the second part of the Natural Sciences Tripos. These gave a more intensive view of many aspects of plant science, and some introduction to tropical plant families from Gilbert Carter. My knowledge of orchids was largely taken from Rendle's first volume on the classification of flowering plants (1904). During the next two years I was Junior Demonstrator at the Botany School, and spent most of my time studying fossil plants under the guidance of Professor Seward. There were fossil ferns but no orchids; however while collecting fossil plants in West Greenland in 1921 with Professor Seward I was interested to see native orchids inside the Arctic Circle.

In 1922 I considered two posts for which I might apply. One was on the staff of the Natural History Museum in London, where A. B. Rendle would have been my chief and which might have offered opportunities for the study of orchids. The other was that of Assistant Director at the Botanic Gardens in Singapore. I decided on the latter and arrived in Singapore in July 1922 with a good general grounding in botany but almost no knowledge in detail of the very complex flora of Malaya. The first job I was asked to do by my new chief, I. H. Burkill, was to put the fern herbarium into order, and thereafter ferns became my main interest, though I had many other matters to occupy my thoughts. I soon found that the taxonomy of ferns (of most of which I had no previous knowledge) was in a state of considerable confusion, and as my knowledge of other plants also more gradually developed I found the same to be true of angiosperms, including orchids. I incidentally realized that a study of native British orchids gives little preparation for the understanding of tropical epiphytic species.

At that time H. N. Ridley, who had been Director of the Gardens in Singapore from 1888 to 1911, was in process of producing his *Flora of the Malay Peninsula* (five volumes, 1922–1925). Ridley had a very wide knowldege of plants but was very uncritical in his study of them. So though he was an excellent field botanist and collected specimens of a large number of Malayan plants little known before (he added two hundred species to the known orchid flora of the Peninsula), his published taxonomic work is very confused and often erroneous; his *Flora* is hardly intelligible without reference to his herbarium. This fact also I gradually came to understand.

In 1925, at the early age of thirty, I was appointed Director of the Gardens and felt very imperfectly acquainted with many aspects of my new responsibility, which included the culture of a wide range of tropical plants and also taxonomic study of the local flora in general. In the course of both aspects of my work I had a wide correspondence with other botanical institutions, especially the Royal Botanic Gardens at Kew and the Botanic Gardens at Bogor (Buitenzorg) in Java, and also with E. D. Merrill, pioneer American botanist in the Philippines, who founded a herbarium but no garden. I visited Bogor in 1926, and this widened my horizons considerably, and brought me into contact with the large collection of Indonesian native orchid plants accumulated over many years by J. J. Smith, who had retired in 1924, and with P. M. W. Dakkus, Curator of the Gardens, who later wrote a book on orchids cultivated in Indonesia.

When one is in charge of a tropical botanic garden, one cannot ignore orchids and their need for special horticultural treatment. I had had no training in the techniques of horticulture, and it was some time before I realized that cultural practice in the Gardens was not as good as it should have been. I came to know local amateur growers of orchids, saw their better results, and tried to learn from them, but no doubt I was slow to learn, and I had a good deal of inertia to overcome in trying to alter the habits of my horticultural staff. The two local enthusiasts from whom I learned most were John Laycock (an English lawyer) and a local resident named Emil Galistan. Galistan produced the most wonderful plants, which made our Gardens efforts look very second-rate. Laycock was beginning to import orchid plants from Indonesia and New Guinea, as well as experimenting with hybrids of tropical American genera brought from Europe. He organized an orchid show, in which the most spectacular exhibits were a plant of his own of *Dendrobium veratrifolium*, covered with flowers, and an *Aerides lawrenceanum* from Galistan bearing more inflorescences than I have ever since seen on such a plant. But though *Arachnis* plants were commonly grown, none was in flower at that time. The only local orchid that could be relied on to produce flowers at all times was *Vanda* Miss Joaquim (Color Plate VIII), and there were no other local hybrids. In the almost seasonless climate of Singapore, with a mean temperature not far from 80°F (27°C) in every month of the year and only slight and irregular spells of dry weather, there were no strong climatic stimuli, and most species of orchids flowered at irregular and infrequent intervals, so that it was impossible to have a really spectacular collective display of flowering orchids.

Then two things happened. Some people in Java began to produce hybrid orchid seedlings, using Knudson's asymbiotic method, and Dr. H. Burgeff visited me in Singapore after spending a few months in Java (where he had been studying saprophytes in preparation for his book *Saprophytismus und Symbiose*, 1932). Burgeff had with him some test tubes containing orchid seedlings, the first I had ever seen, and gave me one containing plants of a *Vanda* hybrid. He explained that one had only to study Knudson's paper of 1921 in the Botanical Gazette (which I had available) and germinating of seeds would be no difficulty. Then I asked him what I should do with the seedlings in the test tube when they were big enough to be taken out. His reply was "give them to the gardener"; but no gardener in Singapore had ever handled an orchid seedling, and my gardeners were still not skilled enough with fully grown plants. So I felt that I had a lot to learn. At the same time Laycock was urging that perhaps if we could produce new hybrids from local orchids they might repeat the perpetual-flowering character of *Vanda* Miss Joaquim (Color Plate VIII). So I bought an autoclave and made up agar-based culture media according to Knudson, and sowed some seeds provided by Laycock and also some of my own, the first being *Spathoglottis aurea* x *S. plicata*.

The other happening about this period was a visit from a rubber planter named C. E. Carr who was living in the middle of Pahang, within reach of large areas of primitive forest. He had been accumulating local orchid plants in his garden, and making very interesting original observations on their pollination mechanisms and the associated insects. He was very short-sighted and made beautiful small drawings in minute detail which was so fine that no printer could reproduce it. He began to find wild orchids that he could not name, and asked my help. I tried to use Ridley's *Flora* and found it very confused, but it was obvious that Carr was finding species not dealt with by Ridley. I introduced Carr to the immense work of J. J. Smith on the orchids of Indonesia (in which he described about eighteen hundred new species) and Carr came to stay a few days with me from time to time, studying J. J. Smith and the Singapore herbarium. He was thus able to name some of his plants, and to decide that others were new and to describe them, following J. J. Smith's model. I visited Carr on his estate at Tembeling, at the junction of the Pahang and Tembeling rivers, and went with him to the summit of Gunong Tahan, the highest mountain in Malaya (2190 m). Through this association with Carr I began to understand the deficiencies in taxonomic knowledge of local orchids and to see the need for a very thorough revision. In all, Carr added about one hundred species to the known orchid flora of Malaya (including twelve of *Taeniophyllum*). He went later to Mount Kinabalu in North Borneo (now Sabah) and made extensive collections there, most of which are still undescribed. He estimated that there were five hundred species of *Bulbophyllum* in Borneo. He then undertook a collecting expedition to southeastern New Guinea (Papua) and unfortunately died there in 1936.

In the decade 1930–1940 I pursued the cultivation of orchid seedlings, from seeds partly provided by Laycock and others, partly from my own crossings. I tried various methods of handling seedlings newly transplanted from flasks, after 1935 with the excellent help of J. C. Nauen (who later died in Thailand as a prisoner of the Japanese). But we were slow to learn the best methods of treatment, and lost many. However, we did make progress. I recorded the results of our work by describing the new hybrids in the Malayan Orchid Review, which was published annually.

During the period also I pursued my study of ferns, and became interested in bamboos, Ridley's treatment of which I found to be even more confused than his account of Malayan orchids (at different times, he described two specimens from the same collection as new species in two genera, and from the descriptions one could not tell whether either genus was correct). I tried also to enlarge my knowledge of the Gardens collections of many plant families, though I did not attempt detailed studies. I kept records of dates of leaf-change of individual deciduous trees (mostly introduced, but including some native species) and discovered that most of them, in an almost seasonless climate, developed leaf-periods that had no relation to the calendar, though a few were rather regular in changing their leaves at six-months intervals, and a few at twelve months. Trees of the same species rarely kept in step with each other, even if planted together (e.g., roadside plantings of *Lagerstroemia flos-reginae*). During this period also Mr. E. J. H. Corner made intensive studies of Malayan trees, resulting in the publication of his book *Wayside Trees of Malaya* (1940), in which about 950 species are described.

Then came the Japanese occupation of Singapore. With the troops came Professor H. Tanakadate who said, "I conserve cultural institutions" and asked me to remain in charge of the Gardens. I did so, but was formally relieved of my charge after about ten months, when Professor K. Koriba, a distinguished plant physiologist, came as Director. He permitted me and Mr. Corner to continue our botanical studies. It was then that I began to write a systematic account of the orchids of the Malay Peninsula, and in so doing I really obtained for the first time a fairly complete perspective on the whole family. I had available all Ridley's specimens and his collection of colored drawings; some of the latter gave important information. I had also all J. J. Smith's papers on the orchids of Indonesia, and those of Hooker, King, and Pantling on the orchids of India. I had further a considerable collection of living native orchid plants, brought to Singapore from various parts of the country over many years, some from Carr, and I examined these every day for flowers. There was also a large collection of orchid flowers in alcohol, which I started after seeing a similar collection made by J. J. Smith at Bogor. I found it difficult to prevent evaporation of the alcohol, which I used at 70 percent; the alcohol evaporated more quickly than the water, and at a certain point did not prevent the development of putrifying fungi. I worked over the herbarium, genus by genus, at the same time taking every opportunity to examine fresh flowers of any kind. I made drawings of these flowers, using a kind of camera lucida, and learned greatly from so doing; making a drawing obliges one to look at every detail, and I often noticed structures that I might otherwise have missed. I found that a vertical longitudinal section of a flower gave a great deal of information not otherwise easily observed; by omitting to make such sections, Hooker failed to observe many important facts about Indian orchids and those Malayan species which he described, and thus helped to lead Ridley astray. But Ridley needed no such encouragement. His attempt at recognizing subgenera in an unnaturally enlarged genus *Saccolabium* was a total confusion, showing that he had no understanding of the generic concepts so carefully formulated by J. J. Smith. I gave up trying to record all Ridley's errors, and redescribed all his species from the type material which was fortunately all available. I also studied such exotic orchids as we had in cultivation, but recognized that I could not identify all of them with the same precision as the native species. I adopted J. J. Smith's generic concepts for native species, as my work was so much dependent on his larger one. As regards general classification, I knew that my knowledge of the family at large did not permit me to make a full critical reappraisement of Schlechter's system. I therefore adopted informal names such as "The Acriopsis Tribe," using as titles for such groups the best-known generic names (plants of *Acriopsis* are common; those of *Thecostele* are not). These were not "names" within the meaning of the International Code of nomenclature, nor intended as such.

Among the living orchid plants in 1942 were a few thousand seedlings in pots, and more in flasks, at various stages of development. As the seedlings flowered I described them. I was fortunate in having a capable Chinese gardener to care for the potted plants, but supplies of all kinds were short (even Derris root as a source of insecticide) and the plants did not make as good growth as they should have done. I also made some more crosses, and with the help of a laboratory assistant experimented with the use of fresh seaweed (*Gracilaria*, I believe) instead of prepared agar-agar.

After a year's intensive full-time work I had completed my preliminary survey of native orchids, covering about 780 species. I then passed on to Zingiberaceae, of which there were also good living collections, many the result of Mr. Corner's field work, and specimens of inflorescences in alcohol. Next I made a complete survey of local Gramineae and Cyperaceae. Thus I developed an interest in monocotyledons as a whole, and after the war I made a study of all the other local families except the palms and aroids, which Dr. C. X. Furtado had made his special field of interest. After the war also I was able to do some new field work in various parts of Malaya, and looked on orchids, gingers, and the rest with a new eye. I noted details of flowers which I saw freshly for the first time, to improve my text. In 1946 I spent twelve days at Cameron Highlands (on the Main Range of Malaya at about 1500 m) and in that time found ten species of orchids of which there were no previous records in Malaya; some were new, some had previously been described by J. J. Smith from Sumatra or Borneo. During periods of leave in England I was able to visit Kew and to look up references to literature, and specimens, not available in Singapore (though we had a good library there), but I had no time to do this as thoroughly as I should have done. The book was published in 1953.

In 1949 I undertook the teaching of botany at the new University in Singapore. Previously the only teaching in biology had been the minimum required for first-year students of medicine. So I had a free hand in devising new courses, and I determined to introduce the students to botanical science in terms of the plants they could see around them, though most of these plants were not mentioned in any textbook. Thus I had to review my knowledge and consider what local plants would best serve as examples of form, structure, and function, both vegetative and floral. In particular, I thought how to introduce the students to the distinctions between monocotyledons and dicotyledons. Besides epiphytic orchids on every old tree, the great monocots of palms, aroids, pandans, gingers, bamboos, and the rest were everywhere a feature of the landscape. I took a *Canna* seed and its germination as more representative of mono-cotyledons generally than maize; I also showed the students a germinating coconut, which is closely similar in general organization. There came into my mind a concept of the sympodial growth of most monocotyledons as due directly to their lack of secondary growth in thickness, thus placing the single-stemmed palms (a minority among native Malayan palms) and the monopodial Sarcanthine orchids as among the few exceptions. (I developed this idea in a paper in Phytomorphology, vol. 5:399–413; 1955.) A correlated idea was that a terminal inflorescence, on each new branch of the sympodium, was primitive in monocotyledons, lateral inflorescences being a secondary development; and so I came to realize that Pfitzer's idea of separating groups of orchid genera as having terminal or lateral inflorescences (Acranthae and Pleuranthae), later adopted by Schlechter, was probably at least in part an unnatural one. Obviously the development of lateral inflorescences had come here and there on separate evolutionary lines. It seemed to me that by making this distinction Pfitzer and Schlechter had unnaturally separated certain groups of orchids. Other much more basic characters need first to be used in characterizing a natural subdivision of the family. It is interesting to note that Schlechter changed the position of Dendrobieae from Pleuranthae (where Pfitzer had correctly placed it according to the strict application of the divisional name) to Acranthae, in order to place Dendrobieae near its apparent allies. In fairness to Schlechter, it should be noted that in the posthumous publication of his final system of classification (Notizblatt des Botanischen Gartens, Berlin, no. 88:563–591. 1926) he expressly stated that there was nothing final about his scheme. It was to me regettable that Schweinfurth made no attempt to alter or criticize it when he wrote the chapter on taxonomy in C. L. Withner's book *The Orchids, a Scientific Survey* (1959).

My knowledge of the orchid family as a whole is certainly inadequate to allow me to pass judgment on newer schemes of classification. I am glad to see that new thought is being devoted to the subject, but it is one of such great complexity that a uniquely satisfying solution is not likely to be established at an early date. I do think however that the main structure of such a scheme ought to be discernible by a mind equipped with enough knowledge. A human mind is a very special kind of computer which, at its best, has far more, and far more subtle, cross-references than any man-made computer. Such cross-references can bring together ideas from different parts of one's mind in very unexpected ways, and may call attention to hitherto unthought-of possible further lines of thought. This is the process of scientific imagination, and it is exactly comparable to poetic or artistic imagination. Though feeding information already available on orchids into a computer may give some help, the process cannot tell how reliable all the information is or indicate where it needs supplementing by new observations and new thought, nor can it be geared to provide the more subtle kinds of imaginative thought. There is no substitute for an active and well-informed mind, and such a mind is not produced without prolonged effort.

I am interested to see that the scheme of classification thought out by Dr. F. G. Brieger for the new edition of Schlechter's *Die Orchideen* goes back in some measure to Lindley. Pfitzer thought that Lindley's scheme depended "too much on the biological correlation of the flower to insect visits for pollination, and too little on a general study of the plant, to be a natural classification" (Rendle, *Classification of Flowering Plants*, vol. 1, p. 373). But there is no doubt whatever that the evolution of orchid flowers has been entirely dependent on the coordinated evolution of pollinators (see van der Pijl and Dodson, *Orchid Flowers, their Pollination and Evolution*,

University of Miami Press, 1966). Vegetative characters are all modifications of the same basic sympodial plan (apart from the few monopodial groups) and similar vegetative habits can be found among genera which are certainly not closely related genetically. The distinction "leaves convolute" as against "leaves duplicate" is not a useful one and was abandoned by Schlechter (it corresponds roughly to the difference between terrestrial and epiphytic orchids). The return to Lindley is interesting because not only was Lindley's *Genera and Species of Orchids* (1830–1840) the first collective account of a major part of the orchid family; its scheme of classification was also one that has stood the test of time. Not all pioneer works of such a nature have been based on such excellent insight. And it was only a part of Lindley's total work.

Since 1954 I have devoted almost all my time to the study of ferns, with two short periods devoted to the bamboos of Malaya and New Guinea. I have been greatly impressed by the progress of orchid culture, and of orchid breeding, in Singapore during visits in 1958, 1960, 1963, and 1969, especially in the increasing range of hybrids among the genera related to *Vanda* (Color Plate VIII) and *Arachnis*. The possibility of further development is still immense, and one cannot foresee the end. These plants offer incidentally a wonderful range of subjects for cytogenetic research. The situation as regards the production of orchid flowers for decorative purposes has been dramatically changed over a period of forty years. In Singapore one can now have a varied and colorful display of orchid flowers at all times throughout the year. It seems to me that more attention should now be given to some other groups of plants, with a view to the production of similar results. If perpetual-flowering orchids can be produced, why not perpetual-flowering (and thus perpetual-fruiting) mangosteens and mangoes?

In recent years I have also been a member of the Orchid Committee of the Royal Horticultural Society, and in that capacity have seen the much slower change in the production of new orchids in temperate-latitude greenhouses where equatorial conditions cannot effectively be reproduced. And for a period also I was a member of the R.H.S. advisory committee on the registration of orchid hybrids, which has had some very vexed questions to handle. The value of the register of grex names depends entirely on the correct identification of parents, especially of new species brought for the first time into the breeding pool. There are not enough orchid taxonomists in the world to maintain a good check on such identifications, and the best of us make mistakes sometimes.

The orchid family within itself represents a complexity of evolutionary development which could repay the study of far more people than are at present devoted to it. I write "repay"; repay in what form? In the form of a deeper insight into biological development, and one can never tell where such insight may lead. Living organisms are incalculably more complex in structure than nonliving, and they represent a system of increasing complexity. Among plants, orchids are among the most highly specialized and diversified of all natural groups; and yet academic botanists have for the most part taken very little notice of them. There are endless ways in which they can be studied, but all such study needs to be viewed against the perspective provided by a full comparative taxonomic account of all known living species. There have never been enough taxonomists, and academic courses in botany tend to discourage detailed taxonomic study (I had no training in such myself), yet today there is a greater need than ever for such people to deal with the immense wealth of species in the tropics, where native forests are being destroyed at an accelerating rate. Taxonomic work is not mechanical nor unscientific, as uninformed academic opinion often considers, but needs the highest mental and imaginative powers. It is strange that in Britain, where hybridization of tropical orchids began and reached a remarkable and carefully documented development, academic botanists and geneticists have rarely taken any interest in the family apart from native species.

PALEOBOTANY

2

Fossil History of
the Orchidaceae

RUDOLF SCHMID and
MARVIN J. SCHMID

Introduction

Since the time of Charles Darwin, the goal of much of systematic biology has been the determination of the evolutionary relationships of organisms. There are a number of means for the determination of phylogenies, but the method *par excellence*, and the only direct one, of course, is the use of the fossil record. Investigators interested in the evolutionary history of a group are most desirous of information from the fossil record to provide, ideally, unequivocal evidence for the early history of that group. Unfortunately for orchidologists, the known fossil record of the Orchidaceae is extremely meager. Consequently, researchers must resort to indirect lines of evidence (phytogeography, anatomy, morphology, chromosomes, etc.) for the construction of the phylogeny of the family.

Most researchers seem to favor a relatively great geologic age for the Orchidaceae (e.g., Ames and Correll, 1952–53; Ayensu, 1974; Brieger, 1958, 1960, 1970–71; Correll, 1950; Croizat, 1960; Darrah, 1940; Dunsterville and Garay, 1959; Garay, 1960, 1964, 1972; Garay and Sweet, 1974; Luer, 1975; Raven and Axelrod, 1974; Sanford, 1974; Stebbins, 1950; and also those authors accepting the Massalongo fossils as validly orchidaceous—see Table 2-2). Relatively few writers, however, have ventured a specific time and/or place of origin. Garay (1960, 1964, 1972; Garay and Sweet, 1974), following Stebbins (1950:501–502), postulates an origin in the early Cretaceous[1] and also proposes Malaysia as the most likely cradle of orchidhood, with most of the transoceanic dispersals having occurred during the Tertiary and epiphytism having originated in the Pliopleistocene. Léon Croizat (personal communication, 1972) believes that the orchids arose "surely not later than the earliest Cretaceous."[2] Raven and Axelrod (1974), in part because the primitive subfamilies Apostasioideae and Cypripedioideae are Laurasian and mainly east Asian, postulate an origin and primary radiation of orchids in Laurasia (specific time not indicated, but "Laurasia" is indicative of at least the Cretaceous), with subsequent long-distance dispersal. Sanford (1974:5) thinks that the "first great expansion" of the family was in the Cretaceous-Oligocene through early Miocene, with subsequent long-distance dispersal. Brieger (1958, 1960, 1970–71:124) favors the early Tertiary and the "united Asiatic-American" tropics (1960:329, specific area not indicated), again with subsequent long-distance dispersal. Apparently following Brieger, Ayensu (1974) is disposed to an early Tertiary origin in tropical Asia. Luer (1975:9), on the other hand, is inclined to the Eocene and southeastern Asia. In contrast, some authors, notably Schultes and Dodson, think that the orchids "show little evidence of great age" (Dodson, 1974:655) or that they may be "a comparatively young group" (Schultes, 1960:1, 1966:1043). While there is some dispute as to the exact time of origin of the

---

[1] See Table 2-1 for a geologic time scale indicating the sequences of geologic periods and epochs.

[2] Croizat's (1960:1235, emphasis his) rather cryptic statement that the "*Orchidaceae are certainly as old as angiospermy*, that is, their age of origin (or, of being) can under no circumstance be any younger than Triassic/Jurassic, with stress on the former era" refers to his belief (Croizat, personal communication, 1972) that the evolutionary potential of the orchids (and of all other flowering plants, in fact) apparently was present in the Triassic/Jurassic during the earliest stages of angiospermy.

Table 2-1. Geologic time scale (pre-Mesozoic omitted; after Harland, Smith, and Wilcock, 1964)

Era	Period	Epoch	Beginning of interval (in millions of years ago)
Cenozoic	Quaternary	Holocene (Recent)	0.005
		Pleistocene (Glacial)	2
	Tertiary	Pliocene	7
		Miocene	26
		Oligocene	38
		Eocene	54
		Paleocene	65
Mesozoic	Cretaceous		136
	Jurassic		195
	Triassic		225

family, nearly all workers (e.g., Brieger, 1958; Dodson, 1974; Dodson and Gillespie, 1967; Dressler and Dodson, 1960; Garay, 1960; van der Pijl and Dodson, 1966; Schultes, 1960) seem to agree that currently, and in the immediate geologic past, the Orchidaceae are in a very active period of evolution.

In general, workers have indicated either that there is no fossil record for the Orchidaceae or that there are only doubtful orchidaceous fossils (see Table 2-2). In contrast, a few persons have stated that true orchid fossils exist (Table 2-2). Most of these authors apparently based their view concerning the fossil record of the Orchidaceae chiefly or only on knowledge of the very dubiously orchidaceous *Protorchis monorchis* and *Palaeorchis rhizoma* described by Massalongo (1857, 1858, 1859a,b) from the Eocene of Italy. Nevertheless, a number of other fossils have also been attributed to the Orchidaceae, most significantly Straus's (1954, 1969) three species of putative orchid fruits (*Orchidacites*) from the Pliocene of Germany. With the exception of Andrews (1970), Gothan and Weyland (1973), Kirchheimer (1957), Melchior (1964), and Němejc (1975), however, most recent workers seem unaware of Straus's finds. These and other taxa will be discussed in detail below.

Orchids are not favorable candidates for fossilization, an obvious conclusion that has not escaped previous authors (e.g., Darrah, 1940; Dunsterville and Garay, 1959; Garay and Sweet, 1974; Krackowizer, 1953, 1964; Krishtofovich, 1957; van der Pijl and Dodson, 1966; Schmid and Schmid, 1973; Schultes, 1960). The following characteristics of most Orchidaceae probably account for their scarcity as fossils: (1) predominant occurrence, both in the present and presumably in the distant past (see discussion above), in the wet tropics, which are areas of rapid decay; (2) herbaceous habit; (3) epiphytic habit, which would generally preclude orchids from the conditions (usually aquatic) most conducive to fossilization (see also Darrah, 1940); (4) production of pollinia (usually) rather than individual pollen grains, and dispersion of these by animal vectors instead of by wind; and (5) minute, easily degradable seeds.

Krackowizer (1953, 1964) and Schimper and Schenk (1879–90), however, apparently believed a rather extensive fossil record of the Orchidaceae is to be expected, and Darrah (1940) and also Krackowizer (1953, 1964) suggested that fossil orchids

Table 2-2. Fossil record of the Orchidaceae as viewed by various workers[a]

No fossil record[b]	Doubtful orchidaceous fossils	True orchid fossils
Ames and Correll, 1952–53 (G)	Darrah, 1940 (R: P, Ot)	Andrews, 1970 (G: O; P = doubtful)
Andreánszky, 1954 (G)	Dodson and Gillespie, 1967 (G)	Churchill, 1962 (G: Ot) [Holocene record]
Brieger, 1960 (G)	Dressler, pers. comm., 1972 (G: O, P)	Cockerell, 1915 (S: A)
Chandler, 1961 (G, for London Clay Flora)	Dunsterville and Garay, 1959 (G: P)	Garay and Sweet, 1974 (G: P, Ot)
Chesters, Gnauck, and Hughes, 1967 (G)	Garay, 1960 (G: P), pers. comm. 1972 (G: A, O, P, Ot)	Godwin, 1960 (G: Ot), 1967 (G: Ot), 1968 (G: Ot), 1975 (S: Ot) [Holocene records]
Correll, 1950 (G)	Gothan, 1921 (G: P)	Gothan and Weyland, 1973 (G: O; P = doubtful)
Coulter and Chamberlain, 1903 (G)	Massalongo, 1858 (S: P), 1859a (S: P), 1859b (S: P)[c]	
Cranwell, 1953 (G)	Meschinelli and Squinabol, 1893 (S: P)[c]	Krackowizer, 1953 (R: P, Ot), 1964 (R: P)
Godfery, 1933 (G)	Němejc, 1975 (G: O, P)	Krishtofovich, 1957 (G: P)
	van der Pijl, 1966 (G: P)	Luer, 1972 (G: P), 1975 (G: P)
	van der Pijl and Dodson, 1966 (G: P)	Melchior, 1964 (G: O; P = doubtful)
	Raven and Axelrod, 1974 (G)	Novák, 1972 (G: Ot)
	Rolfe, 1909–12 (G: P)	Rosa, 1975 (G: P)
	Schmid and Schmid, 1973 (R: A, O, P, Ot), 1974 (S: P)	Schimper and Schenk, 1879–90 (G: P)
	Schultes, 1960 (G), 1966 (G)	Straus, 1954 (S: O), 1969 (S: O)
	van Steenis, pers. comm. 1973 (G: O, P)	Vent, 1965 (S: Ot)

[a] Key to symbols after citations: "R" indicates detailed review for fossil history of the Orchidaceae whereas "S" indicates papers describing in detail particular taxa. Specific fossils on which the views of workers are based are indicated as follows: A = *Antholithes pediloides*, O = *Orchidacites* spp., P = *Protorchis monorchis* and/or *Palaeorchis rhizoma*, Ot = other taxa. Some workers cited in this paper (e.g., Kirchheimer, 1957; MacGinitie, 1953) could not be categorized for inclusion in this table.

[b] The Orchidaceae are not listed in the compilations by Muller (1970) and Potonié (1967).

[c] Massalongo (1858, 1859a,b) and Meschinelli and Squinabol (1893) are included under "doubtful orchidaceous" because they qualified the determination of Massalongo's fossil material with the designation "Protorchidaceae," a term used, to our knowledge, by no one else until our recent reports (Schmid and Schmid, 1973, 1974).

might eventually be encountered in deposits in tropical areas when these become better known.

Fossils that have been attributed to the Orchidaceae (or to the Protorchidaceae) are strictly megafossils (e.g., fruits, leaves, tubers, etc.); orchidaceous microfossils (e.g., seeds and pollen) older than the Quaternary have not been reported in the literature.[3] Discoveries of cuticular remains (as those already found of the Pliocene *Orchidacites wegelei* of Straus, 1954) would seem to offer the best hope for significant additions to the fossil record of the Orchidaceae. Tomlinson (1974) and Williams (1975; personal communication, 1974), however, note that types of stomatal apparatus in orchids are very similar to those of other monocotyledons.

Even if orchid pollen were preserved as fossils, it is a moot point that it would be recognizable as such. Not only might botanists fail to recognize the fossilized pollen of those orchidaceous forms that had not yet evolved pollinia, but they might not be able to identify individual pollen grains derived from pollinia that had broken up. Perhaps significantly, neither the Orchidaceae nor the Asclepiadaceae, the only two angiospermous families possessing pollinia and massulae (Walker and Doyle, 1975), is listed in the recent compilations of fossil pollen and spores by Muller (1970) and Potonié (1967).

Although Chandler's (1964, and works cited therein) extensive investigations (initially with the late Eleanor M. Reid) of the Tertiary London Clay Flora of England over a period of several decades failed to reveal any orchidaceous remains, she suggested (1961:29) that "possibly search for pollen among the finer sediments and residues may eventually demonstrate the presence of this family" in the London Clay Flora. Subsequent palynological work (two 1961 Ph.D. theses by Ma Khin Sein and Jane Pallot at the University of London, both cited in Chandler, 1964, the latter thesis published as Machin, 1971), however, has thus far failed to substantiate this prediction.

We decided to summarize what is known of the fossil record of orchids (1) because there is no account available other than the rather superficial ones by Darrah (1940) and Krackowizer (1953, 1964), (2) because there are a number of misconceptions in the literature that should be corrected, and, most importantly, (3) because a reasonably complete list of fossils attributed to the Orchidaceae could be prepared since we had access to the "Compendium Index of Paleobotany" (see Andrews, 1970, and Eyde, 1972, for accounts of its coverage) and to libraries with extensive holdings in rather obscure publications. The present report, it might be noted, represents an expanded and updated account of our earlier articles on "fossil orchids" (Schmid and Schmid, 1973, 1974).

As recently discussed by Eyde (1972), there are several paths into the paleobotanical literature. We checked a variety of sources for records of orchidaceous fossils, most

---

[3] Many orchidologists have heard rumors about orchid pollen having been discovered in Miocene sediments of western Venezuela, and Garay and Sweet (1974:8), in fact, recently referred to "some undescribed pollen tetrads dating from the Eocene, recently collected in Venezuela" (the date is in error, and "pollen tetrads" should be "pollinia," according to our unpublished information). We have been able to confirm that such a discovery was indeed made. However, we must withhold further details and respect the confidentiality of our source until the findings can be published.

importantly the index by Andrews (1970, including unpublished cards for additions since 1965) and the United States Geological Survey's "Compendium Index of Paleobotany," an unpublished file available for consultation only in the Natural History Building, Room W-300, of the Smithsonian Institution, Washington, D.C. We checked the Compendium Index for most of the temperate genera listed in Schultes and Pease (1963). Most tropical genera, however, were not sought in the Compendium Index due to the minuscule yield that could only result from such a mountain of effort. As noted above, tropical plants are unlikely candidates for fossilization. In addition, most tropical orchids are endemics that presumably evolved during or just before the Quaternary, and hence any fossils of them would be unlikely to be encountered by paleobotanists, most of whom have worked (until very recently, at least) in temperate areas. Finally, any orchidaceous fossils of the pre-Quaternary tropical floras of presently temperate areas would probably be given generic names not based on living taxa.

Reports of Orchidaceous Fossils

Three extinct genera (*Palaeorchis*, *Protorchis*, and *Orchidacites*) have been designated as orchidaceous or protorchidaceous. At least one other fossil taxon, *Antholithes pediloides*, has been regarded as an orchid. In addition, fossil remains from the Quaternary have been attributed to a number of extant, north temperate orchid taxa. Purists who restrict "fossils" to pre-Quaternary remains and therefore regard Pleistocene and Holocene finds as "subfossils" may object to the inclusion of plant remains from the Quaternary in the following enumeration:

Jurassic

The "Compendium Index of Paleobotany," citing Thurmann (1833), lists the following extant species as occurring in the Jurassic strata at Porrentruy, France: *Ophrys myodes* Jacq., *Orchis morio* L., *O. pyramidalis* L., *Satyrium viride* L., and *Serapias rubra* L. This is incorrect. Thurmann did indeed list these species, but only as part of the modern vegetation growing on the Jurassic strata of this region.

Eocene

Protorchis Massalongo (1857:777, *nom. nud.*; 1858:749; 1859a:63).
  Protorchis monorchis Massalongo (1857:777, *nom. nud.*; 1858:749; 1859a:64, *t.* 23, *f.* 3; 1859b:133). See Plate 2-1-**1**, **2**; Plate 2-2-**1a**, **1b**; Plate 2-3-**1a**, **1b**.
Palaeorchis Massalongo (1857:777, *nom. nud.*; 1858:750).
  Palaeorchis rhizoma (Massalongo) Massalongo (1858:750; 1859b:133) (= *Protorchis rhizoma* Massalongo, 1857:777, *nom. nud.*). See Plate 2-2-**2**.
These two species represent the first described and also the geologically oldest fossils that might possibly represent orchids. In 1857, Abramo Bartolomeo Massalongo (1824–1860) listed, without benefit of description or illustration (hence *nomina nuda*), the new generic name *Protorchis*, with two new species *P. monorchis* and *P. rhizoma* based on specimens from the calcareous Eocene deposits at Monte Bolca in northeastern Italy. In 1858, Massalongo validly published *Protorchis monorchis* and also the

Plate 2-1.   *Protorchis monorchis*, showing leaves and fibrous roots attached to tuber, **1**: Photograph reproduced from Massalongo (1859a); approximately × 1.6.
2: New photograph (unretouched) of same specimen (Verona f. M. 66); approximately × 1.5.

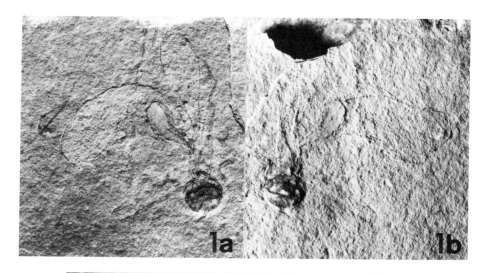

Plate 2-2.
1: *Protorchis monorchis*, part (a) and counterpart (b) (Verona f.M. 575 and f.M. 574, respectively); × 1.2. **2:** *Palaeorchis rhizoma*, showing leaves attached to rhizome bearing circular, papillate leaf scars (Verona f.M. 609); × 1.3.

new combination *Palaeorchis rhyzoma* (the specific epithet is an orthographic error) based on *Protorchis rhizoma*. The next year a more complete description and also a photograph (see Plate 2-1-**1**) of *Protorchis monorchis* were published (Massalongo, 1859a). In his 1858 work Massalongo dated *Protorchis* as "1854," with the added notation "in litt. et in Musaeo" (1858:749). Since the 1854 reference is obviously unpublished, the *nomina nuda* in the 1857 report thus represent the actual first (though taxonomically invalid) publication of the names involved.

Massalongo spent most of his scientific career in northeastern Italy, particularly in Verona (see detailed accounts in Cornalia, 1860; de Visiani, 1861 or 1868). Accordingly, we inquired of several institutions in northeastern Italy for photographs of and additional information on specimens of *Protorchis* and *Palaeorchis*. Plates 2-1 to 2-3 include photographs of six specimens of four plants of *Protorchis* and *Palaeorchis* in the collections of institutions at Padova (= Padua) and Verona (see acknowledgments):

Protorchis monorchis:

Plate 2-1-**1**, **2**: Verona f.M. 66.

Plate 2-2-**1a**, **1b**: Verona f.M. 575 and f.M. 574 (part and counterpart).

Plate 2-3-**1a**, **1b**: Padova No. 5039 and No. 5038 (part and counterpart).

Palaeorchis rhizoma:

Plate 2-2-**2**: Verona f.M. 609.

Of all the fossils discussed in this paper, *Protorchis monorchis* and *Palaeorchis rhizoma* have received by far the most attention (see Table 2-2 and below). However, for all the attention they have received, these fossils have been rarely illustrated. Massalongo (1859a) published a photograph of only *Protorchis monorchis*, reproduced in Schmid and Schmid (1973) and here as Plate 2-1-**1**, but apparently never elsewhere. A photograph of a second specimen of this species appeared in 1953 in the late Ferdinand J. Krackowizer's first brief note on "fossil orchids," but not in his very similar, though more ornately written, second report (1964). Plate 2-3-**1b**, corresponds to the photograph in Krackowizer's (1953) paper. Photographs of a third plant of *Protorchis monorchis*, represented by part and counterpart (Plate 2-2-**1a**, **1b**), appeared in Rosa (1975) and Schmid and Schmid (1974). Plate 2-1-**2**, which is also included in Rosa (1975) and Schmid and Schmid (1974), is of the same specimen as that figured by Massalongo (1859a; Plate 2-1-**1**), but differs from it in several minor respects, particularly details of the roots. Retouching of Massalongo's figure (Plate 2-1-**1**) by his photographer Maurizio Lotze perhaps accounts for these differences. The remaining illustration of *Protorchis monorchis* (Plate 2-3-**1a**) first appeared in Schmid and Schmid (1974). *Palaeorchis rhizoma* (Plate 2-2-**2**) had never been figured until our recent article (Schmid and Schmid, 1974). As far as we can determine, all known fossil material of *Protorchis* and *Palaeorchis* is figured in the present report.[4]

There is some confusion as to the number of specimens Massalongo had available for study. Only one plant of *Palaeorchis rhizoma* was at his disposal (Massalongo, 1859b; Plate .2-2-**2**). However, in one publication (1859b) Massalongo clearly states that

---

[4] Rosa (1975) indicates that three additional specimens of *Protorchis monorchis* exist in a private collection in Verona, and that additional fossils of a more recent age occur in other Italian localities. In view of the lack of any additional information from Rosa, skepticism seems the most conservative approach.

there were two specimens of *Protorchis monorchis*, whereas in another (1859a) he indicates three specimens. Apparently, there were two plants (Plate 2-1-**2**; Plate 2-2-**1**) which involved three specimens, one plant, however, being represented by a part and its counterpart (Plate 2-2-**1a**, **1b**). In fact, the Museo Civico di Storia Naturale at Verona, which contains Massalongo's collections of Protorchidaceae, has material of only two plants of *Protorchis monorchis* (Plate 2-1-**2**; Plate 2-2-**1**; also Fig. 3 in Rosa, 1975; L. Sorbini, personal communication, 1972).

The Istituto di Geologia at Padova possesses fossil material, represented by part and counterpart, of only one plant of *Protorchis monorchis* (Plate 2-3-**1a**, **1b**; G. Piccoli, personal communication, 1972). This material was not studied by Massalongo (1858, 1859a,b) but was collected, apparently at a later date, by Baron Achilli de Zigno, a colleague of Massalongo (G. Piccoli, personal communication, 1972).

In 1893, Meschinelli and Squinabol listed *Protorchis monorchis* and *Palaeorchis rhizoma* in their fossil flora of Italy. According to Krackowizer (1953, 1964), Meschinelli and Squinabol studied newly discovered material of both species in a better state of preservation, but this is not indicated by the latter. Krackowizer in his first note (1953) also states that these workers actually studied the de Zigno collections at Padova (Plate 2-3-**1**). Certainly these are in better condition than the Massalongo collections at Verona (compare Plate 2-3-**1** with Plate 2-1 and Plate 2-2-**1**). We could, however, find no evidence to support Krackowizer's implication (1953:38, 1964:40: "Novas descobertas de exemplares das mesmas plantas . . .") that Meschinelli and Squinabol (1893) had new material of *Palaeorchis*.

Although Massalongo (1857) initially listed his new species under the Orchidaceae, he subsequently (1858, 1859a,b) very carefully indicated the tentatively orchidaceous nature of his fossil specimens by including them in a new taxon, the Protorchidaceae ("Protorchidee" in 1858, 1859a; or the Latinized "Protorchideae" in 1859a,b). Massalongo (1858, 1859a) admitted that he was unable to find in the extant flora counterparts of his fossils. Massalongo (1858, 1859a) noted a resemblance of both his fossil species to the Araceae, which he (1858) apparently regarded as being rather close to the Orchidaceae. A superficial likeness between *Palaeorchis rhizoma* and the fossil alga *Delesserites* was noted but was rejected as indicative of a relationship (Massalongo, 1858). After additional concern that *Palaeorchis rhizoma* might be butomaceous, Massalongo (1858) finally decided to retain this species in his Protorchidaceae. This discussion illustrates the difficulty that Massalongo had in assigning his fossils to an extant plant group. This fact is apparently realized by very few authors since a number (e.g., Darrah, 1940; Dunsterville and Garay, 1959; Krackowizer, 1953, 1964; Rolfe, 1909–12) incorrectly state or imply that Massalongo had regarded his fossils as orchids.

According to Massalongo (1858, descriptive terminology below is his), the Protorchidaceae are next to the orchids and the aroids and consist of small herbs with tubers or rhizomes bearing lateral fibrous roots and several very slender, cuneate-obovate or spathulate leaves with entire margins and fine midribs. Misstatements to the contrary (Gothan, 1921; Gothan and Weyland, 1973; Krackowizer, 1953, 1964; Schimper and Schenk, 1879–90), both species are without tubers. *Protorchis monorchis* (Plate 2-1;

Plate 2-2-**1**; Plate 2-3-**1**) has a round, solitary tuber whereas *Palaeorchis rhizoma* (Plate 2-2-**2**, never illustrated by Massalongo) differs chiefly in having a perpendicularly cylindrical rhizome covered with circular, papillate leaf scars (Massalongo, 1858). The two species also differ somewhat in having spathulate versus oblong to spathulate leaves, respectively (Massalongo, 1858). Massalongo (1859a) subsequently indicated that *Protorchis monorchis* strictly speaking does not have a true tuber, but rather a rounded rhizome (Plate 2-1; Plate 2-2-**1**; Plate 2-3-**1**). In the same publication (1859a) he also added the following information for *Protorchis monorchis*: tuber 7–8 mm in diameter; leaves 3–4 per plant, attenuate into a petiole, 5 cm long, and 12–15–18 mm wide. These dimensions correspond only partially to those of Massalongo's (1859a) figured specimen (Plate 2-1-**1**). Presumably Massalongo took his dimensions for the leaves from the specimen he figured but took the dimensions for the tuber from a second fossil specimen (Plate 2-2-**1**).

Although Massalongo (1859b:133) eventually indicated that his specimens of both *Protorchis monorchis* and *Palaeorchis rhizoma* were seedlings, there is no mention in his previous descriptions (1858, 1859a) of the probable developmental age of these fossils.

Most workers (e.g., Andrews, 1970; Darrah, 1940; Dunsterville and Garay, 1959; Garay, 1960; Gothan, 1921; Gothan and Weyland, 1973; Melchior, 1964; Němejc, 1975; van der Pijl, 1966; van der Pijl and Dodson, 1966; Rolfe, 1909–12; see also Table 2-2), usually referring only to *Protorchis monorchis*, have subsequently concluded that Massalongo's fossils are not truly representative of the Orchidaceae. Only Garay and Sweet (1974), Krackowizer (1953, 1964), Krishtofovich (1957), Luer (1972, 1975), Rosa (1975), and Schimper and Schenk (1879–90) definitely accepted Massalongo's finds as orchidaceous. Van der Pijl (1966; van der Pijl and Dodson, 1966), however, apparently seems tempted to accept *Protorchis monorchis* as validly orchidaceous, no doubt because its Eocene date ties in with his understanding of the evolution of the bees.

Meschinelli and Squinabol (1893) included both of Massalongo's fossil species under the Protorchidaceae (see Table 2-2, footnote c) in the order Microspermae (= Orchidales), but these authors noted, without explanation, that *Palaeorchis rhizoma* is probably a member of the Butomaceae. Krackowizer (1953, 1964) accepted the views of Meschinelli and Squinabol (1893) except that he regarded *Protorchis monorchis* as a true orchid rather than as a protorchid.

Admitting that both of Massalongo's fossils are doubtfully orchidaceous, Leslie A. Garay (personal communication, 1972) nevertheless maintains that of all the fossils attributed to the Orchidaceae, *Protorchis monorchis* is perhaps the most likely candidate for inclusion in the family, largely because of its similarity to the European *Orchis pallens* L. More recently, Garay (in Garay and Sweet, 1974) again confirmed his belief in *Protorchis monorchis*, despite our previously published skepticism of the orchidaceous nature of this plant (Schmid and Schmid, 1973, 1974). Rosa (1975), like Garay, accepts *Protorchis monorchis* as an orchid because of the great similarity of the fossil to an extant species (the Venezuelan *Platystele ornata* Garay). Finally, C. G. G. J. van Steenis (personal communication, 1973) notes that the sterile *Protorchis monorchis* might be *any* tuberous plant with juvenile leaves and that the specimen is hardly evidence for the fossil record of Orchidaceae.

In conclusion, although the better preserved material of *Protorchis monorchis* in the collections at Padova (Plate 2-3-**1**) does seem to substantiate Massalongo's descriptions (1858, 1859a,b) based on his material at Verona (Plate 2-1; Plate 2-2-**1**), it still does not warrant a change of our previous opinion (Schmid and Schmid, 1973, 1974), and that of most workers (Table 2-2), that *Protorchis monorchis* is a very doubtful orchid fossil. In addition, while the hitherto unpublished representation of *Palaeorchis rhizoma* (Plate 2-2-**2**; also in Schmid and Schmid, 1974) likewise also fits Massalongo's descriptions (Massalongo, 1858, 1859b), the very poor preservation of this fossil makes any assignment to the Orchidaceae extremely tenuous. Consequently, the orchidaceous nature of Massalongo's fossils is clearly very questionable. As has already been suggested (Chester A. Arnold, personal communication, 1967; Darrah, 1940; Dunsterville and Garay, 1959), perhaps the most charitable thing that can be said about the affinity of *Protorchis* and *Palaeorchis* is that they are monocotyledonous.

Oligocene

Antholithes pediloides Cockerell (1915:332, *f*. 1). See Plate 2-3-**9**.

T. D. A. Cockerell, the prolific describer of fossils from the western United States,[5] in 1915 delineated from the Lower Oligocene (the age according to MacGinitie, 1953; incorrectly regarded as Miocene by Cockerell, 1915) beds at Florissant, Colorado, a new species in the fossil artificial (or form) genus *Antholithes*. Cockerell attributed the fossil (Plate 2-3-**9**), *A. pediloides*, to the Orchidaceae because of its marked resemblance to the lip of *Cypripedium*, and he also presumed that the several small, "subhyaline" spots scattered over the surface might represent the work of some insect.

Other than the suggestive outline of the fossil, however, the lack of significant detail certainly makes Cockerell's determination of the fossil as an orchid extremely doubtful. In his classic flora of the Florissant beds, MacGinitie (1953:159) reached the same conclusion and disposed of *Antholithes pediloides* among "species of somewhat doubtful taxonomic value" under *incertae sedis*. Garay (personal communication, 1972) suggests that *A. pediloides* is "referable to *Aristolochia* rather than Orchidaceae," but this belief, like Cockerell's, is also based on superficial resemblances.

Miocene[6]

Darrah (1940) briefly discussed, and then discounted as truly orchidaceous, a fossil stem (apparently unnamed) from the Miocene of Hungary that had been described by a Robert Brown (there were several Robert Browns). Since Darrah provided no references in his note, and since after considerable searching we have been unable to locate any additional information concerning this fossil, we can only quote Darrah (1940:149) fully: "A third form [besides Massalongo's *Protorchis* and *Palaeorchis*] was once provisionally accepted as a fossil orchid. This fossil stem, found in rocks of Miocene age in Hungary, included a few structurally preserved hair-like roots which Robert Brown considered to be of some epiphytic orchidaceous plant. . . . As a matter

---

[5] Derek J. de Solla Price (personal communication in Menard, 1971:87) reports an output of 3,904 papers by Cockerell. This is perhaps the all-time record for scientific productivity, but in the case of Cockerell it is directly proportional to superficiality.

[6] See footnote 3.

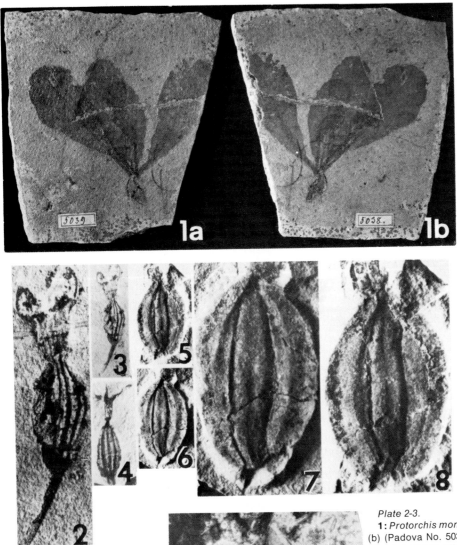

Plate 2-3.

1: *Protorchis monorchis*, part (a) and counterpart (b) (Padova No. 5039 and No. 5038, respectively), showing leaves attached to tuber; preservation is better than in specimens depicted in Plate 2-1 and in Plate 2-2-1; approximately ×1.0. **2-8**: *Orchidacites*, fossil fruits; note three-pronged floral remnants at apices of fruits in **2-4** (rephotographed from Straus, 1969). **2**, *Orchidacites wegelei*, ×2.6; **3**, *Orchidacites wegelei*, ×1.0; **4**, *Orchidacites orchidioides*, ×1.0; **5**, *Orchidacites cypripedioides*, ×1.0; **6**, *Orchidacites cypripedioides*, ×1.0; **7**, *Orchidacites cypripedioides*, ×2.6; **8**, *Orchidacites cypripedioides*, ×2.6. **9**: *Antholithes pediloides*; note spots scattered over surface of fossil (rephotographed from MacGinitie, 1953, courtesy of Carnegie Institution of Washington); approximately ×2.0. **10**: Quaternary fossils, cf. *Epipactis palustris* (according to Vent, 1965), showing fruit (at lower right) and leaf impressions (rephotographed from Vent, 1965); ×1.0.

of fact it was with this organ [the pseudobulb] that Robert Brown attempted to compare his supposed fossil from Hungary."

In a footnote, Krackowizer (1953), writing from Brazil, recalled a recent report, in a European journal, of an orchid fossil from Hungary, but he was unable to provide any further information. Does he mean Darrah's (1940) paper, which, however, appeared in an American journal?

Pliocene

Orchidacites Straus (1954:6, *nom. nud.*; 1969:167).
> *Orchidacites orchidioides* Straus (1954:6, *t.* 1, *f.* 15, *t.* 8, *f.* 6; 1969:167, *t.* 28, *f.* 2). See Plate 2-3-**4**.
> *Orchidacites wegelei* Straus (1954:6, *t.* 8, *f.* 1–5; 1969:167, *t.* 28, *f.* 1a, 1b). See Plate 2-3-**2**, **3**.
> *Orchidacites cypripedioides* Straus (1969:168, *t.* 28, *f.* 3–6). See Plate 2-3-**5–8**.

In 1954, Straus described from the Upper Pliocene of Willershausen, Germany, two species of fruits, *Orchidacites orchidioides* and *O. wegelei*, which he assigned to the Orchidaceae. The two species, especially the former (as suggested by its name), were thought to resemble various species of *Orchis* (Straus, 1954). More recently, Straus (1969) provided for *Orchidacites* a generic diagnosis, which had been omitted from the 1954 report, and described a third species, *O. cypripedioides*, with fruits regarded as similar to those of *Cypripedium*. These taxa are illustrated in Plate 2-3-**2–8**, reproduced from Straus's 1969 paper.

Orchidacites is a form genus proposed for fossil fruits comparable to the capsules of various extant orchid genera (Straus, 1969). According to Straus (1969), the fossil capsules, 1.5 to 2.5 cm long, are ellipsoidal or narrowly ellipsoidal, have several longitudinal striae (Plate 2-3-**2–8**), and often bear the remnants of a corolla at the fruit apex (Plate 2-3-**2–4**).

Straus (1969; also personal communication, 1972) believes that the fossil fruits of *Orchidacites* came from epiphytes growing on rotting branches that eventually were blown into the sediments by wind, and, as a consequence, he has speculated (1969; personal communication, 1972) that many of the present-day orchids (e.g., *Limodorum*, *Neottia*, *Corallorhiza*, and *Cypripedium*) were primitively epiphytic and now are terrestrial "secondary relicts." This echoes the old view of Andrews (1916:205) that some Australian epiphytic orchids "had become terrestrial" because "the trees no longer afforded them the necessary protection [from "the severe and harsh climatic conditions"], whereupon they descended and were preserved in the sandy wastes [of eastern Australia] by the development there of new xerophytic genera." These views, of course, are dissonant with the conventional one that the terrestrial habit is ancestral and the epiphytic derived (e.g., Brieger, 1958, 1960; Dodson and Gillespie, 1967; Dressler and Dodson, 1960; Garay, 1960, 1964, 1972; Garay and Sweet, 1974; van der Pijl 1966; Rolfe, 1909–12; Sanford, 1974).

The Straus fossils have received little comment from either orchidologists or paleobotanists. Andrews (1970), Melchior (1964), and Gothan and Weyland (1973) accepted the fossils as unmistakably orchidaceous. Kirchheimer (1957:650), however, remained skeptical, believing that the inferior, winglike, ribbed gynoecium with a distinct styloid process evokes resemblances to young fruits of *Halesia*, *Pterostyrax*, and other Styracaceae (a completely unrelated family in the dicotyledons). Němejc (1975) agreed with Kirchheimer, although the former noted that the fossils of *Orchidacites* are perhaps the most likely of the few known fossils to be orchidaceous. Straus (personal communication, 1972), in counterargument, however, believes that the fruits he described are truly orchidaceous since fruits of the Styracaceae never show floral remains whereas fruits of the Orchidaceae often do.

On examining the photographs reproduced herein (Plate 2-3-**2–8**), Garay (personal communication, 1972) is also disinclined to accept Straus's fossils as orchidaceous because of the apparently excessive number of ribs (Plate 2-3-**2–8**) for true orchid fruits, which have a maximum of six, and because of the curious three-pronged floral remnants (Plate 2-3-**2–4**). Garay (personal communication, 1972) does not believe that these remnants could represent a perianth since perianth segments of orchids usually wither and rapidly decay, yet he also would not regard the remnants as a column since three-pronged columns do not occur in the Orchidaceae. For similar reasons, Robert L. Dressler (personal communication, 1972) is also skeptical that these fossils are orchidaceous, but he is less certain in excluding *Orchidacites cypripedioides* (Plate 2-3-**5–8**) from the orchids since it "looks rather like a *Cattleya* fruit."

In defense of Straus, we might note that a three-pronged calyx of fused sepals occurs in some modern orchid taxa (e.g., *Pterostylis*, see Fig. 84 in van der Pijl and Dodson, 1966; *Masdevallia*, etc.) and that on orchid fruits a greater number of ribs (than six) may be apparent since these may be variously secondarily divided (e.g., *Trichopilia suavis* Lindl. et Paxton). Unfortunately, Straus (1969) hurts his own cause by interpreting the floral remnants (Plate 2-3-**2–4**) as a corolla since it is perhaps more likely that they represent a calyx. However, it should also be noted that none of these characters are truly diagnostic of the orchids since, as van Steenis (personal communication, 1973) points out, a trimerous perianth of united segments, an inferior ovary, and ribbed fruits occur not only in other monocotyledonous families, but also in several dicotyledonous ones (e.g., *Cryptocarya* of the Lauraceae, which has all of these characters).

Quaternary

Quaternary orchid fossils are included here for completeness, although they are unimportant from the viewpoint of our understanding of the origin and most of the subsequent evolution of the family. The names of at least twenty extant species of orchids are listed in the "Compendium Index of Paleobotany" and are attributed to both the Pleistocene and Holocene (= Recent or Postglacial) of the Quaternary. Most of these listings were compiled around the turn of the century, when the Compendium Index included casual, incidental references to fossils—a practice long discontinued (Eyde, 1972). Unfortunately, a number of these listings are not applicable because the original works discuss the various orchid species as components of the contemporary flora and not as fossils. This is the case with reports of *Goodyera repens* (L.) R. Br. from the Quaternary of Denmark, *Himantoglossum hircinum* (L.) Sprengel and *Ophrys aranifera*

Huds. from the Postglacial of Switzerland, and *Malaxis paludosa* (L.) Sw. from the Holocene of Germany, which the Compendium Index attributes to Andersson (1906), Naegeli (1905, as cited in Brockmann-Jerosch, 1910), and Becker (1874), respectively.

The Compendium Index also attributes the following extant orchid taxa to Sernander's (1894) extensive work on the Quaternary (Würm Glacial and Postglacial) of Gotland, Sweden (names listed as they appear in Sernander):

Anacamptis pyramidalis (L.) Rich.   *Malaxis monophyllos* (L.) Sw.
Cephalanthera ensifolia (Sw.) Rich.   *Neottia nidus-avis* (L.) Rich.
Corallorhiza innata R. Br.   *Orchis angustifolia* Wimm. et Grab.
Epipactis palustris (L.) Crantz   *O. maculata* L.
Gymnadenia conopsea (L.) R. Br.   *O. militaris* L.
G. odoratissima (L.) Rich.   *O. ustulata* L.
Listera cordata (L.) R. Br.   *Platanthera bifolia* (L.) Rich.
L. ovata (L.) R. Br.   *Sturmia loeselii* (L.) Reichb.

However, Sernander (1894) merely discusses these and other orchid species in terms of a phytosociological survey of the modern bog vegetation of Gotland. The bogs Sernander studied did indeed contain identifiable fossils, but none of these were orchids.

To our knowledge, there are only four published reports of Quaternary fossils attributed to the Orchidaceae. In 1965, Vent (p. 200) described leaf and fruit impressions from the Riss-Würm Interglacial of Weimar-Ehringsdorf, Germany, and assigned these to "cf. *Epipactis palustris* (Mill.) Crantz" in the Orchidaceae. Garay (personal communication, 1972), however, discounted the orchidaceous nature of these fossils after examining Vent's photograph (Plate 2-3-**10**).

Finally, Godwin (1967, 1968; also in Turner, 1970) presented a pollen diagram of a core of Old Buckenham Mere, Norfolk, England, which includes an entry for an "orchid-tetrad" (no further explanation given) dating from the Holocene, about 1100 B.C. Similarly, orchid pollen from about 150 B.C. (again, no further information) was discovered in Viper's Track, Somerset, England (Godwin, 1960). Still other orchid pollen (representing 3 percent of total tree pollen) was found in a Mesolithic site (about 7500 B.C.) at Thatcham, Thames Valley, Berkshire, England (Churchill, 1962; also in Godwin, 1975). Recently, Godwin (1975:378) was able to identify the "separable pollen tetrads" at the Buckenham Mere site as belonging to "*Orchis* sp." There are also unpublished records (Sir Harry Godwin, personal communication, 1973) of orchid pollen of similar age in peats from Amberley Wild Brooks, near Arundel, southern England, and Port Talbot, southern Wales. Such subfossils, however, are obviously of trivial importance from the standpoint of the fossil history of the Orchidaceae.

Conclusions

Fossils dating from the Eocene to the Quaternary have been referred to the Orchidaceae, but objections have been raised against the orchidaceous nature of all of these fossils. These fossils are hardly reliable records for the Orchidaceae. Since they were assigned to the Orchidaceae on purely superficial resemblances (as discussed above), this manner of determination represents little more than wish fulfillment (see, for example, Dilcher, 1974, for the pitfalls of such simplistic matching of fossils with presumed modern counterparts). Of the aforementioned fossils, the most likely to be orchidaceous (though still very doubtfully so) nevertheless remain Massalongo's famous fossils from the Eocene of Italy—*Protorchis monorchis* and *Palaeorchis rhizoma*— and especially Straus's recent finds from the Pliocene of Germany—*Orchidacites orchidioides*, *O. wegelei*, and *O. cypripedioides*.

In conclusion, then, the Orchidaceae, unfortunately from the standpoint of orchidology, have no positive or useful fossil record. In this sense the orchids present a striking parallel to several well-known gods of mythology: Athena, who sprang fully grown and fully armored from the head of Zeus, and the Aztec Huitzilopochtli, who was borne fully grown and fully armored from Coatlicue. Less martially, and perhaps much more appropriately, one might analogize the orchids to Aphrodite (Venus), the goddess of beauty and love, who sprang fully formed from the foam of the sea and was wafted to the shores of Cyprus.

Acknowledgments

We are greatly indebted to Dr. Lorenzo Sorbini, Museo Civico di Storia Naturale, Verona, and Prof. Giuliano Piccoli, Istituto di Geologia, Università di Padova, for information on Massalongo's fossils and for the negatives used to prepare some of the accompanying figures (Plate 2-1-**2**; Plate 2-2-**1**, **2**; Plate 2-3-**1**).

Literature Cited

Ames, O., and D. S. Correll. 1952–53. Orchids of Guatemala. Fieldiana (Bot.) 26:i–xiii, 1–727.

Andersson, G. 1906. Die Entwicklungsgeschichte der skandinavischen Flora. Résultats Sci. Congr. Int. Bot., Vienne (1905), p. 45–97.

Andreánszky, G. 1954. Ósnövénytan. Akadémiai Kiado, Budapest.

Andrews, E. C. 1916. The geological history of the Australian flowering plants. Amer. J. Sci. 192:171–232.

Andrews, H. N., Jr. 1970. Index of generic names of fossil plants, 1820–1965. U.S. Geol. Surv. Bull. 1300. (Also 1975 supplement by A. M. Blazer, covering 1966–1973. U.S. Geol. Surv. Bull. 1396.)

Ayensu, E. S. 1974. Beautiful gamblers of the biosphere. Nat. History 83(8):36–45.

Becker, G. 1874. Botanische Wanderungen durch die Sümpfe und Torfmoore der Niederrheinischen Ebene. Verh. Naturhist. Vereines Preuss. Rheinl. Westphalens 31:137–158.

Brieger, F. G. 1958. On the phytogeography of orchids. Proc. 2d World Orchid Conf., Honolulu (1957), p. 189–200.

——. 1960. Geographic distribution and phyllogeny [*sic*] of orchids. Proc. 3d World Orchid Conf., London, p. 328–333.

——. 1970–71. Botanische Grundlagen der Orchideenforschung, p. 1–142. *In* F. G. Brieger, R. Maatsch, and K. Senghas (eds.), Rudolf Schlechter's Die Orchideen: Ihre Beschreibung, Kultur und Züchtung. 3d ed. Verlag Paul Parey, Berlin. (Brieger's article in Pts. 1–3, issued 1970–71; entire work incomplete; Pts. 4–7 issued 1973–75.)

Brockmann-Jerosch, H. 1910. Die Änderungen des Klimas seit der grössten Ausdehnung der letzten Eiszeit in der Schweiz, p. 55–71. *In* Die Veränderungen des Klimas seit dem Maximum der letzten Eiszeit, Ber., Exekutivkomitee 11. Int. Geol.-Kongr., Stockholm, 1910.

Chandler, M. E. J. 1961. The Lower Tertiary floras of southern England. I. Palaeocene floras: London Clay Flora (supplement). British Museum (Natural History), London. (Text and plates separately bound.)

——. 1964. *Idem*. IV. A summary and survey of findings in the light of recent botanical observations. British Museum (Natural History), London.

Chesters, K. I. M., F. R. Gnauck, and N. F. Hughes. 1967. Angiospermae, p. 269–288. *In* W. B. Harland *et al.* (eds.), The fossil record. Geological Society of London.

Churchill, D. M. 1962. The stratigraphy of the Mesolithic Sites III and V at Thatcham, Berkshire, England. Proc. Prehistoric Soc., Ser. 2, 28:362–370.

Cockerell, T. D. A. 1915. Notes on orchids. Bot. Gaz. 59:331–333.

Cornalia, E. 1860. Sulla vita e sulle opere di Abramo Massalongo. Atti Soc. Ital. Sci. Nat. (Milan) 2:188–206.

Correll, D. S. 1950. Native orchids of North America. Chronica Botanica, Waltham, Mass.

Coulter, J. M., and C. J. Chamberlain. 1903. Morphology of angiosperms. D. Appleton, New York.

Cranwell, L. M. 1953. New Zealand pollen studies: the monocotyledons: a comparative account. Bull. Auckland Inst. and Mus. No. 3:1–91 *and* Harvard Univ. Press, Cambridge, Mass.

Croizat, L. 1960. Principia botanica. The Author, Caracas. (1 vol. in 2. Published 1961.)

Darrah, W. C. 1940. Supposed fossil orchids. Amer. Orchid Soc. Bull. 9:149–150.

Dilcher, D. L. 1974. Approaches to the identification of angiosperm leaf remains. Bot. Rev. 40:1–157.

Dodson, C. H. 1974. Orchidales, p. 648–656. *In* Encyclopaedia Britannica, Macropaedia, Vol. 13.

Dodson, C. H., and R. J. Gillespie. 1967. The biology of the orchids. The Mid-America Orchid Congress. (No city of publication given.)

Dressler, R. L., and C. H. Dodson. 1960. Classification and phylogeny in the Orchidaceae. Ann. Missouri Bot. Gard. 47:25–68.

Dunsterville, G. C. K., and L. A. Garay. 1959. Venezuelan orchids illustrated. Vol. 1. Andre Deutsch, London. (Also introduction in Spanish in Vol. 2, 1961.)

Eyde, R. H. 1972. Note on geologic histories of flowering plants. Brittonia 24:111–116.

Garay, L. A. 1960. On the origin of the Orchidaceae. Bot. Mus. Leaflets, Harvard Univ. 19:57–96. (Also *in* Proc. 3d World Orchid Conf., London (1960), p. 172–196.)

——. [1964.] Evolutionary significance of geographical distribution of orchids. Proc. 4th World Orchid Conf., Singapore (1963), p. 170–187.

——. 1972. On the origin of the Orchidaceae, II. J. Arnold Arb. 53:202–215.

Garay, L. A., and H. R. Sweet. 1974. Orchidaceae (ix, 235 pp.). *In* R. A. Howard, Flora of the Lesser Antilles: Leeward and Windward Islands. Arnold Arboretum, Harvard Univ., Jamaica Plain, Mass.

Godfery, M. J. 1933. Monograph & iconograph of native British Orchidaceae. Univ. Press, Cambridge.

Godwin, H. 1960. Prehistoric wooden trackways of the Somerset Levels: their construction, age and relation to climatic change. Proc. Prehistoric Soc., Ser. 2, 26:1–36.

——. 1967. Pollen-analytic evidence for the cultivation of *Cannabis* in England. Rev. Palaeobot. Palynol. 4:71–80.

——. 1968. Studies of the Post-Glacial history of British vegetation. XV. Organic deposits of Old Buckenham Mere, Norfolk. New Phytol. 67:95–107.

——. 1975. The history of the British flora: a factual basis for phytogeography. 2d ed. Cambridge Univ. Press, Cambridge.

Gothan, W. 1921. H. Potonié's Lehrbuch der Paläobotanik, 2d. ed. Gebrüder Borntraeger, Berlin.

Gothan, W., and H. Weyland. 1973. Lehrbuch der Paläobotanik. 3d ed. by H. Weyland. BLV Verlagsgesellschaft, Munich. (Same information on "fossil orchids" in 1954 and 1964 editions.)

Harland, W. B., A. G. Smith, and B. Wilcock (eds.). 1964. The Phanerozoic time-scale. Geological Society of London. (Issued as a supplement to vol. 120 of Quart. J. Geol. Soc. London.)

Kirchheimer, F. 1957. Die Laubgewächse der Braunkohlenzeit. Veb Wilhelm Knapp, Halle (Saale).

Krackowizer, F. J. 1953. Orquídeas fósseis. Rev. do Circulo Paulista de Orquidófilos 10(3):36–38.

——. 1964. Orquideas fósseis. Orquídea (Rio de Janeiro) 26:39–40.

Krishtofovich, A. N. 1957. Paleobotanika. 4th ed. Gosudarstvennoe Nauchno-tekhncheskoe Izdatel'stvo, Leningrad.

Luer, C. A. 1972. The native orchids of Florida. The New York Botanical Garden, Bronx, N.Y. (See Schmid, 1976, for review.)

——. 1975. The native orchids of the United States and Canada excluding Florida. The New York Botanical Garden, Bronx, N.Y. (See Schmid, 1976, for review.)

MacGinitie, H. D. 1953. Fossil plants of the Florissant beds, Colorado. Carnegie Inst. Washington Pub. 599:i–iii, 1–198.

Machin (née Pallot), J. 1971. Plant microfossils from Tertiary deposits of the Isle of Wight. New Phytol. 70:851–872.

Massalongo, A. B. 1857. Vorläufige Nachricht über die neueren paläontologischen Entdeckungen am *Monte Bolca*. Neues Jahrb. Mineral., Geognosie 1857:775–778.

——. 1858. Palaeophyta rariora formationis tertiariae agri Veneti. Atti R. Ist. Veneto Sci., Ser. 3, 3:729–793.

——. 1859a. Specimen photographicum animalium quorumdam plantarumque fossilium *Agri Veronensis*. Vicentini-Franchini, Verona. (Dual text in Italian and Latin.)

——. 1859b. Syllabus plantarum fossilium hucusque in formationibus tertiariis agri Veneti detectarum. A. Merlo, Verona.

Melchior, H. 1964. Reihe Microspermae (*Orchidales, Gynandrae*), p. 613–625. *In* H. Melchior (ed.), A. Engler's Syllabus der Pflanzenfamilien. 12th ed. Vol. 2. Angiospermen. Gebrüder Borntraeger, Berlin-Nikolassee.

Menard, H. W. 1971. Science: growth and change. Harvard Univ. Press, Cambridge, Mass.

Meschinelli, A., and X. Squinabol. 1893. Flora tertiaria Italica. Sumptibus Auctorum Typis Seminarii, Patavi.

Muller, J. 1970. Palynological evidence on early differentiation of angiosperms. Biol. Rev. 45:417–450.

Naegeli, O. 1905. Ueber westliche Florenelemente in der Nordostschweiz. Ber. Schweiz. Bot. Ges. 15:14–25.

Němejc, F. 1975. Paleobotanika. IV. Systematická část: rostliny krytosemenné. Academia, Nakladatelství Československé Akademie Věd, Prague.

Novák, F. A. 1972. Vyšší rostliny: Tracheophyta. 2d ed. 2 vols. Academia Nakladatelství Československé Akademie Věd, Prague. (Same information on "fossil orchids" in 1961 edition.)

Pijl, L. van der. 1966. Pollination mechanisms in orchids, p. 61–75. *In* J. G. Hawkes (ed.), Reproductive biology and taxonomy of vascular plants. Pergamon Press, Oxford.

Pijl, L. van der, and C. H. Dodson. 1966. Orchid flowers: their pollination and evolution. Univ. of Miami Press, Coral Gables, Fla.

Potonié, R. 1967. Versuch der Einordnung der fossilen Sporae dispersae in das phylogenetische System der Pflanzenfamilien. Forschungsber. Landes Nordrhein-Westfalen 1761:1–310.

Raven, P. H., and D. I. Axelrod. 1974. Angiosperm biogeography and past continental movements. Ann. Missouri Bot. Gard. 61:539–673.

Rolfe, R. A. 1909–12. The evolution of the Orchidaceae. Orchid Rev. 17:129–132, 193–196, 249–252, 289–292, 353–356; 18:33–36, 97–99, 129–132, 162–166, 289–294, 321–325; 19:68–69, 289–292; 20:204–207, 225–228, 260–264. (General discussion in 20:225–228, 260–264.)

Rosa, M. D. 1975. Moltiplicazione meristematica delle orchidee. Rotary Club di Roma Sud Ovest, Rome. 15 pp.

Sanford, W. W. 1974. The ecology of orchids, p. 1–100. *In* C. L. Withner (ed.), The orchids: scientific studies. Wiley-Interscience, New York.

Schimper, W. P., and A. Schenk. 1879–90. Palaeophytologie. Pt. 2. *In* K. A. Zittel (ed.), Handbuch der Palaeontologie. R. Oldenbourg, Munich. (Also the 1891 translation into French by C. Barrois *et al.*: Paléophytologie. Pt. 2. *In* K. A. Zittel [ed.], Traité de Paléontologie.)

Schmid, R. 1976. Review of Luer (1972, 1975), cited above. Syst. Bot. 1:97–98.

Schmid, R., and M. J. Schmid. 1973. Fossils attributed to the Orchidaceae. Amer. Orchid Soc. Bull. 42:17–27.

——. 1974. On Massalongo's fossils: *Protorchis* and *Palaeorchis*. Amer. Orchid Soc. Bull. 43:213–216.

Schultes, R. E. 1960. Native orchids of Trinidad and Tobago. Pergamon Press, New York.

——. 1966. Orchid [in part], p. 1041–1043. *In* Encyclopaedia Britannica, Vol. 16. (Also in subsequent editions through 1973.)

Schultes, R. E., and A. S. Pease. 1963. Generic names of orchids: their origin and meaning. Academic Press, New York.

Sernander, R. 1894. Studier öfver den Gotländska vegetationens utvecklingshistoria. Doctoral Thesis, Univ. Uppsala. 112 pp. (Printed copy.)

Stebbins, G. L., Jr. 1950. Variation and evolution in plants. Columbia Univ. Press, New York.

Straus, A. 1954. Beiträge zur Pliocänflora von Willershausen. IV. Die Monocotyledonen. Palaeontographica 96B:1–11.

——. 1969. Beiträge zur Kenntnis der Pliozänflora von Willershausen (VII). Die Angiospermen-Früchte und -Samen. Argumenta Palaeobotanica 3:163–197.

Thurmann, J. [1833.] Essai sur les soulèvemens Jurassiques du Porrentruy, avec une description géognostique des terrains secondaires de ce pays, et des considérations générales sur les chaines du Jura. Mém. Soc. Hist. Nat. Strasbourg 1 (book 2, article "L"):1–84.

Tomlinson, P. B. 1974. Development of the stomatal complex as a taxonomic character in the monocotyledons. Taxon 23:109–128.

Turner, J. 1970. Post-Neolithic disturbance of British vegetation, p. 97–116. *In* D. Walker and R. G.
West (eds.), Studies in the vegetational history of the British Isles: essays in honour of Harry Godwin.
Univ. Press, Cambridge.

Vent, W. 1965. Neue Pflanzenfunde aus den interglazialen Ilmtaltravertinen von Weimar-Ehringsdorf.
Geologie 14:198–205.

Visiani, R. de. 1861. Relazione della vita scientifica del dott. Abramo Bartolommeo Massalongo. Atti
R. Ist. Veneto Sci., Ser. 3, 6:241–305.

——. 1868. Das wissenschaftliche Leben des Dr. Abraham Bartholom. Massalongo zu Verona. Translated
from the Italian (see de Visiani, 1861) by A. v. Krempelhuber. Verh. K.-K. Zool.-Bot. Ges. Wien
18:35–94.

Walker, J. W., and J. A. Doyle. 1975. The bases of angiosperm phylogeny. Ann. Missouri Bot. Gard.
62:664–723.

Williams, N. H. 1975. Stomatal development in *Ludisia discolor* (Orchidaceae): mesoperigenous subsidiary
cells in the monocotyledons. Taxon 24:281–288.

HISTORY—SYSTEMATICS

3

Orchids in Rumphius'
Herbarium Amboinense

HENDRIK C. D. de WIT*

* This chapter is dedicated to Suzanneke, because of her smile when she looked at the orchids in my little garden, long ago.

Outline of Rumphius' Life

Georgius Everhardus Rumphius, to his family and friends Jeuriaen Rumpf, was born, probably in 1627, at or near the town of Hanau (Western Germany). I pointed out some years ago (de Wit, 1959:2) that his mother's name, Anne Elisabeth (family name unknown), made her being Dutch very possible. In addition Rumpf enlisted with the Dutch East India Company as "Jeuriaen," a typically Dutch Christian name, and he was also known as "Jörg," the equivalent name in low-German. Half of Hanau's population were Dutch refugees, adherents to the Evangelical Church, a sect to which the Rumpfs belonged. Having reconsidered this historical evidence I feel more convinced than ever that Jeuriaen's home language was Dutch, which explains his descriptions of plants in a racy Dutch. So thorough a command of a foreign language can hardly be acquired. I hold that writing Dutch was what Rumphius was wont to do, that it was his mother tongue.

Jeuriaen finished the Hanau "Gymnasium" and soon after was recruited as a soldier by an officer alleged to be in the service of the Republic of Venice. He set out to explore the world, eighteen years old, believing himself bound for Venice. He embarked on "De Swarte Raef" (The Black Raven), destination South America, in the service of the Dutch West India Company, which was fighting the Portuguese in Brazil. Captured by the Portuguese, Rumphius was brought as a prisoner to Portugal to be inducted into the Portuguese Army. As he roamed through Portugal his taste for exotic plants developed and at Lisbon, and possibly other ports, he saw and heard about the marvels and adventures in the Far East. In 1648/49 he returned to Hanau and stayed there three years. He left the island harbor of Texel in the north of Holland on December 26, 1652, on the East Indiaman "Muyden," as midshipman Rumpf. His motive was "the elucidation of Amboina's plants, this surely being first of all the reason for proceeding to India," as he stated, many years later, in an official letter. He arrived in Batavia (Jakarta) in 1653, and in the Ambon Archipelago in 1654. Three years later he became second merchant at Larike (in southwestern Ambon), in 1660 chief ("opperhooft") of the northern Peninsula, Hitu, and in 1662 "first merchant."

In 1663 he requested permission to be allowed to have books purchased in Holland and have them sent to him because "I stand in need of various good and trustworthy authors, who might serve me in these Indian wildnesses as a compass and a stay to the Memory." He got his books.

In 1666, Rumphius became temporarily "secunde" at Ambon, serving directly under the Governor. But only temporarily, because he was replaced by an officer enjoying "protection" in high places. As a consolation a "certain bit of land . . . not thought to yield more than a hundred 'rijcksdaelders' [dollars] when sold" was presented to him. It was a vacant lot near the town hall; Rumphius made it serve as a small botanical garden, his "Tuyn," where he grew among other plants some of his orchids.

When his contract as a merchant expired (1667) Rumphius applied for permission to retire and to stay eight or ten months in Ambon as a private person to prosecute his "curious studies." This was declined. Europeans were permitted to remain in the

East Indies only if they were servants of the East India Company. His contract was therefore extended for another year, under condition that leisure is granted to "promote said curious studies." Rumphius felt his merchantship was "a masque I am compelled to wear . . . to earn a living for myself and my dependents." At the end of the year he had to leave for Europe, but hedged: the ship supposed to carry him and his family he judged unsafe. He stayed on, after all, a merchant, but busy in his year-old botanical garden, roaming through the island, collecting and observing plants, and writing *Herbarium Amboinense*.

In April 1670, Rumphius, suffering from an eye disease, was practically blind but he had won the respect and admiration of the Government for his character and work; Governor Maetsuycker ordered that he be allowed to remain with all his dignity.

An earthquake killed Rumphius' wife and youngest daughter on February 17, 1674: "very sad it was to perceive that man sitting beside these dead bodies, and to hear his lament, both on this disaster and his blindness."

A great fire largely destroyed the town of Ambon on January 11, 1687. Rumphius' library, many of his manuscripts, and his own original illustrations of *Herbarium Amboinense* were lost. New illustrations were made in later years by helping hands, but Rumphius could neither see nor correct them. He is not responsible for discrepancies between his text and the figures. Nevertheless the number of errors is surprisingly low. Undaunted, Rumphius set to work to repair the damage, helped in various ways by the East India Company to prevent him from "ending his days in melancholia."

In 1701 he completed the last part of the *Herbarium*, "being an Auctuarium or Final Gift." On June 15, 1702, Rumphius died; the task was done.

Herbarium Amboinense

The *Amboinsche Kruid-Boek* or *Herbarium Amboinense* is Rumphius' main work; there are also published letters and notes on various subjects, mainly plants and animals, and a *Rariteit-Kamer* (mainly shells).

Rumphius' son, Paul August, executed the only known portrait of his father, and many plant drawings. Philip van Eyck was sent in 1688 to Ambon to draw plants for the *Herbarium Amboinense*. So were Daniel Crul (ca. 1680) and the soldier Pieter de Ruyter, schooled by van Eyck, who after his teacher's return (1696) stayed with Rumphius, probably till his master's death. Another able draughtsman was J. Hoogeboom. Johan Philip Sipman worked four years with Rumphius before departing for Holland (1696). He interrupted his return voyage in Jakarta to put into order the manuscripts of *Herbarium Amboinense* which were kept there.

Christiaen Gieraerts, related to Rumphius by marriage, accompanied him on collecting trips and helped copy manuscripts. The manuscripts of the first six books were dispatched to Batavia in 1690 and shipped to Holland in 1692. Governor-General Camphuys had ordered the manuscripts to be copied before they were shipped, and owing to this fortunate precaution the *Herbarium Amboinense* was not lost when the originals went down with the "Waterland," sunk by the French. A new copy was made and in 1696 the first nine books arrived safely in Holland, thanks to Isaac de St. Martin's and Cornelis Chasteleyn's work at Batavia. The final three books reached Holland in 1697, together with Sipman and van Eyck, and the Auctuarium (afterward published as the seventh volume but bound in the sixth volume) arrived in 1704. In the meantime Cornelis Abramsen, a one-time servant of Rumphius, made a considerable number of colored drawings, from specimens collected near Batavia.

It was not until 1736 that Professor J. Burman, who held the Chair of Botany in the University of Amsterdam, applied for permission to publish *Herbarium Amboinense*. He had it published in six volumes between 1741 and 1750 (the Auctuarium in 1755). The original Dutch text was accompanied by a careful Latin translation, and etchings were made from the drawings and colored figures in the original manuscript. Burman added a paragraph of notes (mainly references to literature) to each Rumphian chapter.

The *Herbarium Amboinense* consists of 1660 folio pages of fine print and nearly 700 plates. About 1200 plant species are treated.

Its nomenclature is pre-Linnean (the Auctuarium excepted, but that doesn't follow the binomial system). Nevertheless, more than 350 nomenclaturally correct binomials rest on, or are typified by, the *Herbarium Amboinense*. The orchids are included in the fifth (1747) and sixth (1750) volumes. To quote the relevant chapters in full would certainly be rewarding (although the graphic, vigorous wording in the Dutch language necessarily stands to lose much of its flavor and force by translation), but this demands many more pages than are available. Below, Rumphius' orchids are listed together with some highlights and an introductory evaluation of his contribution to orchidology. Details helpful to the tracing of Rumphian orchids on Ambon in their natural habitat are added.

Interpretation of *Herbarium Amboinense*

Rumphius' work is the best ever on Moluccan botany. It is an authoritative source today. No herbarium specimens exist on which the descriptions rest. Identifications often are supported by specimens collected in later years, e.g., by Robinson (1913). General interpretations were listed by me in 1952 (de Wit, 1959:1–12). Linnaeus himself, although fully acquainted with it, has fewer than twenty references in his *Species Plantarum* of 1753. Merrill's (1917) excellent study "An Interpretation of Rumphius's *Herbarium Amboinense*" was revised by me (de Wit, 1959:339–460), but I added hardly any significant data. Merrill in particular based his interpretation on specimens collected by Dr. Ch. B. Robinson, Jr., on Amboina. Robinson started fieldwork on July 15, 1913, and was killed (through a tragic misunderstanding) on December 5 of the same year. The orchids are named according to Merrill's (and de Wit's) publications, but it is to be noted that J. J. Smith identified the orchids for Merrill's book. Smith's work on Indonesian orchidology is a standard reference, and his identifications are almost completely accepted in the annotated list of the orchids in *Herbarium Amboinense* presented below. If mentioned without further reference, Smith's contribution in Merrill's book (1917) is meant.

Rumphius as a Botanical Author

Let us suppose that Rumphius when he left for the East Indies was familiar with the taxonomical or botanical literature of his day. What might he have been taught, at school and afterward, but before the end of 1652? That was the year he left Europe, center of all botanical learning, to which he never returned. After 1652, information or the views of others reached him by means of letters or books. Another limitation was that his eyesight was gone by 1670. Nature was and had to be his main source of information, as long as his eyes served him. He must have made all descriptions between 1653 and 1670.

The study of botany, by means or method acceptable to modern thought, had been resumed in the first half of the sixteenth century. German and Dutch scientists or botanists had the works of Brunfels, Bock (Tragus), Fuchs, Camerarius, Dodonaeus, Clusius, Lobelius, and J. and C. Bauhin as the main sources of reference. For his orchids Rumphius consulted Bock, Dodonaeus, and J. Bauhin. In addition he referred to Kircher, a second-rate author. However, these literature sources were of no value to Rumphius; they contained next to nothing that he could use.

Some information of tropical plants was recorded by the abovementioned authors. There were also Jan Huyghen van Linschoten, Garcia ab Orta, and de Bondt, the first two writing on Indian and the last on Javanese plants. Rumphius owned de Bondt's *Notae in Garcia ab Horto*, but again this was no help.

When Rumphius left Europe, there was no information worth mentioning about tropical orchids. Belief in *generatio spontanea* still stood firm (Harvey's slogan "*Ex ovo omnia*" of 1651 had just appeared in print). Cells were seen only in 1665 (and misunderstood) by Hooke. The discovery by Nehemiah Grew that stamens represented male organs took place in 1682.

De Tournefort, easily the best plant-describer and taxonomist of the second half of the seventeenth century, still hardly bothered about segregation of species ca. 1700 (and achieved but little in that field). On the other hand, he delimited genera adequately. Written fifty years after Rumphius' departure from Europe, the *Institutio* by de Tournefort never reached the blind botanist in Ambon.

I think that Rumphius is the first botanist in history who noted the presence of pollen in orchids. And more: perusing Dodonaeus' book I was surprised to find no record of orchid-fruits. Rumphius recognized orchid-fruits without the slightest doubt and though he obviously hesitates to declare that the "flour" or "fine sand" inside were the seed, he nevertheless arrived at that conclusion. I suggest that Rumphius is the first author ever to describe orchid-fruits and seeds, while he tacitly rejects the tales about their reproduction (cited below) found in the scientific literature of his day. And he described the epiphytic, nonparasitic growth of many orchids, contrasting this to terrestrial growth.

Chapters of the *Herbarium Amboinense* are devoted to one main taxon, consisting of one or more species. Often data on allied species or taxa are added to the descriptive part. The description is followed by an explanation of the name or names used. Then the growing stations are noted. Ecological data often are added, and as a rule they have not been improved upon since. Finally the various uses are recorded.

Occasionally the literature within Rumphius' reach is discussed objectively and never in a condescending way (which might have been a temptation for other men in the privileged position to observe in the field, and so to obtain information not available to the European authors).

Rumphian plant descriptions are excellent and I have stated my appreciation before. He used no specialist's, not even a professional botanist's, terminology, or even the small number of specialized terms available in his day. Dutch current in the seventeenth century provided all he needed for phytography as a fine art. His pen-portraits are so well written that if a Rumphian description is checked against a living specimen one feels growing satisfaction and pleasure in perceiving the quality of his work. And here lies the reason why Rumphius' *Herbarium Amboinense* is an ever-green, exemplary, and never to be forgotten work of phytography.

Our present-day phytography is part of the handicraft of the professional taxonomist, who performs what he is required to do and was trained for. The descriptions produced are modeled in a strict pattern. Within narrow permissible limits the modern describer treats a sequence of organs. Each category is treated in every desirable or necessary detail, again according to a rigid model considered suitable for the description of an organ. The describer may be allowed the freedom of first mentioning number and surface, then shape followed by measurements, or a different sequence. However, once adopted for a general treatment, the pattern is set, and any change is an oversight, or, at best, a deliberate liberty indulged in for good reasons.

The result is that no modern technical plant or species description causes any emotion. The description is adequate and right if it contains, in a surveyable and easily checked arrangement, the data necessary for identification. Modern phytography, as demanded for monographic taxonomical treatment, can be entered into a computer program without hitch. It is made by a highly trained observer who proceeds, notes, and records objectively. Any personal commitment is to the detriment of his work, its value and trustworthiness. An observer who reports today on his findings from investigations of plant specimens aimed at determining their identity and systematic place, must keep aloof, must be absent from his phytography. As a result his descriptions are dead. It is impossible to retain a graphic mental image after reading a page of modern phytography. Rumphius, an unusually gifted observer, an enthusiastic scientist, deeply interested in the appearance and behavior of his plants, personally presented to the reader what he saw and heard, felt and thought, and what he wanted the reader to see and hear also. Rumphian phytography is part of himself and therefore alive, and that makes his book an evergreen.

Rumphius as an Orchidologist

As a systematist Rumphius performs reasonably well, when judged by the state of knowledge in the middle of the seventeenth century. He appears to recognize orchids almost without fail, even if he admits two species of *Curculigo*. The first, *C. orchioides* Gaertn., *Orchis amboinica major radice Raphanoide*, book XI, chap. 14 (*HA* 6, p. 117, plate LIV, fig. 1), indeed superficially resembles an orchid. Another plant he called

"Involucrum," or "Daun bonkus" (wrapper plant), "inwindzel" [(book XI, chap. 12 (=*HA* 6, p. 114, plate LIII)]. It was identified by Merrill (1917:142) as *Curculigo capitulata* (Lour.) O.K. = [*Molineria capitulata* (Lour.) Herb.].

It is significant that Rumphius, though following as it were a taxonomist's insight by correctly putting the orchids together, unhesitatingly adds these two *Curculigo* species. He feels no qualms about the first *Curculigo*: it is an orchid.

About the second, however, he stated (*HA* 6, p. 114): "The flowers and fruits appear peculiar, they resemble no anggrek [orchid],[1] but a Globba," and he continues to give details leading to an identification. Rumphius placed them with his orchids because the habit and leaves resemble those of orchids. To him (and his contemporaries) habit and leaf characters were at least as important as floral characters. In the eighteenth century the flower will be, gradually, acknowledged as being of foremost importance in classification. It is intriguing to find Rumphius troubled by the appearances of flower and fruit, which make him doubtful about his classification on the basis of vegetative characters.

Rumphius arranges his taxa, first of all, according to their usefulness. His twelve "books" carry titles indicating this model. The *Herbarium Amboinense* is a description of the taxa (all taxa found in Ambon, and other Indonesian islands), a survey of their life cycles, their names, their uses. It is not a "taxonomical" arrangement.

Book XI (vol. 6) deals with "wild herbs thus far untreated," and so it contains the wild orchids. One orchid, not recognized, closes Book X. *Flos susannae*, the only orchid segregated from all others, is treated in Book VIII (vol. 5) because this deals with "the domesticated plants, serving as food, medicine or ornament." *Flos susannae*, being grown as a garden ornamental, belongs there.

The orchids, having been assembled, are now arranged, first of all, according to their use and status. *Angraecum scriptum* comes first. It grows on trees, in high places, and it is a privilege, reserved for local nobility, to wear its flowers on festive occasions—two reasons why it heads the procession of orchids.

Ornamental epiphytic orchids follow, and then we are acquainted with less spectacular orchids. Now it is the color of the flowers that indicates how to assemble a number of species and varieties. Then, Rumphius continues (p. 106): "One should not assume that the luxurious wilderness of Amboina brings forth no more species of Anggreks than those which we presented in the beginnings of the eleventh book, where I lost courage to find out everything; but because I found some new species since, which I judged worthy to be described for reason of their singular shape, I will now proceed to present some, one after the other."

This remark makes it clear that Rumphius certainly wanted to report on all useful plants but also wished to include those devoid of usefulness: profit is not all. He is moved by the luxurious wilderness and the singular shape of its denizens to describe and to study. Here is the link to the modern naturalist.

The procession of noble orchids (epiphytes, above the ground) is closed by five species, all carrying the name of "*Herba supplex*," *Daun subat* (suppliant herbs). Rumphius declares (chap. 9): "This herb will consider itself belonging to the clan of

---

[1] Rumphius writes "angrec," "angreck," "angrek," and "angrekum." The presently preferred spelling in Indonesia, "anggrek," is used throughout this article for simplicity.

Anggrek, and amidst its Nobility it may be seen as a Parasitus or courtier who in good custom follows the court; there are five kinds, one small or common, and four large." Next comes the chapter (10) introducing "the peasant's kin of Anggreks, which do not grow on trees any more, like the twelve preceding, but on the earth."

This closes Rumphius' arrangement of the orchids; it is perhaps unnecessary to note that he and his contemporaries used "species" (*soorte*) and "genus" (*geslagte*) in an entirely different sense than in present-day taxonomy. The Aristotelian concept, followed by Rumphius, is that immortal timeless "*essentiae*" manifest themselves in living organisms. An animal or a plant is, as it were, the echo, reflection, or imprint in living matter of an unchangeable "*essentia*" that in itself is perfect. According to circumstances, an *essentia* is represented by one or another living being, including plants. Thus, if we accept the more common or best-known group of similar plants as the usual or normal representation of an *essentia*, then will other groups of similar plants (more or less resembling the first-mentioned group) be seen and indicated as "alterations," i.e., modifications of the identical master pattern. All pre-Linnean taxonomy (including Rumphius') is to be understood by means of this concept—a deductive way of reasoning which in practice often leads to the same results as those obtained by modern (Adansonian) inductive taxonomy.

Rumphius gave considerable thought to the ways of dispersal of his orchids. He described the fruit of each species, never failing to find a mealy content (a "flour"), but he hesitated to say that this would be the seeds (see *Grammatophyllum*).

Where do the orchids come from? Rumphius consults Tragus (Bock), and is told that orchids originate from the "seed" of thrushes and blackbirds, who copulate in spring meadows and pastures; sometimes one may come across their ejaculations. Kircher believes, Rumphius tells us, that all terrestrial orchids originate from the rotting corpses of animals which still contain some seminal virtue, or from the selfsame seed of animals which sport on the mountains or in the fields. Proof of this is found in the appearance of the flowers of the orchid that sprouted from the seed of the beast which it resembles, or in the similarity to that insect which grows commonly from a dead carcass of any beast. Kircher, of course, alludes to *Ophrys*. Orchid seeds were a complete mystery. To him the appearance of orchids is caused by something closely akin to *generatio spontanea*.

While noting the redundancy of the reasoning in Kircher's 1665 publication, we can't help approving when we find Rumphius, at the same time, avoiding either support or criticism when quoting Bock and Kircher. He simply did not accept things on faith. Rumphius looked at his orchids. Again and again he discussed their epiphytic habitat, the way they maintain themselves and how they spread and reach their growing places. Not finding orchids sprouting from carcasses—once he is amazed at observing grasses pricking through subterranean tubers—he remained puzzled, as he should be, and this is exactly what his time and his means (unaided eyesight, the state of biology, unbiased observation, lack of previous records or comments) allowed him to do.

The descriptions are all shaped in the same way. Vegetative characters (roots, pseudobulbs, leaves, habit) receive as much attention as the flowers and the fruits. The floral characters as seen by the naked eye are admirably observed and depicted in words and considered in every visible detail. The column, stigma, and pollinia are noted and described. Rumphius realized that the pollinia were comparable to anthers (pollen), and that is as far as he was able to proceed. The seeds are "flour" or "fine sand" to him. Subterranean parts are, of course, carefully described. The age-old interest of the rhizotomists and herbalists in the virtues of roots and tubers accentuated botanical observation all through the middle ages and into the seventeenth century. For centuries the subterranean parts of the orchids were better known than the flowers (one may consult the herbals of the fourteenth through the seventeenth centuries to realize this peculiar historical development).

After the morphology, Rumphius notes the growing localities or environment. He lists names of various origins and meanings, and records all ethnical data (local lore; medicinal, magic, and food uses).

This arrangement is much the same as that in present-day taxonomical treatments. An essential difference, however, is that Rumphius tells about plants which are alive—living nature. A wealth of descriptive data coupled with his vivid style portrays his objects as living plants. His gifts as a naturalist and writer of prose provide the basis from which research on the identity of still doubtful Rumphian plants should start (rather than from the identification of general Ambon collections). The vegetation of the land where Rumphius worked has largely been destroyed. Still it seems best to set out from the places where Rumphius once lived and allow him to lead the way.

Among many other fields of Moluccan botany, Rumphius inaugurated East Indonesian orchidology, and set the standard for devoted, unbiased, but warm-blooded research.

The Orchids in *Herbarium Amboinense*

Platanthera susannae (L.) Lindl.; *Flos susannae*; *HA* 5,[2] p. 286, tab. 99.

Lit.: Merrill (1917:168–169) de Wit (1959:398–399, 430).

It was collected in August, 1913, by Robinson on grassy hillsides in Ambon, Soja road and Way Tommo. Linnaeus (1753) published *Orchis susannae* (*Species Plantarum*, p. 939), which was afterward referred to *Habenaria* and to *Platanthera*. Holttum suggested that these genera be united, but J. J. Smith (Backer and Bakhuizen van den Brink, 1968, 3:248) keeps them apart.

The anther chambers are elongated at the base forming a tube which encloses the long, threadlike caudicle. In *Platanthera* the stigmas are together on the flat head of the column, separated by a groove. In *Habenaria* the stigmas are free, each on a knob.

Describing the flower, Rumphius notes that "in the center one sees a concave corollar leaflet, shaped like a small hood, that has two lateral hornlets, which bend and curve turning toward the inside, and disappear under the hood, and carry yellow anthers like the white lilies. Under the hoodlet one sees white and glossy knobs or glands, below which is a tube descending to the stalk."

[2] *Herbarium Amboinense*, Vol. 5.

Rumphius counts six ribs on the fruit and he notes that at maturity the fruit wall disintegrates into six narrow ribbons or small straps but, he says, there are no seeds, only fawn-colored woolly hairs. One to three tubers (shaped like testicles, a comparison made in every herbal) are present; one is the larger, the other wrinkled. In the rainy season *Flos susannae* produces a stem and large white flowers; in the dry season all aerial parts die. At the time of its new growth it can be uprooted and will thrive in a new station; when transplanted in flower it will not return next year. It is worthwhile to grow in pots and tubs. Rumphius certainly cultivated it in his garden, otherwise he could not have known these particulars of its life cycle. Moreover, he would not have entered *Flos susannae* into Book VIII.

Rumphius tried eating the tubers (tubers of terrestrial orchids are eaten by the Ambonese wherever they occur in quantity). He had them dug out and cleaned, and after some days in water, they were boiled in sugar. The result he judged unsatisfactory.

Flos susannae is the lovely and moving epitaph for Rumphius' first wife, apparently an Ambonese girl; the following little note is all that is known about her: "Because I could not find a Malay or an Amboina name, I named this flower in Latin *Flos susannae*, in Malay Bunga Susanna, in memory of her who during her life was my first Companion and Helpmeet in the search for herbs and plants, and who showed me this flower for the first time."

Habenaria rumphii (Brongn.) Lindl.; *Flos susannae minor, Orchis amboinica minor*; *HA* 5, p. 287; *HA* 6, p. 118, tab. 54, fig. 2 (Plate 3-12).

Lit.: Merrill (1917: 169, 549); de Wit (1959: 378, 430; see also p. 56).

Collected by Robinson on grassy hillsides in Ambon, Soja road.

In Book XI (vol. 6), Rumphius returns to *Flos susannae*. He explains that Susan's flower was placed in Book VIII because it was closely allied to *Amica nocturna* (*Polyanthes tuberosa*). It is the first and the most beautiful of four "species." He now proceeds to describe the three other terrestrial orchids (*Angrekum terrestre*). These are different from those treated just before and truly *Orchis*, by which Rumphius tacitly unites tuberous terrestrial orchids as a segregate, apart from the tuberless taxa. The third treated (XI, vol. 6) is *Orchis amboinica minor*; in Malay it might be called "Anggrek kitsjil" (small orchid). Rumphius correctly guessed the close relationship to *Flos susannae*.

Its habitat he described: "It grows like the preceding on airy hills, and also in grassy flats in swards under which it is hard to discover, if without flowers. One always finds it together in large numbers, where the grass remains low and short, like on the red mountain near Victoria Castle, where the whole congregation flowers simultaneously and withers simultaneously. It loves a black and hard soil; if one wants to transplant it, the root ought to be dug out after flowering, to be cleaned from the root fibers, to be kept dry for some days, and then be transplanted in suchlike earth, but it wants to be put in a slightly raised place, not in shadowy or moist stations."

Rumphius tried candied tubers—he tried all kinds—and found them rather tasty, but they were hard to get.

Anoectochilus reinwardtii Bl.; *Folium petolatum*, Daun petola, het Petola blad.; *HA* 6, pp. 92, 93, tab. 41, fig. 3.

Lit.: Merrill (1917:169, 549), de Wit (1959:347, 431).

Robinson collected *A. reinwardtii* on November 5, 1913, at Hitoe lama, Ambon. The specimen was cultivated and came from the adjacent hills. *A. reinwardtii* is known to occur on Java and Flores. I have not seen a specimen from Ambon, and Robinson's specimen was sterile. The occurrence of *Anoectochilus* is certain but the specific identity needs confirmation.

Book X (vol. 6) ends with this orchid, the only one among the "wild herbs haphazardly arranged" (*de herbis agens silvestribus promiscue*). By a happy coincidence Book XI "continues" by treating the acknowledged orchids.

It is interesting to note that Dr. Robinson found the cultivated plant sterile. Rumphius declares: "I took many pains to transplant it into the gardens, where it grew some time, but again and again it died without seed. The Ambonese, who sometimes plant it in their mountain gardens, are more succesful."

This small low grassy herb, consisting of few leaves, "is a masterpiece of nature, which we intend to be the end of this tenth book. The leaves are as cleverly decorated as if this were done by art. It has a single soft stem, not over two or three inches high, and so the little plant well-nigh rests on the earth. On top it bears three leaves, almost to a triangle spread, and below the same still two or three smaller, which more or less divide the stem into joints, and by their sheaths part of the way encase it, etc.

"The larger leaves rather resemble *Arundinella latifolia* [*Commelina*]. However they are shorter and rounder, some perchance heart-shaped, thickish, but pliable. On the upper side they are chestnut-brown, or slightly deeper colored, soft to the touch like velvet, and a little glossy, very prettily delineated by light-red or yellow lines, running together or athwart, by which they exhibit some square or unknown characters as though they were drawn by an artist-painter by means of a fine brush. The undersides of the leaves are reddish purple-colored, without characters. Unchanged it remains a long time, without showing anything else but these three or four painted leaves.

"Finally it produces from its center a single tender stalk, round, woolly, five or six inches high, partitioned in three or four dark segments, on which some white florets come forth, which soon disintegrate; and below selfsame the stalklet begins increasing and shapes a three-sided fruit, in the manner of *Empetrum acetosum* [*Begonia muricata* Bl.], to wit an oblong husklet, made of three thick pellicles or wings, but narrower than that of *Empetrum*, colored by a blend of green and brown, retaining on top the withered flower a long time.

"This capsule at least splits into three parts, but below and on top remaining intact, and then a little sandy seed falls out therefrom, resembling that of *Empetrum*, while still three single filaments remain present between the straplets. The root is trifling, made of a few thick white fibers, weakly seated in the earth, because always it occurs in a loose and moist soil."

Rumphius goes on to explain that the Malay name Daun petola reflects its resemblance to a costly silken tissue called Petola which is dyed in many colors. It is found but rarely, and is mostly unknown to natives. Daun petola always grows on high and remote mountains, under the intermittent shadows of high trees, where the ground is humid.

Uses, Rumphius says, are not yet known, and so it is "only brought back from the mountains as a curiosity, and exhibited; likewise I have not been able to picture it by pencil or brush because of the intricate lineaments of the leaves, wherefore I glued the whole herblet in this place onto a piece of paper, the more so as the dried one keeps its colors best."

Grammatophyllum scriptum (L.) Bl.; *Angraecum scriptum*, Bonga loki, Anggrek Krinsing, het geschreven Anggrek; *HA* 6, p. 98, tab. 42 (Plate 3-1).[3]

Lit.: Merrill (1917:177), de Wit (1959:378, 415).

Dr. Robinson collected *Gr. scriptum* on October 29, 1913, epiphytic, at an altitude of 10 m, at Paso, on Ambon, and noted the native name "manumpang."

Book XI (the second in vol. 6) starts on p. 95: "Now we will describe Nobility among the wild plants, which they impersonate by desiring to dwell always in exalted stations upon other trees, and never lowly on the earth; likewise generally Noble Castles and Strongholds are seen to be erected on the heights, also in that an exceptional manner of habit and appearance is proper to them, similar to Nobility flaunting its fashionable attire. The third argument is adduced by the Moluccan Princesses, who rule that the flowers will not be worn but by Young Ladies of Rank. Among this Nobility, as it happens likewise in our human society, one meets suchlike persons that change into Peasants, and grow on the earth, and who seem to represent a different kin. Which compels me to divide all Anggreks into two main groups: One of noble lineage, growing only on trees, and secondly the Peasant's stock, which sprouts out of the soil, and they are all kindred to that herb which is named in the herbals Helleborine [e.g., *Orchis* spp.] and *Calceolus mariae* [*Ophrys* spp.], and segregated in so many species that I shall be unable by far to describe them all. However, I comprehended the Noble race into twelve here following kinds, the first and most beautiful of which, *Angraecum scriptum*, I shall describe in this Chapter.

"*Angraecum scriptum* is a singular plant in the manner of Mistletoe thriving on the trees, on which it waxes on the thickest branches, and mostly fornent their origin, or from the axils, with innumerable tough and white fibrils attaching themselves to the bark, and it holds erected many white prickles like a Hedgehog, but it stings not.

"From this emerge at first several large, slightly flattened and cone-shaped purses, transversely divided in segments and furthermore lengthwise deeply fluted or grooved, inside of a herbaceous and slimy nature; herefrom sprout three or four long and narrow leaves, clasping each other, similar to those of white *Helleborus*, or of *Hyris* [*Iris*], thick, rigid, below narrow, gradually widening, over one foot long, three fingers wide, pervaded in their length by three nerves, which protrude but little, but the middle nerve forms a furrow on the interior side; adjacent to this purse another stalk arises from the root, terete, and without leaves, four and five feet long, in the upper part somewhat bent, whereon the flowers one above the other come forth, in the manner of Hyacinths. Each on its own bandy foot stalklet.

[3] The legends for the twelve plates in this Chapter are as Rumphins had them, with very slight alterations.—ED.

Plate 3-1.
The forty-second plate. Engraved or Piebald Anggrek, growing on the trunk of a Calappus tree (Cocos). A: Unopened flower bud. B: Open flower, side view. C: Open flower, front view, natural size. D: Fruit. E: Root, attached to the Calappus tree.

"These flowers now are also peculiarly fashioned and appear to resemble those of *Satyrium* [orchids], attaining the size of a daffodil, made of five outer floral leaves, at the rear narrow, toward the front wide, some yellow, some yellow-green; on these one discerns broad spots and characters, like Hebrew lettersigns, but not to be interpreted, and all brown-red, also in one flower different from the next.

"In the center stands another hollow leaflet, involute like a small goblet, lighter colored, striped by brown or violet lines; in its cavity one sees a small but thick column, with an enlarged head, and furthermore the flower is scentless. The first expanding flower is yellow-green interiorly, and its characters dark brown, but in time it turns bright yellow, and the characters become red; it remains fresh a long time, also on broken-off stalks, which offer one flowers for eight days if placed in a room, one flower opening after the other. Finally they begin to wither, but do not drop, and their feet begin increasing and becoming pouchy, and make the fruit, which resembles a young Blimbing [*Averrhoa bilimbi* L.] or a six-edged thick capsule, its sides having raised ribs, of which three are large and furrowed and split in the upper part; the three other stick out less far and are unfurrowed. It is five inches long, one and a half thick, in the uppermost part largest, carrying the withered flower on top, in the rear narrowing, outside with a green, thick, herbaceous bark, inside entirely filled by a yellow, flaky flour.

"The ripe ones become dark grey and open up readily in six parts in such a manner that by their backs they hang together, at the top and base, like an Imperial crown, and then the yellow flour is largely shed and is blown away on the wind; but whether this is endowed with a seed-virtue, and settles to grow on other trees, is still unknown.

"The pouch, which carries the leaves, is, as stated, inside herbaceous, but when the leaves have fallen, they become inflated and finally dry, having inside a strong and fibrous mess, in which ants usually settle.

"Some variations of the above-mentioned plants are known, but they do not warrant the segregation of a distinct kind. Because, firstly, the plants growing on Mangas [*Mangifera indica* L.] or the like, trees with a juicy bark, have larger leaves than the forgoing, to wit seven to eight and twenty inches long, and over a hand breadth, and with no other distinguishable lengthwise nerve than the middle one, instead of three, which were found in the before-mentioned, and resemble the young leaves of the 'spatwortel.'

"At one time I possessed a flower-bearing stalk, four and a half feet long, repeatedly curved, on which fifty-two flowers were open simultaneously. The characters thereon resemble Hebrew not so clearly, but are more like ancient Latin capital letters, and some of them also suggest Samaritan letters, from which some names might be fabricated if here and there a leaf from a flower were taken and arranged. The branch of a Mango tree, on which Anggrek and similar herbs are standing if it feeds them well, will bear no or few fruits, which must be borne in patience, to gain a beautiful spectacle."

I translated the first third of Rumphius' chapter on *Grammatophyllum* to illustrate his approach and way of thinking. Having explained its "idea" (nobility; Platonian origin), he subdivides into twelve "species" (Aristotelian method). To aid the imaginative faculties of the reader of his description, he introduces comparisons (helleborine, *Satyrium*, daffodil, Hebrew letters, *Averrhoa*, imperial crown).

The markings on the petals catch his special attention, here and later in the chapter: one might even obtain some word by arranging them. This, of course, is the age-old belief, also adopted in the mystic theories of Paracelsus, of "signature," the presence of visible signs of the plant's "virtue" apparent by the shape, color, or habit. Rumphius does not follow, nor abandon: he prefers the benefit of the doubt and never displays a willingness to accept without supporting controllable evidence.

He finds it hard to believe that the flour in the fruits might be orchid seed, which is amazing indeed. On the other hand, Rumphius is suggesting that the flour might one day turn out to be the orchid's seed. He is also repeatedly considering the matter of epiphytic against parasitic regarding orchids, but although he is not clearly in favor of either, it can be concluded that the orchids are seen by him as either epiphytes or terrestrials, not parasites. The reference to the feeding of orchids does not infer parasitism (see below).

Rumphius indicated another "variation," occurring on the Kalappus tree (*Cocos*), which is believed by many to be a particular species, and he "therefore will describe it explicitly." A reasonably close description follows. He does not mention any growing locality, has no Ambonese name for it, and the Balinese reject the name Anggrek kringsing for it. Rumphius named it provisionally Anggrek kalappa. Sometimes it is called Anggrek lida "because of the smooth and stiff leaves, which resemble a large tongue."

Hasskarl suggested that this might represent *Cymbidium wallichii* Lindl. (J. J. Smith according to Merrill, 1917:177), but he stated that the description by Rumphius contradicts his own interpretation. Smith offers no other name. Some research in Bali, I suggest, may well reveal which species Rumphius intended.

Listing the names on record Rumphius noted: *Angraecum scriptum*, *Helleborine mollucca*, Bonga Boki, Bonga putri; on Ternate, Saja baki, that is *Flos principissae*. There is also Saja ngawa, and Ngawan (in Balinese, Anggrek kringsing). In Javanese all these flowers are called Langrec. Rumphius goes on to say that "the Portuguese call them Fulha alacra or Fulha lacre, although in reality this is a peculiar species in Java, smelling like musk, and so called because of the resemblance to a scorpion, which is suggested by the tail of the flower."

Dr. Smith (in Merrill, 1917:177) rejects this as a reference to *Arachnis flos aëris* (L.) Rchb. f., but I submit that Rumphius was aware of the presence of *A. flos aëris* on Java, that it differed from *G. scriptum*, and that it can be deduced that this Bornean endemic was an ornamental in Java since the first half of the seventeenth century or earlier.

Continuing, Rumphius declared that some Malay call all Anggreks "Api api," and they are also of the opinion that they sprout from the seed or the excrement of certain birds, and in particular they accuse the little bird Cacopit, which is a kind of *Regulus* (possibly *Dicaeum vulneratum*; cf. van Bemmel in de Wit, 1959:55). Rumphius judges this improbable "because said little Bird is not often seen in the Mangi-mangi [various coastal trees, e.g. *Calophyllum, Avicennia, Garcinia*], but in the interior on shrubs bearing flowers, from which it sucks nectar or dew; however it has to accept the repute that it sows all mistletoes or viscums by its excrements.'

"It grows nowhere but on heavy branches of trees in the country and on the mountains, similarly on *Canarium* trees and on the beach on a variety of Mangi-mangi tree, and it is known in all these easternmost islands; if cautiously taken up with all its rootlets, then it may be transplanted on a Mango tree nearby the houses if first of all a bit of loam is smeared on the branches, and if it is then tied onto this with a piece of string, where it brings its flowers every year, though they are in this way not as lovely yellow as those growing in the wild."

This shows that the orchid is being fed and not believed to be a parasite. And now we meet Rumphius experimenting in his little botanical garden. "I have also repeatedly tried to plant it in the garden and in the soil, where they produced nothing but leaves, but I never succeeded in having the flower come forth, though they stood for long years over; after that I came across a half-rotten stump in the forest on which it grew, and I brought this home, and put it deep into the soil, and the Anggrek throve and flowered, but when the stump came to nought, it also vanished.

"Remains to investigate whether one may keep it if a green branch in its entirety is chopped off and buried horizontally in the ground. Otherwise we must be contented that nature allows us to nourish this beautiful showpiece on our Manga trees nearby."

Rumphius finds it difficult to guess how these plants manage to become settled on the trees under natural circumstances. "Obviously it is unwarranted to believe that they arise from the detritus of the bark, like Moss and the Kinds of Ferns, because they would assume on widely different trees a much changed appearance also, and it would be impossible to transplant them in the above-described manner, but because one observes that they are as it were placed upon them, even on slippery and smooth barks, like that of Canary trees, it therefore seems more probable that they are either sown by the wind by virtue of their own seed, or by the birds, like the Waringa trees [*Ficus benjamina* L.] and a variety of species of *Viscum*."

This citation shows Rumphius considering the views of Bock and Kircher and finding Kircher's statements especially to be logically at fault. (Note that Rumphius avoids mentioning these authors here.) If the contents of the fruits really are seeds, they can be assumed to be carried by the wind. If not, birds may be responsible, as they are responsible for *Ficus benjamina* (here the earliest record of the dispersal of the strangler figs species, to which *F. benjamina* belongs) and for the mistletoes, and they are not the Cacopit birds.

I cannot explain Rumphius' next remark on watery grains, though I am convinced that he saw this and there is a natural explanation: "It might be supposed that the true seed-virtue is hidden in some grains of the size of a small bean, which are sometimes encountered in the forementioned yellow flour of the fruits, albeit that they are rather watery. Similar grains, larger than the others, in the fruits of various Waringas are believed to be seed-grains similarly."

Rumphius mentions some uses. "The flower serves for nothing but as a pleasure to behold, if they are cut on a complete stem and placed in a room during some days, not in water but just stuck in a clump of earth, because this plant entered into water emits a foetid smell like sewage, and like the majority of Orchids the fresh juice also smells.

"In Ternate the ladies of Exalted rank, *viz* the Ladies of the House, sisters, and daughters of their Kings (who are all called "Putri" in Malay, and in Moluccan "Boki") consider these flowers their own in such manner that a woman of common family, let alone a slave woman, would certainly offend them greatly by wearing this flower on the head. For this reason they send for this flower into the forest, to put it into their hair, declaring that nature herself indicates that these flowers are not fitting for people of lowly station, as it occurs nowhere but in high places, wherefrom it is endowed with its above-mentioned names.

"If anyone is stricken by whitlow ["quick-lawe," a small inflamed tumor, usually below the skin, on the end-joint of a finger], he should apply the juice marrow from the tuber, rub it with some *Curcuma* and salt water, and tie it on top, and the swelling will be brought to ripen quickly, although it will sometimes disappear, when it has not yet taken.

"The pouches of the large Anggrek, when peeled, and the interior marrow mashed and rubbed, with a little ginger, and smeared over the belly, evokes some itching at first, but not long, and thereafter it kills the worms, and at the same time expels all bad humors from the bowels, indeed it causes a swollen spleen or Tehatu to melt; the selfsame tied onto swollen legs is also applied to extract the dropsy.

"The marrow from the bulbs when chewn in the mouth, so that the juice appears, rinses the mouth, and reduces aphtha, because it is insipid and cools strongly.

"The Ambonese have a secret but superstitious trick to prepare a *filtre* from the yellow flour in the fruit, saying that a woman who has partaken of this flour must run after the one who put it into her food or drink. It is otherwise also added to food to stop the bloody flux [*roode loop*] and it lacks all taste."

Rumphius ends this chapter with a survey of literature, on which I have commented already.

Phalaenopsis amabilis (L.) Bl.; *Angraecum album duplex*, Anggrek poeti, *Angraecum album majus*; *HA* 6, p. 99, tab. 43 (Plate 3-2; Color Plate I).

Lit.: Merrill (1917:177, 178, 550), de Wit (1959:395, 396, 414).

Dr. Robinson collected *Phal. amabilis* at Amahoesoe on Ambon in August, 1913, as an epiphyte, almost at sea level.

Rumphius noted the velamen on the roots, "dirty white without, green inside," and recorded the absence of pseudobulbs. "The flower is made of five outer petals, soft and snowwhite, of which the two laterals are largest; toward their interior one notices an asembly of three also white petals, more or less creating the appearance of a Seahorn or of a Slipper, because the two lowermost bend together by a circular outline.

"The uppermost leaflet is more erect, and has at its ends two long beard-hairs, curled like a moustache. In the center of this circle one observes another thick leaflet, like a small pillar, dividing itself in two minute heads painted with yellow and purple; this circle is not exactly in the center of the flower, but slanting toward one side;

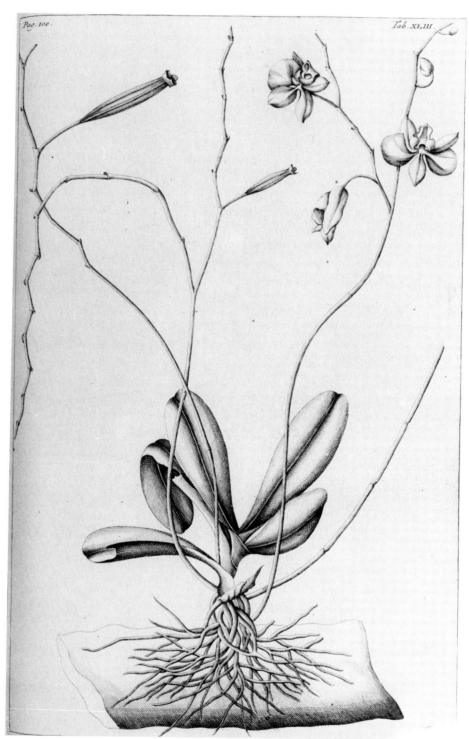

Plate 3-2.
The forty-third plate. Large White Anggrek.

right in the center of the flower is a white knoblet, from where the circle rises; in the said knoblet one finds two yellow grains, seeds as it were.

"These yellow grains are visible in the white knoblets, like two eyes, and simulate the head of a locust; and furthermore [the flower] is scentless."

It is worthwhile to note that Rumphius observed the main character of *Phalaenopsis*: the position of column and labellum.

Rumphius continues "This species has yet another alteration, where the flower admittedly is similarly fashioned, inside white, but outside with a purple hue." Dr. Smith unhesitatingly considers this the same species: "specimens with the sepals purple on the outside are not rare" (Merrill, 1917:178). There remains, nevertheless, the problem of the distribution and occurrence of *Phal. deliciosa* Rchb. f. (*Phal. hebe* Rchb. f.) on Ambon.

Finally, Rumphius recorded: "Item: another alteration still, of which the flower consists of five widespread leaflets, among which the pair of laterals are very broad, entirely white, only the little inner hillock is yellow.

"Name: In Latin, *Angraecum album majus*; in Malay, Anggrek poeti besaar and Bombo terang; in Dutch, Flying Pigeon; in Balinese, Anggrek Colan (that is the male, because they take this to be the female); with the Ambonese it still has no name, but on Loehoe it is called Wanlecu."

Again, Dr. Smith (in Merrill, 1917:178, 542) refers this to *Phal. amabilis*, but I follow him with some misgivings. It is a peculiar fact that *Dendrobium crumenatum* Swartz figures nowhere among the Rumphian orchids identified by Dr. Smith. The Rumphian names cited above are partly for *Phal. amabilis*, and partly, it seems, they are not. There is the Dutch[4] name (in the twentieth century Pigeon Orchid applies certainly only for *Dendrobium crumenatum*) and there is a distinction between male and female made by the Balinese. Information from Loehoe about "Wanlecu" is needed. Rumphius also noted for his first "alteration" that the shape of the flower was similar to that of *Phal. amabilis*, but he certainly suggests a different shape for the second. He does not mention pseudobulbs, but he appears to consider their presence in this group of little importance. The evidence is not sufficient to identify Wanlecu as *Dendrobium crumenatum* but a search *in loco* may clarify matters.

Dendrobium ephemerum (J.J.S.) J.J.S.; *Angraecum album minus*, Anggrek poetih ketjil, Anggrek kassian, Beursjes Anggrek; *HA6*, pp. 99, 100, tab. 44, fig. 1 (Plate 3-3).

Lit.: Merrill (1917:174, 550), de Wit (1959:365, 366, 414).

In November, 1913, Dr. Robinson collected *Dend. ephemerum* in Hitoe lama, Ambon.

The description of the habit, flower, and fruit in general agrees with *Dend. ephemerum* (J.J.S.) J.J.S., which Dr. Smith at first considered to be a variety of *Dendrobium papilioniferum* J.J.S. He also stated that *Dend. ephemerum* might be of hybrid origin (Merrill, 1917:174).

"It occurs on old rotting trees, growing on airy hills, which have fallen down, near the Caju poeti forests [*Melaleuca leucadendra* (L.) L.] but it is difficult to transplant because the roots are too brittle and too far-spreading."

---

[4] And English.—ED.

Plate 3-3.
The forty-fourth plate. First figure: Little White Anggrek, which is the Pennangu Maravara of Hort. Malab., vol. 12, tab. 3. Second figure: The Red Anggrek, described in the next chapter.

Rumphius refers to an allied taxon which seems intermediate to Daoen soebat (*Dendrobium* spp., probably *Dend. acinaciforme* Roxb.), which might be *Dend. suaveolens* Schltr. because it is "somewhat fragrant" and closely allied to *Dend. ephemerum*, but there is no certainty. A search in the growing localities might yield some information.

Renanthera moluccana Bl.; *Angraecum rubrum*, Anggrek mera, het roode Anggrek, *HA* 6, p. 101, tab. 44, fig. 2 (Plate 3-3).

Lit.: Merrill (1917:179, 550), de Wit (1959:402, 415).

Dr. Robinson collected *R. moluccana* in Ambon, during September, 1913. He noted that the orange-red flowers were spotted with red all over, and that the tip of the column was white. Native names were Bunga karang and Manumpang karang.

"The fourth kind of Anggrek," Rumphius begins his description, "is the red one, represented by a single tribe, still more ropelike than the preceding [*Dendrobium ephemerum* (J.J.S.) J.J.S.], because it is a long rope, and runs with long branches in the scrub among all kinds of low growth; its roots are not found to have taken hold in the earth, but here and there on an old rotten tree; the branches are scarcely a finger thick, round, hard, and stiff, but snap off when broken; the leaves are standing thereon and not in particular groups as in the former but on this the flower-bearing stalk, taking turns one above the other. . . .

"The stalk, carrying the flowers, is three and a half span [one span is about 23 cm, the distance between tip of thumb and tip of little finger when hand is fully extended] long, round, and stiff. It is divided in several side-branches, to which the flowers are attached. They are of the size of common Hyacinths, close together and standing athwart from the stalk, made of five small petals, of which the two widest are bent downward and the three narrowest are bent upward. Their color deep yellow generally, densely spotted by red lines and dots, so the whole raceme seems fire-red."

Dr. Smith identified this as *Renanthera moluccana*, but I fail to see why *Renanthera coccinea* Lour. would not meet the Rumphian data just as well or possibly better, in case these two species are really different.

"The fruits are over one finger long, half a finger through, pointed at both ends, dirty yellow in color, somewhat triangular but with six protruding ribs, striped lengthwise; inside one sees the yellow-threaded marrow similar to other Anggreks; on top one sees the remnant of the flower, being a six-leafed starlet.

"The Ambonese have no particular name but in Latin it is *Angraecum rubrum* and in Malay Anggrek mera.

"It grows mostly on the beach, running with many tendrils through the scrub, although it starts always on a rotten block or old root. In the valleys and along the riverbanks, one meets it clambering up the trees, and there it offers a handsome spectacle in the greennesses.

"And then it is rarely used, save the young leaves which may be put into Vinegar and Salt, either alone or mixed with other Atjar [sour pickles], and then they taste like Cappars [fruits of *Carissa carandas* L.], though one may suck but very little therefrom because they are exceedingly fibrous, and one draws well-nigh nothing more from it than the taste of Capper. To this end one ought to choose the thickest and fattest leaves, waxing on the beach and open scrub, because these have a pleasant saltiness, and thereby are better than those from the forest."

Rumphius records another "changeling," an alteration, of mingled fashion, between this "*Anggrek rubrum*" and the next "*Octavum sive furvum.*"

"The leaves are somewhat larger, five and six inches long, two wide, having a double top; the flowers are red, yellow, or orange, like the dried Mace of the Nutmegs, without spots, and have similarly five leaflets, of which the two widest are hanging downward and the three others are pointing upward, and the flower stalk is divided in some side-branchlets. This genus one sees not on trees like the other Anggreks, but thriving on the beach in scrub, like the preceding, with long, woody branchlets like ropes, which have a vein and watery marrow inside.

"I am unable to say, however, that both these species have their origin from the earth, because they run so far and long through the densest thickets that one cannot reach the root, and those few which I encountered had themselves established on old rotten stumps and mouldering branches."

Although Rumphius observed carefully and refused to draw a conclusion before he had sufficient observations available, the plant must still be identified with certainty. Dr. Smith stated: "I do not understand the exact status of the form of this plant described by Rumphius" (Merrill, 1917:179).

Vandopsis lissochiloides (Gaud.) Pfitz.; *Angraecum quintum, Angraecum scriptum minus,* Anggrek kringsing ketjil; *HA* 6, p. 102.

Lit.: Merrill (1917:178), de Wit (1959:410, 414).

Rumphius begins the fourth chapter of Book XI (vol. 6): "The fifth species is a small subspecies of the large or first, but because of its variation I have allowed it a special chapter. It has, to begin with, a large bunch of leaves, which grows also peculiarly, standing all within each other, and embracing each other, fourteen and fifteen inches long, two wide; frontally the tip is remarkably split, and there one side of it is longer. Beside this gathering, from the root itself, rises a flower-bearing stalk, round, stiff, four feet long, on which stand the flowers somewhat laxly, alternating one above the other, on bent stalks."

The description of the flower is picturesque and convincing. As a result, the identification is easy and certain. Having recorded the names, Rumphius described its habitat and cultivation.

"It grows on the beach on the Mangium caseolare or Waccat [*Sonneratia ?alba* J. Smith], wherefrom sometimes its stems hang so far down that they touch the water, because these trees stand during high tide in sea-water and are dry during ebb; I guess that the Malay for this reason named this flower Renda casian, that is, meek and poor, because they hang down so humbly. Those cut off may keep a long time indoors. The Balinese plant these . . . often on the trees of Sajor poeti [*Pisonia grandis* R. Br. var. *sylvestris* (T. *et* B.) Heim] where they wax luxuriously, which they implement as follows. They cut off the whole of the stock from the mother stem, together with a piece of its bark, then tie selfsame by means of ropes of Comuto [*Arenga pinnata* (Wurmb.) Merr.] on the thick branches of aforesaid trees, and smear this on the outside with mud, and so it adheres thereto."

Dendrobium spp.; *Angraecum flavum*, Anggrek casturi, Anggrek hemon; *HA* 6, p. 102.
    Lit.: Merrill (1917:174), de Wit (1959:414).
    Rumphius devoted chapter 5 of Book XI (vol. 6) to "the yellow Anggrek," which is represented by five yellow-flowered species of orchids. The flowers are marked slightly or not at all, the leaves are not massed in "peculiar bunches" but stand alongside of or sidewise to the branching flower stalk. There are many species and two are described in chapter 5 (Book XI).

Dendrobium strebloceras Rchb. f.; *Angraecum (flavum) sextum moschatum sive odoratum*; *HA* 6, pp. 102, 103.
    Lit.: Merrill (1917:174), de Wit (1959:366, 414).
    Dr. Smith (Merrill, 1917; see also Backer and Bakhuizen van den Brink, 1968, 3:358) identified *Angraecum sextum moschatum* as *Dend. rumphianum* T. et B. He makes no mention of the floral fragrance, which is reported by Rumphius after a delightful description of the habit and the flowers. "At daybreak, when the flower is just open, it has an agreeable sweet scent, almost like daffodils, or here in this country the Tanjong flowers [*Mimusops elengi* L.], not penetrating but stronger than of other Anggrek species.
    "On Bali its fragrance is still more enchanting, and for this reason they fable that Dewa, who is their God, which other Indian heathen called Dewata, Lewata, Rewata, and Rewa, visits this flower at night, and touches it with a whiff of Musk or Civet wherefrom it has its name. The flower-bearing stalk does not push forth right from the assembly of the leaves but often appears among the said leaves sidewise, as though it were inserted therein.
    "Its settlements are on the Waccat, or Mangium caseolare [*Sonneratia ?alba* J. Smith], and Citrus trees, which stand in the forest-gardens of the Ambonese."
    While I have preferred to identify *Angraecum (flavum) sextum moschatum* as *Dendrobium strebloceras*, it is to be noted that the Bali plant might represent *Dend. moschatum* Swartz.

Dendrobium mirbelianum Gaudich.; *Angraecum (flavum) septimum*, Anggrek tsjampacca; *HA* 6, p. 103, tab. 45 (Plate 3-4; Color Plate II).
    Lit.: Merrill (1917:174), de Wit (1959:366, 414).
    Dr. Smith found it impossible to distinguish between tab. 45 (Plate 3-4) and tab. 46, fig. 2 (Plate 3-5). He suggested that both may represent *Dend. mirbelianum*. It seems to me that the flowers in tab. 45 (Plate 3-4) are subtended by a bract and have no undulation in the perianth, whereas the flowers in tab. 46, fig. 2 (Plate 3-5) are without bracts and clearly show undulations. I am, however, unable to suggest another interpretation, which must rest, first of all, on the descriptions they are declared to represent.
    The description and drawing of *Angraecum flavum septimum* agree with *Dend. mirbelianum* Gaud. Rumphius compared the flower to a "flying hornet," made of five

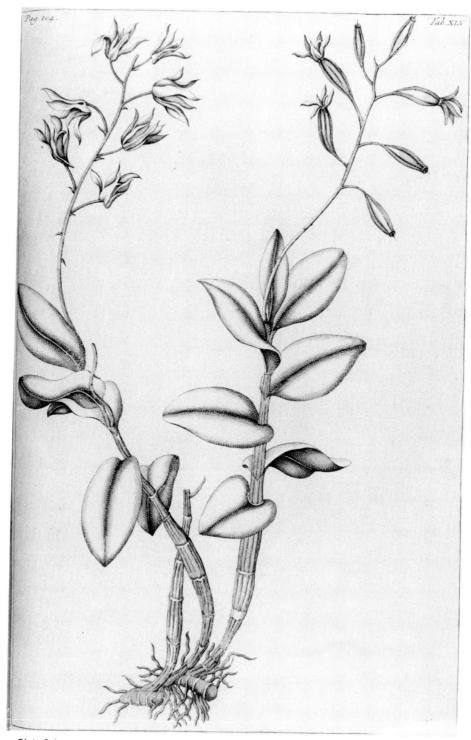

Plate 3-4.
The forty-fifth plate. Seventh or Yellow Anggrek, which was described in this chapter as the second species.

leaflets, of which the uppermost is slightly leaning over and represents the back, two suggest the wings, two other lateral ones are shorter and overlap a middle leaflet, which has two lobes on the sides enclosing the middle little column; the outermost leaflets are slightly striped like the Kananga flower [*Cananga odorata* (Lmk.) Hook. f.] outside yellow, inner surface deep yellow, like the Tsjampacca flower (*Michelia champaca* L.); the lip ("*helmke*") with a rim like a tongue, is bent outward and striped with purple. The lowermost part of the flower ends in a horn, like larkspurs (*Delphinium*), being "the head of the hornet."

It flowers in the rainy season, and Rumphius, testing everything as a dish, found the leaves "sourish, somewhat brackish," and they "blunt the teeth." *Dend. mirbelianum* is found, again, on the aforementioned Mangi-mangi trees and other trees standing in salt water.

Vanda furva (L.) Lindl.; *Angraecum* (*flavum*) *octavum sive furvum*, Anggrek kitsjil glap; *HA* 6, p. 104, tab. 46, fig. 1 (Plate 3-5).

Lit.: Merrill (1917:178), de Wit (1959:410, 414)

There can be no doubt as to the correct name of *Angraecum octavum*. Linnaeus made the Rumphian plate and description the type of his *Epidendrum furvum* (*Species Plantarum*, ed. 2, 1763, p. 1348). However, the circumscription and synonymy are less evident. The specific identities of *Vanda furva* and *V. celebica* Rolfe are in need of further studies.

One may keep the cut flowers in the house for a long time. Its fruits are "six-edged capsules, a hand long and wide, a finger thick, divided in six ridges, inside with a similar yellow and hairy marrow, from which hangs a yellow and fine sand.

"It grows on the aforementioned Waccat trees, both on growing and lying trunks, and on half-rotten branches. It is not easily transplanted, because of its spreading roots."

Dendrobium rumphianum T. *et* B.; *Angraecum* (*flavum*) *nonum*, Anggrek lemon kitsjil; *HA* 6, p. 104, tab. 46, fig. 2 (Plate 3-5).

Lit.: Merrill (1917:174), de Wit (1959:366, 414).

Rumphius stated: "*Angraecum nonum* has the smallest leaves, equal to our common *Sempervivum*, about one finger long, and hardly two wide, without nerve except a dark furrow, at the top not much cleft, thick and stiff, tasting unpleasantly sour."

The flower stalks appear on top or sidewise, and the flower resembles most nearly *Angraecum sextum*, but is usually smaller, "which makes it seem but a small kind of the latter." *Dend. rumphianum* is rather like *Dend. strebloceras* in appearance.

In Rumphius' description I found nothing contrary to the present identification, which is in agreement with Dr. Smith's conclusion.

Luisia confusa Rchb. f.; *Angraecum* (*flavum*) *decimum* and *A. angustifolium*; *HA* 6, p. 104.

Lit.: Merrill (1917:178, 550), de Wit (1959:385, 414).

Dr. Robinson collected *Luisia confusa* as an epiphyte at 2 m altitude at Paso on Ambon, in July, 1913 (flowers yellowish-green, lip lilac-purple, yellow-margined).

"This is the smallest of all yellow Anggreks, growing mostly on Canary trees [*Canarium* sp.]. It has thick, narrow leaves, like the pods of Catjang tsjina [*Vigna*

Plate 3-5.
    The forty-sixth plate. First figure: The Dark Anggrek or the Eighth. Second figure: The Ninth
Species of Anggrek.

cylindrica (L.) Skeels], six or seven inches long, not terete but flat, which stand around a straight stem.

"The flower is very small, two or three are borne together from the lap of the leaves, pallid yellow, of five leaflets, of which the two uppermost and narrower hang over, with a purple lip [*helmken*] inside."

Coelogyne rumphii Lindl.; *Angraecum nervosum,* zenuwachtig Anggrek; *HA* 6, p. 106, tab. 48 (Plate 3-6).

Lit.: Merrill (1917:169, 549), de Wit (1959:414).

Dr. Robinson collected *Coelogyne rumphii* at Soja and Bato merah on Ambon in August, 1913. It occurs also on Buru and Ceram.

Coelogyne rumphii was also referred to *Pleione* and *Epidendrum.* It would appear, however, that the taxon described by Rumphius and tab. 48 represent *Coelogyne celebensis* J. J. Smith (Backer and Bakhuizen van den Brink, 1968, 3:279–280). Rumphius stressed the presence of quadrangular pseudobulbs and four to five prominent longitudinal veins. These are characteristics of *Coelogyne celebensis* J.J.S. The drawing shows the raceme to be longer than 20–30 cm, and the leaves rather wide. *C. rumphii* is described in *Flora of Java* as having pseudobulbs (no ribs are mentioned, and the key implies that they are smooth), rather narrow, slightly pleated leaves, and racemes shorter than 30–50 cm. On the other hand, floral characters of *C. rumphii* agree with Rumphius' description. I have refrained from considering possible nomenclatorial consequences.

Angraecum nervosum grows on the Kinar trees (*Kleinhovia hospita* L.) and on ironwood [*Intsia bijuga* (Colebr.) O.K.].

"The flower resembles other Anggreks of middling size, consisting of five leaflets, the three outermost of which are largest and white-yellow in color, of which one is standing up and two hang downward; then there are two narrow ones, like straplets, which point backward; inside is the usual little hood, made of two leaflets, outside white and slightly turning yellowish, inside brown dotted.

"This flower pictures a flying gadfly if one takes the angular stalklet for the head, the lowermost broad leaflet for the tail, and the two narrow leaflets for the wings.

"The fruits are still unknown . . . ; the taste of the leaves is bitter and unpleasant. This Anggrek is peculiar in that it has veined leaves, and the flower stalk rises from the pouch proper."

Sarcanthus subulatus (Bl.) Rchb. f.; *Angraecum pungens,* steekend Anggrek; *HA* 6, p. 106.

Lit.: Merrill (1917:179), de Wit (1959:403, 414).

Dr. Smith collected *Sarcanthus subulatus* in Ambon during 1900. Rumphius declares that it is found "on a tree of Caju matta buta [*Excoecaria agallocha* L.], produces no pouches, but sends a thick creeper along the branches, and hangs down usually, here and there bearing a stalk, on which the leaves are standing, and between them again others appear." His description of the terete leaves, with a suddenly contracted subulate top, is excellent: "The leaves stand one by one, twelve to fourteen inches long, scarcely one little finger wide, at the summit with a tip, about one finger-joint

Plate 3-6.
   The forty-eighth plate. Veined Anggrek, which possibly is the Erythro-bulbus, with folded leaves of the white Hellebore, ''Red Bulb,'' that is, ''roode bol,'' so named by our [Dutch] nation (after Plukn. Mantiss., p. 70, and the Chichultic Tepetlanhxochite of Hernand. by Recch., p. 368).

long, which seems to be placed on top of the leaf, furthermore stiff, and without obvious nerves, which protrude at the lowermost part slightly, and upwards make the leaf somewhat hollow, like a smooth furrow, in colour dark green, and the older turn to fawnish, the stinging tips drop from the old leaves. . . .

"From its stalk waxes the fruit, hardly an inch long, striped, and triangular, shaped like a young clove, carrying the flower still a long time on top, inside filled with a coarse whitish flour."

Vanda saxatilis J.J.S.; *Angraecum saxatile*, Klip Anggrek; *HA* 6, p. 107, tab. 49, fig. 1 (Plate 3-7).
    Lit.: Merrill (1917:178), de Wit (1959:410, 415).
    Dr. Smith (1928) described *Vanda saxatilis* on the basis of the Rumphian description.
    Rumphius described the habit of *Angraecum saxatile* as similar to that of *Sarcanthus*, "creeping over the rocks, the leaves crowded in bunches, eight and ten inches long and one inch wide, on the upper side furrowed, on the lower with a sharp back, at the top cleft, having two tops, of which one is not only conspicuously longer than the other, but also stinging like a soft thorn.

"Between the hindmost leaves appear also long, round, and somewhat tortuous stems like cords, tough and unbreakable, white without, and at their end forking into two or three branches, which again take root in the bark of the trees.

"The flower stems are two span long, bear in the upper part small flowers, yellow-red in the centre, yellow margined; yellow is also the color of the lip [*helmken*]." The fruits have "a flat starlet on top, made of five tips and a blunt knoblet in the centre."

Rumphius clearly described a *Vanda*. The specific delimitation of species allied to *Vanda saxatilis* requires further study, in particular as regards *V. celebica* Rolfe.

Eria moluccana Schltr. *et* J.J.S.; *Angraecum angustis crumenis*; *HA* 6, p. 107.
    Dr. Smith had to identify *Angraecum angustis crumenis* almost entirely from the description of pseudobulbs and leaves because the flowers were unknown to Rumphius.

Angraecum sediforme; *HA* 6, p. 107.
    Lit.: Merrill (1917:179), de Wit (1959:393, 415).
    Rumphius wrote that this species was "rightly named, because the leaves resemble a *Sedum or Sempervive*; some are one, others are three inches long, two fingers wide, without any ribs, with a stiff tip, thick smooth and juicy, but without milk, otherwise one might take it for a *Nummularia lactea* [*Dischidia* sp.]. The flower is not yet seen. It grows with thin and tangled cords among and through the roots of other Anggreks."
    There is no evidence that an orchid is described. Dr. Smith declared: "unrecognizable." By looking at epiphytic orchids in their Ambonese habitats one might come across plants answering Rumphius' description. I am tempted to think of *Drymoglossum piloselloides* Pr. or *Cyclophorus nummularifolius* C. Chr.

Bulbophyllum sp.; *Angraecum uniflorum*; *HA* 6, p. 107.
    Lit.: Merrill (1917:177), de Wit (1959:352, 415).

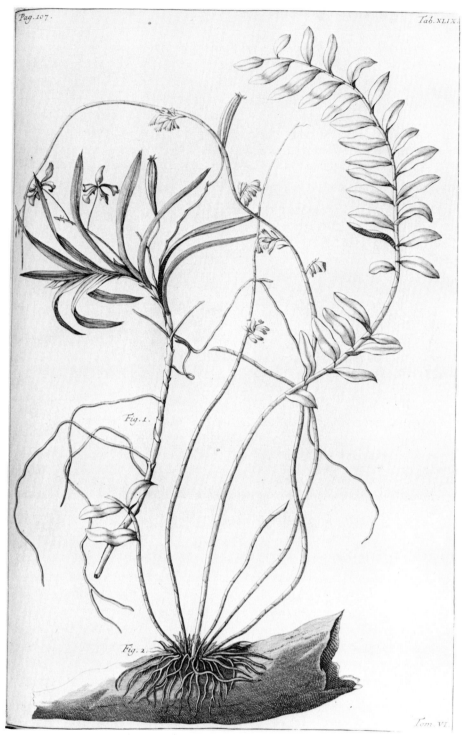

Plate 3-7.
   The forty-ninth plate. First figure: Rock Anggrek, the Tsjerou Mau Maravara of Hort. Malab., vol. 12, tab. 5 [to which was added by Plukn. (Almag., p. 87) the Monomopatense *Caryophyllus* with nervy leaves of the Bupleurum, hollow inside, producing blue flowers, and with stalks winged longitudinally (Phyt. tab. 275, fig. 1)]. The second figure shows the Purple Anggrek, which is the first species described in the eighth chapter.

"*Angraecum uniflorum* has leaves in shape and size resembling a tongue, to wit on top rounded, and slightly cleft in two, thick, stiff, and without any nerves exept a shallow furrow in the upper surface. Each leaf rests on a short pouchlet made of four or five sharp ridges; some are smooth with two edges.

"The flower stalk rises aside the pouch, round, one span high, each carrying one single flower, more or less similar to Anggrek angin,[5] made of three leaves, of which the largest and foremost is tongue-shaped, below wide, on top narrow, on the back sharp-ridged, curved backward over the whole flower; at the sides stand two leaflets similarly broad and thick below, on top narrow and soft, bent toward each other like sickles.

"In the middle stands a small head, its color brown, on which one sees many white-yellow points or eyelets, some circular, others square, furthermore without scent.

"It grows with a simple root on the branches of wild trees, and sometimes shows a flat layer as though made of some Moss, wherefrom here and there rise the pouchlets and single leaves."

Dr. Smith identified this as a *Bulbophyllum* sp., which is still the best description. Rumphius' data are, however, probably sufficient to decide upon the specific identity if *Bulbophyllum* species could be studied in Ambon in their natural habitat. *B. uniflorum* (Bl.) Hassk. may be taken into consideration first of all.

Liparis treubii J.J.S.; Anggrek gajang; *HA* 6, p. 108.
    Lit.: Merrill (1917:172), de Wit (1959:384, 414).

After careful study, Dr. Smith decided on *Liparis treubii* as the correct name for Anggrek gajang. He certainly understood which taxon Rumphius described, but it seems to me that the genus *Liparis* in the Moluccas and Indonesia is very much in need of revision. The data given by Rumphius agree with what is now called *L. condylobulbon* Rchb. f. (Backer and Bakhuizen van den Brink, 1968, 3:307).

Rumphius compares the shape of the fruits to a "wheat-grain but larger," which is exactly the way they look. "They are also six-edged, at maturity bursting along the sides while the top remains whole. The contents are at first yellowish and juicy, but change to a yellow sandy flour when ripe.

"It flowers in the rainy season, and one finds it on the Gajang trees [*Inocarpus edulis* Forst.], which grow in the wild in the valley of Ayer Cotta Lama. This species one also finds on other trees, and also on the east coast of Celebes, where the leaves are applied against swollen and hardened bellies, withered over a fire, till they become limp, then the abdomen rubbed therewith, and the marrow of the sliced bulbs chewn in the mouth, and the juice is swallowed."

Dendrobium sp.; Anggrek jamboe; *HA* 6, p. 108.
    Lit.: Merrill (1917:176), de Wit (1959:366, 414).

Dr. Smith at first suggested *Dendrobium pruinosum* T. *et* B. as an identification. Dr. Robinson, according to Dr. Smith, suggested in his field notes *Pseuderia foliosa* Schltr. Merrill (1917:176) prefers to refer Anggrek jamboe to the genus *Dendrobium*. Rumphius described it as follows:

[5] Dog's Anggrek, shown in Plate 3-8.—Ed.

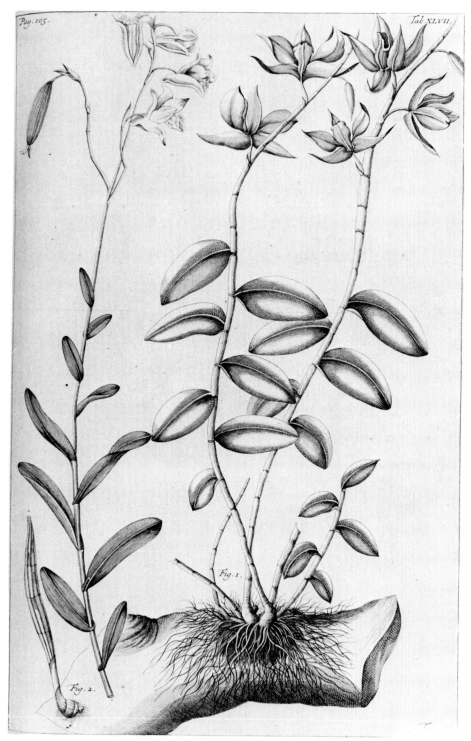

Plate 3-8.
The forty-seventh plate. First figure: Dog's Anggrek. Second figure: The Pouchy Anggrek.

"Anggrek jamboe has narrow, stiff leaves, five inches long, two fingers broad, ending in a stiff top, tasting at first unpleasantly, but later sweet like the juice of Liquorice.

"The small flowers come in opposite pairs, on little feet along the stem, and are made of five thick lemon-yellow leaflets, all bent inward like bird claws, and in the center one sees a violet-blue lip. The fruits are still unknown, and it grows on the wild Jamboes trees [*Eugenia* spp.] pendant, with long stems."

Angraecum taeniosum; *HA* 6, p. 108.

Lit.: Merrill (1917:179), de Wit (1959:393, 415).

Dr. Smith is of the opinion that *Angraecum taeniosum* belongs in the Sarcanthinae. Rumphius described it as follows:

"*Angraecum taeniosum* or straplets orchid grows by a single somewhat woody stem along which the leaves are placed solitarily and without order, resembling thick straplets or thongs on either side, with a furrow lengthwise, as though it were made of two parts, four and five inches long, and in thickness slightly exceeding a straw.

"At side of the uppermost leaves a short flower stalk arises, of which the flowers are still unknown.

"Afterward follow three or six fruits, being oblong ribbed capsules, one joint of a thumb long, like fruits on other Anggreks; on the outside they are divided in three larger and three smaller ridges, with a little crown on top, being the remnant of the flower; inside they are full of a sandy fluff. The root is long, single, creeping athwart, slightly woody, and it produces no pouch."

Only field observations of Ambonese epiphytes may solve this puzzle.

Eria sp.; *Angraecum lanuginosum*; *HA* 6, p. 108.

Lit.: Merrill (1917:177), de Wit (1959:371, 414).

"*Angraecum lanuginosum* is rather different from the common Anggreks in appearance, because it produces a single stem, three or four feet long, without swelling or pouch, of which the lowermost half is naked, and in dark joints divided. The upper part is densely leafy, round, and woolly.

"The leaves are fashioned like small Anggreks, very irregularly placed about the stem, three and four inches long, two fingers wide, thick, stiff, without a conspicuous vein, ending in a short stiff tip, which is slightly curved.

"The upper side is like worn velvet, and the three or four uppermost leaves, the youngest, are on both sides woolly.

"From the lap of the upper leaves emerges the flower stalk over one finger long, on this are the little flowers arranged, on short stalklets, which are also woolly, and they are bean-sized.

"These have below a hollow leaflet, like a small boat, wherein lies a hollow floret in three thick yellow leaflets expanding; among these a violet tonguelet peeps out, together suggesting a lion's mouth its tongue sticking out.

"It has but little root, consisting of few rootlets, and it grows among other Anggreks on wild trees at Toleeuw, a village of easternmost Amboina."

Surely, it ought to be possible to discover *Angraecum lanuginosum in loco*; I suspect it might belong in *Eria monostachya* Lindl., around which name a number of taxa have been segregated.

Dendrobium sp.; *Angraecum purpureum et nudum*, Anggrek jambu, Anggrek kassumba, Rangrec; *HA* 6, p. 107.

Lit.: Merrill (1917:175, 176), de Wit (1959:366, 414).

Rumphius begins chapter 8 of Book XI after chapter 57 of the Auctuarium, which was inserted between chapters 7 and 8 in the following way:

"The twelfth species was seen so rarely with leaves that many suppose it to be leafless. I have noted this difference in that the one growing on beach rocks and trees usually is without leaves, but the one that grows toward the interior and on the trees has its own leaves, and so it were possible to make two species thereof, which is, however, not necessary, because the difference is too small."

Dr. Smith believed that Rumphius had a *Dendrobium* sp. in mind but was unable to identify *Angraecum purpureum* (the seaside "species") any closer.

The following characters are mentioned: a stem consisting of numerous uneven fusiform joints, more slender near the base than near the apex; alternating leaves, five inches long and more than an inch wide; and a cleft top.

"This stem becomes about one foot high and bears nothing but leaves which drop at their old age and leave a bare stem behind, and this is why one thinks it is leafless, because at the side of the aforementioned stem arises another particular stem from the root, two or three feet high, rather slender below, near the root, and then continues by similar fusiform joints. In the conjunction of these joints, which is always at the narrower end, the flowers grow in hanging bunches close together, like whirls or the inflorescence of Jamboe [*Eugenia* sp.], around the joints or on one side.

"These florets have a peculiar shape, differing from the preceding, because they have actually five leaflets, which are not spreading, but adjacent to each other like a small tube, open at the underside, and thereto a small pouchlet or hornlet, like the Orchids, an inch long or less and hardly one inch thick. At the top, the edge is divided in tips, and inside, the lower leaflets cover a hoodlet colored purple or rose-red like the Cassomba color [*Bixa orellana*], entirely without scent. These bunches hang about the middle of this stem, and near the tops it is almost bare; the fruits are still unknown; the root is insignificant and made of short fibers.

"This species is found on the shore, both on short and thick trees, and on steep cliffs, on which lie mouldering branchlets and twigs."

Research in the field will very likely lead to the correct identification. The alteration, or "land species," differs only in having more leaves. Rumphius continues adding data. The flowers are seen in November and December. The vernacular names are the same, and the Latin is *Angraecum purpureum silvestre*. It grows on wild trees, like the waringa, samaria, and clove trees.

"The pulped stems are warmed and smeared upon 'curè Mataa ican,' or boils on hands and fingers, if a boil refuses to break out, to shatter the swelling and destroy it, or otherwise to make it open up if it has already become large.

"On high forest trees these stems attain a length of seven or eight feet, from the lower side side up generally bare, in the middle with flowers, and in the upper end again with some leaves; they are full of a tough slime, which exudes abundantly if they are cut or broken, but because of their obvious toughness one cannot break them off." This Dr. Smith reduced without hesitation to *Dendrobium purpureum* Roxb. Dr. Robinson collected it on Ambon, at Waë, in November, 1913, and found it in flower as Rumphius had indicated. At an altitude of 50 m it was pendant epiphyte, with lilac flowers, the sepals tipped with green.

Dendrobium moluccense J.J.S.; *Herba supplex minor*, Daun subat, het ootmoedig kruid; *HA* 6, p. 110, tab. 50, fig. 2 (Plate 3-9).
 Lit.: Merrill (1917:175, 550), de Wit (1959:366, 437).
 Dr. Robinson collected *Herba supplex minor* on Ambon, at Roemah tiga, in July, 1913. It is epiphytic and found at sea level usually on *Calophyllum inophyllum*. The flowers are dark red.
 Rumphius begins chapter 9 (Book XI) by stating:
 "Among the kindred of Anggrek this herb may be arranged, and among selfsame Nobility it may be seen as Parasitus or courtier, who customarily follow the court; one has five species of this, one small or common and four large."
 Rumphius goes on to describe the plant in detail. It is pictured accurately in tab. 50, fig. 2. Dr. Smith at first (1905) identified it as *Dendrobium atropurpureum* Miq.
 This small epiphyte, consisting of stems bearing decussate, crowded, subfalcate leaves, flowers only after several years, and the flowers are small ("short, slender calyces, high-brown"). It would seem that Rumphius had it in his garden. It "keeps unchanged a long time when broken off and kept hanging in the house."

Dendrobium acinaciforme Rxb.; *Herba supplex major prima*, Sibane (Luhunese), Daun subat parampuan, Herba supplex femina; *HA* 6, p. 111.
 Lit.: Merrill (1917:173), de Wit (1959:365, 437).
 "*Herba supplex major prima* also has several stems on one root, which are in their lower part bare over some length, after that up to a height of two feet clad by leaves, of the same shape as the preceding, but larger; then the stem grows longer for another one and a half feet, the upper part hung with solitary little flowers, which are yellow and resemble a small helmet, drop easily, and leave the stalk behind; few turn into fruits, which are triangular berries, filled by a similar flour."
 Rumphius noted that this plant is thought to be the female of the preceding, the male one.
 "These two species got their names because the leaves are inserted one into the other, if one turns the leafy bunches upside down, like the fingers of two hands that intend to supplicate, which reason is also given for the name of the preceding grass Daun subat.
 "Because of this fashion the Malay and Hituese use it in Amboina like the Ternateans use the forementioned grass: to wit, between lovers who send it to each other when they beseech each other and want to pray forgiveness, and to this they are wont to add

Plate 3-9.
The fiftieth plate. First figure: Purple Anggrek, the second species, described in the eighth chapter. The second figure illustrates the Suppliant Herb, and in reality its first species, which comes close to the Thalia Maravara of the Hort. Malab., vol. 12, tab. 4. The third figure pictures the other Wild or Peasant Anggrek, described in the eleventh chapter, with its fruit (A).

this refinement that men ought to send the leaves of the first species, which has its leaves more rigid, and so is more passionate.

"But the second and next species are sent by the women, meaning to acknowledge that they are, when beseeching and praying, much more fickle and dissembling than men.

"The Reader should not scoff at these triflings overmuch, because in the Indies it often stands him in very good stead, when he understands these Hieroglyphic Art-fulnesses to avoid being deceived.

"Furthermore the Alfurese of Ceram put these leafy stems with the flowers into their arm-rings, which they wear around their arms if they plan to set out for robbing or to hunt heads, as by their faith it makes them courageous or, I suspect, to obtain good fortune, because it seems that on account of their permanent greenness they deem these herbs lucky."

Dr. Smith pointed out that tab. 51, fig. 1 (Plate 3-10) cannot be accepted as representing *Herba supplex femina*, as stated. This is, possibly, some other *Dendrobium* species. The yellow flowers are so unusual in species allied to *Dendrobium moluccense* that Dr. Smith concluded that Rumphius described *D. acinaciforme*, although stems as long as those described he "never saw."

Rumphius' description was given here in full to facilitate further research *in loco*.

?Dendrobium sp.; *Herba supplex major secunda*; *HA* 6, p. 111.

Lit.: Merrill (1917:176), de Wit (1959:366, 437).

"*Herba supplex major secunda* was taken also to be a female, and it agrees more with that *Gramen supplex* [*Digitaria adscendens* (H.B.K.) Henr.] because it has much thinner and narrower leaves than both aforegoing, and so better resembling grass. They are also inserted one into the other; each leaflet is five inches long, and less, and has a small knee in the middle, but mostly they stand shriveled and macerated, being eaten through and up to the top; beside these leafy bunches emerge very thin and rigid rampant stalklets, which produce kneelets, release rootlets, and produce new leaf-producing bunches, whereas the stalklets do not continue straight on, but sidewise, always giving rise to smaller bunches up to the end. It grows along the shore on old trees, which lean forward tipping over, and also on rocks bearing some soil and fully exposed to the sun."

It is not pictured; tab. 51, fig. 1 (Plate 3-10) represents *Herba supplex femina* s. *secunda*, not *Herba major secunda*. Dr. Smith (in Merrill, 1917:176) judged the description too vague to be sure that a *Dendrobium* is meant. It seems even doubtful to me that an orchid was described. Rumphius apparently saw neither flowers nor fruits and was guided by the appearance of the leaves and habit of the plant. Research *in loco* may bring the solution.

?Dendrobium sp.; *Herba supplex major tertia*; *HA* 6, p. 111.

Lit.: Merrill (1917:176), de Wit (1959:366, 437).

"*Herba supplex major tertia* produces stems, low, down near the root, edged and somewhat bulging, divided in sharp ribs, like the Anggrek. The leaves resemble the second species of *Herba supplex* and stand in bunches together, flattened, but in such manner that [the bunch] divides upward in two or three other bunches, and the upper stem then shoots forth for quite a distance carrying some leaves, till the uppermost stalklet, which carries sparse little yellow flowers like the second species; after the flowers the studded stems are bare, here and there a fruit hanging on a thin stalk, three-cornered, but the interspaces are fluted by ribs, a fingernail long, inside with a yellow flour.''

Dr. Smith thinks that this probably is a *Dendrobium* of the section Rhopalanthe, and certainly not *D. atropurpureum* Miq.

Dendrobium sp.; *Herba supplex major quarta*; *HA* 6, p. 111.
   L.: Merrill (1917:175), de Wit (1959:366, 437).
   "*Herba supplex major quarta* possesses leaves and stems like the second, but, as a rule, larger, the stems being a yard long and more, and on them few leaves; on top it also carries two or three flowers, semilunar in fashion, each opened seated on a thin stalklet, like a little boat or slipper. The lowermost leaflet is divided in five tips standing out, which suggest the heels of a shoe; above stands still another leaflet bent backward like the nose of a shoe, entirely white, with a touch of yellow on the inner side of the uppermost leaflet. Scentless.''

To Dr. Smith the description of the flower suggested *Dendrobium confusum* Schltr., but that species does not seem to reach the measurements noted by Rumphius.

Dendrobium calceolum Roxb. *Herba supplex quinta*; *HA* 6, pp. 111–112, tab. 51, fig. 2 (Plate 3-10).
   Lit.: Merrill (1917:173), de Wit (1959:365, 437).
   "*Herba supplex quinta*, closely described, hangs like a rope from the trees, while fourteen and sixteen stems rise from a single root, near their origin thin, flat, and very tough; from there grow three others up to the length of one fathom and more, which produce at the very end short side branchlets, transversely directed. The leaves are a finger long, and scarely one wide, stiff, with a long acumen fashioned like a lancet; the flower is of the size of a small Anggrek, fashioned as aforesaid. The fruit is still unknown. Of this a drawing was made.''

Dr. Smith indicated that Roxburgh did not correctly cite Rumphius.

Spathoglottis plicata Bl.; *Angraecum terrestre primum purpureum* s. *album*, Daun corra corra Ahaan, het eerste land-Anggrek; *HA* 6, p. 112.
   Lit.: Merrill (1917:172, 549), de Wit (1959:406, 415).
   In chapter 10 (vol. 6) Rumphius continued the story of the orchids as follows: "Now follows the Peasant's kin of the Anggreks, which do not grow on trees, like the twelve preceding, but on the ground. . . . " Apparently Burman forgot to rectify the text. When preparing the manuscript for the press, he intercalated chapter 57 between chapters 7 and 8. This placed the treatment of ten species, which are found in chapter 57, in advance of chapter 10. Burman therefore should have changed "twelve" to "twenty-two.''

Plate 3-10.
    The fifty-first plate. First figure: The Suppliant Herb, actually the female or second species. The second figure illustrates the fifth species of the Suppliant Herb with a flower, hanging from a tree on which it grows, with its flower (natural size).

Some of these "peasants" approach the *Helleborus*, and some *Orchis* species, says Rumphius. The treatment of *Angraecum terrestre primum* is an excellent example of Rumphius' powerful phytography. Only a few highlights are selected here.

"After the leaves one sees four or five pointed knobs, together with the roots, but above the soil like small Combilis [*Dioscorea esculenta* (Lour.) Burk.], divided in dark joints, like the pouches of other Anggreks, with many fibers anchored in the earth. At the side of these knobs the flower-bearing stalks come, four and five feet tall, round, and largely bare, but somewhat jointed. In the top part they carry many purple flowers one above the other in the fashion of Columbine.

"Each is hanging on a rather long stalklet, and is made of five leaves, the three narrower of which stand expanded, light-purple like a *Colchicum* or 'tyloos.' In the center stand two other leaflets, somewhat folded together at one side, and at the other they cover another leaflet cleft on top and resting on a yellow stalklet decorated with purple lines. At their side stand another two narrower leaflets, and in front of selfsame another third one, curved somewhat upward above the said stalklet, all purple-red, and covered by the first two leaflets without main stalk, fashioned like the small bag on the neck of a crammed goose, purple and yellow mingled; as soon as the flower opens, the stalk begins to wax pouchy and striped, step by step changing itself into a fruit."

Rumphius knows of a second kind, *Angraecum terrestre primum album*, which is believed to be the female, largely similar but with very much smaller leaves. These are ribbed lengthwise and folded, but with fewer ribs and folds. The flower is similarly shaped but entirely white or sometimes slightly violet-tinged, also scentless. The pouches near the roots are also somewhat narrower and more pointed.

"The pouches of the first species, if it grows on heavy clay, sometimes attain a size comparable to the tubers of Combilis [*Dioscorea*], and on the whole plant now and then one sees nothing but these knobs, four and five together, without leaves and stalks, inside herbaceous and fibrous, at first slimy but afterward changing into a dry spongelike substance, as was described previously for *Angraecum scriptum*. But planted in the gardens it produces no thick tubers."

The Malay name, says Rumphius, is derived from the shape of the leaf, which suggests the cavity of a Karakar (Korra korra: Moluccan boat). Some call it by a general name: Daun tana; the Ambonese call it Ahaan, a name in common with the following Involucrum [*Molineria capitulata* [Lour.] Herb.), because they consider both herbs to be of one kind.

"These species are condescending insofar as they come down from the trees and grow on the ground; however, they do not come to the plain, but they are always found on steep places, mostly in vales where the land has slid down, and thereon grows nothing but long grass, of the kind that is called Hulong [*Imperata cylindrica* (L.) Raeusch]. The white kind is rarely found; both are often seen on the steep slopes of Alf river, where they are sometimes difficult to get, and one can also transplant them in the garden where they stand at least for a year before bearing flowers.

"The flowers are only used for ornament [*cieraat*], and with the leaves they are tied to the Sagueer-pots [for palmwine, of *Arenga pinnata* (Wurmb.) Merr.], and many kinds of fruit are wrapped therein, which are brought to the market for sale, as will be recorded for the next Involucrum [*Molineria*]. In the leaves and roots an obvious acridity is present, which suggests the taste of *Helleborus*."

Dr. Robinson collected *Spathoglottis plicata* in Ambon, in the town, on Soja road, Batoe gadja, and Hitoe messen, in July, August, and November, 1913, between 10 and 150 m altitude.

In the *Herbarium Amboinense* tab. 52, fig. 1 (Plate 3-11) is erroneously referred to here. According to Dr. Smith it represents *Phaius amboinensis* Bl.

Phaius[6] *amboinensis* Bl.; *Angraecum terrestre alterum*; *HA* 6, pp. 113–114, tab. 52, fig. 1 (Plate 3-11), not tab. 50, fig. 3 (Plate 3-9).

Lit.: Merrill (1917:170/171), de Wit (1959:395, 415).

"The second species of terrestrial Anggrek has a rather thick, creeping root, almost like *Curcuma*, from which some thick stems issue, lengthwise striped with sharp ridges, and transversely jointed. The leaves are also inserted one around the other, and resemble a young sprouting Pinang [*Areca cathecu* L.] or a *Helleborus albus* [*Veratrum*] two and a half span long, one and half hand wide, lengthwise divided by five ribs, smooth, and bright green."

Rumphius describes the flower:

"The flower has on the outside five white leaflets, and inside a wide yellowish hoodlet, which embraces with its wings the central three-cornered small pillar, and both are placed straight under the upper leaflet, being one of the aformentioned five, which is also like a little boat bent over the flower."

It creeps over flat ground, Rumphius declares, "its roots creeping over the soil like worms, on bald mountains, where one finds a little dell, and some vegetation, as in flat valleys, on the riverbanks among the grass, and it is easily transplanted into the garden. The taste is less biting than that of the preceding, more like true Anggrek, but no uses are known."

The next chapter (12) treats the "Involucrum" [*Molineria*]; for details see above, p. 54.

Dr. Smith noted that tab. 52, fig. 1 (Plate 3-11) was erroneously referred in *Herbarium Amboinense to Angraecum terrestre primum purpureum*, and tab. 50, fig. 3 (Plate 3-9) to *Angraecum terrestre alterum*. According to Dr. Smith, tab. 52, fig. 1 (Plate 3-11) "undoubtedly" belongs with *Phaius amboinensis*, and tab. 50, fig. 3 (Plate 3-9) is *Phaius gratus, Angraecum terrestre primum album.*

Calanthe furcata Batem. ex Lindl.; *Flos triplicatus, Helleborus amboinicus*, Bonga tiga lapis, Ahaan albal, Ahaän Malona, de drievoudige bloem; *HA* 6, p. 115, tab. 52, fig. 2. (Plate 3-11).

Lit.: Merrill (1917:170), de Wit (1959:353, 430).

Rumphius finds *Flos triplicatus* most of all resembling "*Helleborus albus* or *Gentiana*" and so different from the kinds of Anggrek that he would prefer to set it apart as another herb by its own, but the natives keep it as a companion species of the preceding

---

[6] The name of this genus is spelled both *Phaius* and *Phajus* in the Orchid literature.—ED.

Cacopit

B

A

Fig. 2.

Fig. 1.

Plate 3-11.
The fifty-second plate. First figure: The First Terrestrial Anggrek, with its flower (A) detached, and a little bird named Cacopit. The other terrestrial Anggrek is pictured in the fiftieth plate. Illustrated in the second figure are the Threefold Flower (described in the thirteenth chapter), with the fruit drawn separately (B).

Involucrum. So Rumphius follows this preference, and proceeds to describe it in his usual manner.

"[The flowers] show a peculiar shape, different from all Anggreks, because they appear like three kinds of flowers one above the other, but all white, and without scent, of which the lowermost part is made of five leaflets, smaller and narrower than a Jessamine flower; the larger stand in a triangle, the middle one more or less like a hoodlet, in the mouth of which one sees something yellowish and mossy, like little fine threads with a little tail, similar to Larkspurs. The third and upper part opposite the hoodlet has another four leaflets, of which the middle pair are diverging, like the Astronomical sign of Aries.

"Each flower has a longish neck, and near its origin a green leaflet. After the flower withers, the neck or stalk thickens gradually, and a longish, ridged or angular capsule comes into being, an inch long, like those of other Anggreks, in which small sandy seed lies hidden if one opens the ripe capsule, and when the seed is rubbed between the fingers, it assumes the color of lead.

"The root consists of many thick fibers, much like worms, bare above the soil, below smoke-colored, on the upper side green, and inside with a tough sinew, tasting insipid at first, later very acrid like some *Gentiana*, burning in the mouth, causing the lips to swell and making the throat raucous; which acridity is also somewhat encountered in the leaves, by which it differs from all Anggreks. It flowers in October.

"It grows in the mountain forests, in particular where much scrub and dry leaves are amassed and rotting. I found it in the light forests of Cajoe poeti [*Melaleuca leucadendra* (L.) L.], below the creeping fern of *Filix calamaria* [*Gleichenia linearis* (Burm. f.) Clarke] where a black and somewhat moist soil occurred, covered by rotting leaves, with its snake-shaped roots so loosely clinging to the earth that it was easily detached, but it is found only occasionally.

"Planted in the gardens it considers a long time whether it will decide to grow, but surrounded by its natural mountain soil and rock it produces its leaves and flowers, and these disintegrate annually down to the roots.

"It has an alteration, as regards the leaves, and a way of growth similar to the preceding; the flowers also are white, but not so obviously three-parted.

"Because this herb is in its entirety very acrid, it ought to be applied with caution, which is still little known, against swollen hands, which is called Hismi, that is, blessed or enchanted. These roots are taken with some nutmegs, Bangle [*Zingiber purpureum* Roxb.], Tsjonker [*Syzygium aromaticum* (L.) Merr. *et* Perry], and ginger, rubbed together, and tied onto the swelling.

"The Natives are so hardened in their mouth that they hazard to use the acrid root internally, chewing selfsame with Pinang [*Areca cathecu* (L.) L.], nutmeg and ginger against prolonged diarrhea, caused by cold or moistness."

Dr. Robinson collected *Calanthe furcata* on Ambon, at Koesoekoesoe sereh, in August 1913, at an altitude of 150–300 m.

?*Eulophia* sp.; *Orchis amboinica major radice digitata*; *HA* 6, p. 116.
   Lit.: Merrill (1917:172), de Wit (1959:372, 446).

The four species of terrestrial Anggreks treated in Chapters 10, 11, 12, and 13 resemble Helleborine and Helleborus, says Rumphius, who proceeds to treat four others, resembling Orchis, and therefore to be included among Ambon orchids. The first and most beautiful one was described in the book 8 (see above) under the name *Flos susannae*. The three remaining ones are dealt with in two chapters, entitled *Orchis amboinica major* and *Orchis amboinica minor*.

Orchis amboinica major radice digitata has only one or two leaves, rather like those of Daun corra corra [*Molineria capitulata* (Lour.) Herb.]; they are much smaller, narrower, sword-shaped, upright, ribbed. They appear with the flowers in January, and the two-and-one-half-foot-long stem carries at its top a few flowers fashioned like the usual Anggrek flower with five leaflets and "with a small short pouch, whitish with purple lines, but the lip [*helmken*] has purple dots."

"The root resembles the Lampoejang or Ginger [*Zingiber zerumbet* (L.) Sm.], because it sticks obliquely in the earth like a clump made of many fingers or claws, of which two or three hang together, with narrow necks like Calbahaar poeti [possibly *Dioscorea* sp.]. Outside it is whitish, held against the day or a candle, half-transparent, full of tough slime, bitterish and unpleasant, smelling like dogs."

Dr. Smith finds Rumphius' description closely applicable to Eulophia, but knows of no species answering all details.

The second species of *Orchis amboinica major* is phrased "radice Raphanoide." It is described in some detail (and pictured on tab. 54, *sub* fig. 1). Clearly it is not an orchid. The fruit contains angular black seed and is evidently that of *Curculigo orchioides* Gaertn. (collected by Dr. Robinson on Ambon, at Batoe gadja, on open hillside at an altitude of ca. 150 m, and associated in the way Rumphius describes; see below).

"Both species grow on bald and windswept mountains, and highland plains below the sward, and the grass Hulong [*Imperata cylindrica* (L.) Raeusch]. They are common on Leytimor on bald mountainous rocks near Victoria Castle. They are certainly not seen throughout the year but about January. Often the sharp points of this grass pushing upward penetrate the tubers of *O. amboinica major radice digitata* like awls. The root most nearly resembles that of *Satyrium*. It may be candied, but first it must be dried till it becomes transparent like amber; it remains very tough and fibrous when chewn, retaining traces of its foul smell. Finally, however, it melts in the mouth, and then the youngest tubers are always to be preferred, to wit, those which are the whitish in the cluster or carry flowers for the first time."

"The Ternateans use the root [of the first-mentioned species] against the Apostemes [swellings] called Sassiri-isso, which are broad, bluish, and cause but little pain, but discharge much pus; large, red, and hot swellings, like boils and furuncles they call Sassiri-bara. They take the root crushed, tie it in a leaf of Boero malacco, that is *Oculus astaci* [*Cissus adnata* Roxb.], heat it over a fire, and then clap it over the mentioned Apostemes."

Habenaria rumphii (Brongn.) Lindl.; *Orchis amboinica minor*, Anggrek kitsjil; *HA* 5, p. 287; *HA* 6, p. 118, tab. 54, fig. 2 (Plate 3-12).

Lit.: Merrill (1917:169, 549), de Wit (1959:378, 430; see also p. 57, above).

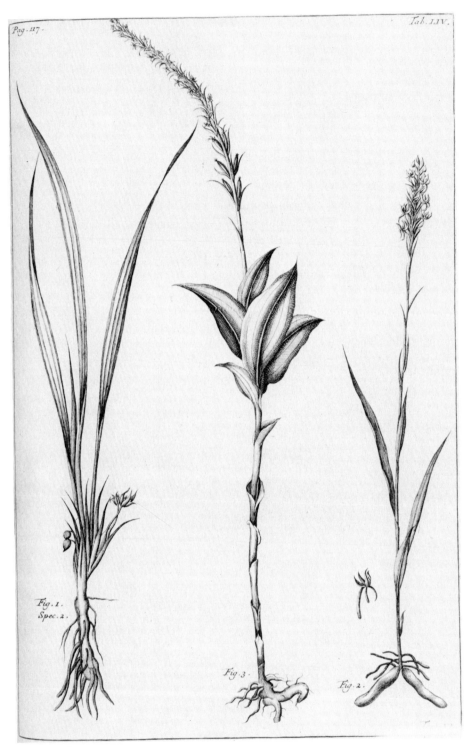

Fig. 1.
Spec. 2.

Fig. 3.

Fig. 2.

Plate 3-12.
   The fifty-fourth plate. First figure: The second species of the Large Ambon *Orchis*. The second figure illustrates the Little Ambon *Orchis*, actually the first species. The third figure represents the second species of the Little *Orchis*.

"The fourth species is also a true *Orchis*, in growth smaller than all preceding."

Rumphius describes the leaves and stem and continues: "On top it carries a thick, short spike, and thereon many white florets closely crowded, fashioned much like our common Orchis, except that they have no pouches behind; in front they gape, and have above two small leaflets, like two winglets, a curved small horn pointing forward, and below a long little beard, bent hindward, altogether white; the upper part of this spike has almost always closed florets.

"The fruits are small angular capsules, inside with a fatty flour, but few reach maturity. The root is very small consisting of a few white, short, and thickish fibers, and below them hang usually two, rarely one, oblong glands, like testicles, whereof one is generally smaller and wrinkled, outside gray, inside white and juicy, fatty, and sweetish of flavor, well-nigh a boiled Combilis [*Dioscorea esculenta* (Lour.) Burk.].

"It flowers at the end of the rains and the beginning of the dry monsoon, and after aestivation the whole stem disintegrates, and so one cannot find it any more. If it is pulled up nothing remains attached but the upper root fibers. The long glands are anchored rather firmly in the earth, and that is why they must be dug out.

"Among the natives it is unknown, but I found it more amenable to be candied, and tastier, than the preceding, the sweetmeat being somewhat crumbling, crackling, but sweet in the mouth and without that bad smell. But to find and to dig it out is difficult, because the roots are best before flowering begins, but then they are hard to find under the grass, and when the herb has disintegrated, I had digging done in the same places, but was unable to find glandlike roots, so it appears to grow quickly, and to perish quickly."

Rumphius described "a second species of this," *Orchis amboinica minor altera*, which is somewhat taller. There is a spike one span (ca. 23 cm) long, closely covered by little florets, hollow, like those of *Herba supplex* (see above), and divided in five tips, whitish-yellow.

"The root consists of two oblong small spheres, of which the larger is one little finger long and one finger thick, mostly standing sidewards; the other is much smaller and slenderer, placed right below the plant, outside fawn-colored, inside white and watery."

Dr. Smith is certain that this refers to a *Peristylus* but is unacquainted with any species like this from Ambon. I suggest considering *P. goodyeroides* (D. Don) Lindl. as a possible interpretation.

One purpose of this survey of Rumphian orchids is to enable a botanically interested person stationed on Ambon to trace the species treated in *Herbarium Amboinense*. A knowledge either of Latin or Dutch (the language of the *Herbarium*) is not required because sufficient detail is available in the present article. Moreover, the rare and costly original *Herbarium Amboinense* is not needed on the spot for this so very pleasant and exciting field work and for a preliminary, reasonably trustworthy identification.

As a biologist Rumphius has been studied and praised repeatedly; there is neither need to ask for closer attention nor to lay renewed emphasis upon his merits. The present study nevertheless shows again that among botanical writings of the seventeenth century Rumphius' work reaches far beyond local Ambonese or Eastern Indonesian plantlife.

Rumphius appears to be the first botanist to have realized what represented orchid-fruits and seed, to understand that orchids might grow in the earth or on other plants and that the latter were not parasites, and the presence of pollinia. This in addition to his pen-portraits of orchids, which are infinitely better than anything written before. And his graphic descriptions were never surpassed afterward.

It seems to me that the time draws near for biosystematics to produce readable and workable monographical treatments of taxa. These are to be many-sided (human-plant relations, past, present, and future connected with all aspects of natural sciences and mathematics) and so to become detailed and fundamental general essays. The biologists composing them will need the quiet unbiased power of observation and of judgment, the perseverance and curiosity, and the mastery of plant-description of Rumphius. Very likely they will not equal him, but clearly they have to find their own quality. To those who want to stimulate their talents and so perform in their own right at the highest attainable level, Rumphius showed the way and set the standards.

Literature Cited

Backer, C. A., and R. C. Bakhuizen van den Brink, Jr. 1968. Flora of Java. Vol. 3:215–451. Wolters-Noordhoff, Groningen.

Merrill, E. D. 1917. An interpretation of Rumphius's *Herbarium Amboinense*, p. 168–179; p. 542–543; p. 549–550. Bureau of Printing, Manila.

Smith, J. J. 1900–1901. Ambon. Teysmannia 12:81, 157, 322.

——. 1905a. Die Orchideen von Ambon. Batavia Landsdrukkerij.

——. 1905b. Die Orchideen von Java. Vol. VI. Flora von Buitenzorg. Leiden.

——. 1920. Aanteekeningen over Orchideeën. II. Teysmannia 31:8.

——. 1928a. Orchidaceae buruenses. Bull. Jard. Bot. Buitenzorg 3(9):440.

——. 1928b. Orchidaceae seranenses. Bull. Jard. Bot. Buitenzorg 3(10):85.

de Wit, H. C. D. (ed.). 1959. Rumphius Memorial Volume. Sponsored by Greshoff's Rumphius Fonds, Hollandia, Baarn.

PHYTOCHEMISTRY

4

The Distribution and Chemistry of Alkaloids in the Orchidaceae*

MICHAEL B. SLAYTOR

* The survey of literature for this paper was completed in March, 1976.

Introduction

Until now, classification by morphological characteristics has been the most successful method devised for plants. One of the more promising recently developed aids to plant classification is the utilization of chemical constituents, particularly secondary metabolites. Their restricted distribution and chemical diversity render them taxonomically important. At present secondary metabolites can only reinforce classical systematic botany because no plant family has been screened exhaustively for possible compounds. Such a survey would involve studying plants at various stages of growth and fully characterizing all secondary metabolites which may be present. A task of this magnitude is certainly beyond the current resources of phytochemistry. The paucity of phytochemical information is nowhere more evident than among the Orchidaceae where the number of known secondary metabolites is very small particularly in relation to the total number of species. Further, the literature is scattered and not easy to master. Therefore this review will (i) cover major papers dealing with the distribution of alkaloids within the family, and (ii) present complete coverage of papers on the chemistry of the orchid alkaloids.

Distribution

In the last ten years the secondary metabolites in orchids have received increased attention and many investigations have been devoted to alkaloids. Characterization of the alkaloids (described in the chemistry section) was preceded by a screening of 1500 species (Lüning, 1964, 1967; Lawler and Slaytor, 1969, 1970). Their distribution in the family has been discussed within the classifications of Schlechter (as summarized by Schweinfurth, 1959, and Pfitzer, 1888). This choice is arbitrary because the taxonomy is confusing (Garay, 1972) and there is certainly not enough information on alkaloid distribution to favor any one system. Genera in 62 out of the 88 subtribes used by Schlechter have been screened for alkaloids. The majority of alkaloids isolated from orchids come from three subtribes, Dendrobiinae, Liparidinae, and Sarcanthinae. Within Dendrobiinae, the genus richest in alkaloids is *Dendrobium* (Lüning, 1966). Scattered through phytochemical reports there are numerous isolated reports of alkaloid-positive tests from orchids. Unfortunately, however, many of the orchids are described only at the generic level. For example, in a major alkaloid survey of New Guinean plants (Hartley *et al.*, 1973), 106 orchids from 35 genera were screened but only two of these were identified at specific level.

Chemistry

Alkaloids which have been characterized are discussed according to their frequency of occurrence. Most of them fall into one of two classes: pyrrolizidine-based alkaloids and the dendrobine-type bases. The remaining ones are of mainly unrelated structures. Many of these are found in the genus *Dendrobium* which contains many alkaloid-rich species. In addition, a few simple alkaloids (which are of wide distribution in plants) have been found.

Pyrrolizidine-based Alkaloids

Several alkaloid esters containing an amino alcohol and a substituted *p*-hydroxy-benzoic acid radical have been characterized from the Liparidinae. Most of the amino alcohols are stereoisomers of 1-hydroxymethyl pyrrolizidine. The four stereoisomers lindelofidine (1), isoretronecanol (2), laburnine (3; $R_1 = R_2 = H$), and trachel-anthamidine (4) are found in either the esterified or free form in alkaloids of the closely related species, *Liparis*, *Malaxis*, and *Hammarbya* (all Liparidinae) as well as species of *Vanda*, *Vandopsis*, *Phalaenopsis*, *Kingiella*, and *Doritis* among the Sarcanthinae. In the Liparidinae, laburnine is the only free 1-hydroxymethyl pyrrolizidine to have been reported. It has been found in *Liparis bicallosa* Schltr. and *L. hachijoensis* Nakai (Nishikawa and Hirata, 1968).

lindelofidine (1)

isoretronecanol (2)

laburnine; $R_1 = R_2 = H$ (3)
laburnine acetate; $R_1 = CH_3CO$, $R_2 = H$
kumokiridine; $R_1 = H$, $R_2 = CH_3$

trachelanthamidine (4)

Malaxin (5), first isolated (Leander and Lüning, 1967) from *Malaxis congesta* (Lindl.) Deb, is an ester of laburnine (3; $R_1 = R_2 = H$) and malaxinic acid (3-isopentenyl *p*-glucosyl benzoic acid; 6; $R_1 = Glu$; $R_2 = H$). Malaxin has also been found in *Liparis bicallosa* Schltr. and its variant *L. hachijoensis* Nakai (Nishikawa and Hirata, 1968; Nishikawa, Miyamura, and Hirata, 1969). Hammarbine (7), closely related in structure, is the minor alkaloid from *Hammarbya paludosa* (L.) O. Ktze. Hammarbine is an ester of 3-methoxy-malaxinic acid (6; $R_1 = Glu$; $R_2 = OCH_3$) and lindelofidine (7; Lindström and Lüning, 1972). Lindström and Lüning (1972) also showed that keitaonine (8) from *L. keitaoensis* Hay is an ester of the same acid and laburnine (3; $R_1 = R_2 = H$). Keitine (9), the minor alkaloid from *L. keitaoensis*, is the aglycone of keitaoine but it is possible that it may be formed from (8) by *post mortem* enzymatic hydrolysis (Lindström and Lüning, 1972).

malaxinic acid; R_1 = Glu, R_2 = H
3-methoxy-malaxinic acid; R_1 = Glu, R_2 = OCH_3
nervogenic acid; R_1 = H, R_2 = $(CH_3)_2$ C = $CHCH_2$
nervosinic acid; R_1 = ara-glu, R_2 = $(CH_3)_2$ C = $CHCH_2$
kurameric acid; R_1 = glu, R_2 = $(CH_3)_2$ C = $CHCH_2$

Several alkaloids are esters of glycoside derivatives of nervogenic acid [6; R_1 = H; R_2 = $(CH_3)_2$ C = $CHCH_2$]. Nervosine (10) from *Liparis nervosa* Lindl. (Nishikawa and Hirata, 1967; Nishikawa, Miyamura, and Hirata, 1969) is the ester of lindelofidine and nervosinic acid [6; R_1 = ara-glu; R_2 = $(CH_3)_2C$ = $CHCH_2$] which is the arabinosyl-glucosyl derivative of nervogenic acid. In nervosiose, a disaccharide, L-arabinose and D-glucose are in the furanoside and pyranoside forms, respectively. They are linked 1 → 2 between the arabinose and the glucose, but the configuration is unknown. The glycosidic linkage between nervosiose and nervogenic acid is β. Other derivatives of nervogenic acid have been found in *L. kurameri* French et Sav. and *L. kumokiri* F. Maekawa (Nishikawa, Miyamura, and Hirata, 1967, 1969).

Kuramerine (11) from *L. kurameri* is the choline ester of kurameric acid [6; R_1 = glu; R_2 = $(CH_3)_2C$ = $CHCH_2$], which is in turn the β-D-glucoside of nervogenic acid. Kumokirine (12) from *Liparis kumokiri* is the ester of kurameric acid and kumokiridine (N-methyl laburnine; 3; R_1 = H; R_2 = CH_3). Auriculine (13; Nishikawa and Hirata, 1968; Nishikawa, Miyamura, and Hirata, 1969), an alkaloid from *L. auriculata* Blume, appears to be the laburnine ester of kurameric acid. The structural assignment is probable rather than absolute because of small quantities of alkaloid available. An alkaloid with the constitution assigned to auriculine has been isolated from *L. loeselii* (L.) L. C. Rich (Lindström and Lüning, 1971). The major alkaloid from *Hammarbya paludosa*, paludosine (14), is the ester of kurameric acid and lindelofidine (Lindström and Lüning, 1971). Finally, grandifoline (15), from *Malaxis grandifolia* Schltr., is a glycosidic derivative of nervogenic acid. The disaccharide, 2-O-β-D-glucopyranosyl-L-arabinose, is presumed, on the basis of optical rotation, to be linked α- to the nervogenic acid which is esterified with laburnine (Lindström, Lüning, and Siirala-Hansen, 1971).

The 1-hydroxymethylpyrrolizidines are also widely distributed in the Sarcanthinae either free or again as esters. Laburnine acetate (3; R_1 = CH_3CO; R_2 = H) was first isolated from *Vanda cristata* Lindl. (Lindström and Lüning, 1969). Laburnine and lindelofidine, together with their acetates, have been isolated from several *Vanda* and *Vandopsis* species (Brandänge and Granelli, 1973). *Vandopsis lissochiloides* Pfitz produces laburnine and lindelofidine and their acetates. Laburnine acetate has been isolated from *Vanda hindsii* Lindl. *Vanda helvola* Blume produces both laburnine and its acetate. An extract of *Vanda luxonica* Loher contains either laburnine or its enantiomer.

Table 4.1. The distribution of phalaenopsine T, La, and Is

Species	ph. T	ph. La	ph. Is
Phalaenopsis amabilis[a,b] (Color Plate I)		+	
P. amboinensis	+		
P. aphrodite		+	
P. equestris (Color Plate IV)			+
P. fimbriata		+	
P. hieroglyfica	+	+ or	
P. lueddemanniana	+	+ or	
P. mannii[b]	+		
P. sanderiana	+	+	
P. schilleriana	+		
P. stuartiana	+	+	
P. sumatrana	+		
P. violacea	+	+ or	
Kingiella taenialis[c]	+		
Doritis pulcherrima	+	+ or	

[a] Lüning, Tränkner, and Brandänge (1966)
[b] Brandänge and Lüning (1969)
[c] Brandänge, Granelli, and Lüning (1970)

More complex 1-hydroxymethylpyrrolizidine esters are found in *Phalaenopsis* species. The commonest are esters of mono methyl (−)-2-benzylmalate reported to be esterified with trachelanthamidine (4) laburnine (3), and isoretronecanol (2). These alkaloids were named phalaenopsine T (16), phalaenopsine La (17), and phalaenopsine Is (18), respectively (Brandänge, Lüning, Moberg, and Sjöstrand, 1972). The naturally occurring 2-benzylmalate esterified with phalaenopsine La has the R-configuration (Brandänge, Josephson, and Vallen, 1973). Their distribution in the genus *Phalaenopsis* and related species is summarized in Table 4-1.

Cornucervine (19) from *Phalaenopsis cornu-cervi* Rchb. f. is an ester of trachelan-thamidine (4) and monomethyl 2-isobutylmalate (Brandänge, Lüning, Moberg, and Sjöstrand, 1971). The 2-isobutylmalic acid has the R-configuration (Brandänge, Josephson, and Vallén, 1973).

Chysin A (20) and chysin B (21) are (+)-1-methoxycarbonylpyrrolizidine and (+)-1-ethoxycarbonylpyrrolizidine, respectively. They were isolated from *Chysis bractescens* Lindl. (Color Plate III), but *Catasetum* species contain small amounts of related compounds (Lüning and Tränkner, 1965). Chysin B, with its unusual ethyl ester group, is perhaps an artifact. The compound was not mentioned in the full report on chysin (Lüning and Tränkner, 1968). The UV absorption of chysin has an anomalous peak at 290 mm. This has now been shown to be due to the presence of small amounts of 1-methoxycarbonyl-$\Delta^{1,8}$-dehydropyrrolizidine, formed by dehy-drogenation of chysin during preparative GLC (Brandänge, Lüning, and Lundin, 1973). The physical characteristics of the pyrrolizidine alkaloids unique to the Orchidaceae are summarized in Table 4-2.

Dendrobine-type Alkaloids

Chemically, the most interesting alkaloids to be isolated from the Orchidaceae are the rearranged sesquiterpenoid ones found in the genus *Dendrobium*. Dendrobine (22), the major alkaloid from *D. nobile* Lindl., was first isolated in 1932 from a preparation of the orchid known as Chin-Shih-Hu (Suzuki, Keimatsu, and Ito, 1932a,b, 1934a) and reported thereafter (Suzuki, Keimatsu, and Ito, 1934b) in *D. linawianum* Rchb. f. *D. nobile* was reinvestigated subsequently (Inubishi, Ishii *et al.*, 1964) and the elucidation of the structure and stereochemistry of dendrobine has been carried out by three groups (Yamamura and Hirata, 1964; Onaka *et al.*, 1964; Inubishi, Sasaki, *et al.*, 1964; Inubishi, Sasaki, Tsuda, and Nakano, 1965; Inubishi, Katarao, Tsuda, and Yasui, 1964).

Altogether fourteen alkaloids of the dendrobine type have now been isolated. There are eight bases and six quaternary compounds. 2-Hydroxydendrobine (23) and dendrobine have been isolated from *Dendrobium findlayanum* Par. *et* Rchb. f., a species closely related to *D. nobile* (Granelli, Leander, and Lüning, 1970). Other oxygen derivatives of dendrobine are 6-hydroxydendrobine (dendramine; 24; Inubishi, Tsuda, and Katarao, 1966; Okamoto *et al.*, 1966b) and dendrobine N-oxide (25; Hedman and Leander, 1972), both of which are minor alkaloids from *D. nobile*. Dendramine has also been found in *D. hildebrandii* Rolfe (Elander and Leander, 1971) and *D. friedricksianum* Lindl. (Hedman, Leander, and Lüning, 1971). Two further quaternary derivatives of dendrobine were reported from *D. nobile*, namely N-methyldendrobine (26), isolated as N-methyldendrobinium iodide, and N-isopentenyldendrobine (27), isolated as N-isopentenyldendrobinium bromide (Hedman and Leander, 1972). Another minor alkaloid in *D. nobile* is dendrine (28), a carbomethoxymethylene derivative of dendrobine (Inubishi and Nakano, 1965). Dendrine has been synthesized and its absolute configuration determined (Granelli and Leander, 1970).

The second most abundant alkaloid in *Dendrobium nobile* is nobilonine (nobiline, 29; Yamamura and Hirata, 1964; Onaka *et al.*, 1965), which has also been reported to occur in *D. hildebrandii* (Elander and Leander, 1971), *D. friedricksianum* (Hedman, Leander, and Lüning, 1971), and in small amounts in *D. findlayanum* (Granelli, Leander, and Lüning, 1970). Nobilonine, or a closely related compound, would appear to be a biogenetic precursor of dendrobine. 6-Hydroxynobilonine (30) has been characterized from *D. hildebrandii* (Elander and Leander, 1971) and also found in *D. friedricksianum* (Hedman, Leander, and Lüning, 1971).

A third variant of the dendrobine alkaloids is dendroxine (31), first isolated from *Dendrobium nobile* (Okamoto *et al.*, 1966a). Its derivatives have also been found in *D. nobile*: 4-hydroxydendroxine (32; Okamoto *et al.*, 1972) and 6-hydroxydendroxine (33; Okamoto *et al.*, 1966b). N-isopentenyldendroxine (34) and N-isopentenyl 6-hydroxydendroxine (35) have been characterized as the chlorides from *D. friedricksianum* and *D. hildebrandii* (Hedman, Leander, and Lüning, 1971) and from *D. nobile* (Hedman and Leander, 1972).

The most recently reported dendrobine-type alkaloid is dendrowardine (36) from *Dendrobium wardianum* Warner (Brandänge, Gawell, Leander, and Lüning, 1973). It was isolated as the chloride.

An excellent review of the chemistry of the alkaloids known up to 1967 is available (Porter, 1967). The absolute configuration of dendrobine alkaloids has been determined by circular dichroism (Behr and Leander, 1972). A preliminary account of the biosynthesis of dendrobine confirming the mevalonate origin of the carbon sekeleton has been published (Yamazaki, Matsuo, and Arai, 1966).

Table 4-2. Physical properties and first reported occurrence of pyrrolizidine alkaloids from Orchidaceae

Structure	R_1	R_2	R_3
	glu	H	laburnine[a]
	glu	OCH$_3$	lindelofidine[a]
	glu	OCH$_3$	laburnine[a]
	H	OCH$_3$	laburnine[a]
	ara-glu	lindelofidine[a]	—
	glu	choline[a]	—
	glu	kumokiridine[a] (N-methyllaburnine)	— —
	glu	laburnine[a]	—
	glu	lindelofidine[a]	—
	glu-ara	laburnine[a]	—
	trachelanthamidine[a]	—	—
	laburnine[a]	—	—
	isoretronecanol[a]	—	—
	trachelanthamidine[a]	—	—
	CH$_3$	—	—
	CH$_2$CH$_3$	—	—

[a] Parent alcohol.

Alkaloid	Melting point (°C)	$[\alpha]_D$ (solvent)	Plant source	Reference
Laburnine acetate (3; R_1=CH_3CO; R_2=H)	oil	$[\alpha]_D^{24} + 13$ (EtOH)	*Vanda cristata* Lindl.	Lindström and Lüning, 1969
malaxin (5)	151–159	$[\alpha]_D^{22} - 31$ (EtOH)	*Malaxis congesta* comb. nov (Rchb. f.)	Leander and Lüning, 1967
hammarbine (7)	amorphous	$[\alpha]_D^{28} + 9$ (EtOH)	*Hammarbya paludosa* (L.) O.K.	Lindström and Lüning, 1972
keitaonine (8)	amorphous	$[\alpha]_D^{23} - 13$ (EtOH)	*Liparis keitaoensis* Hay	Lindström and Lüning, 1972
keitine (9)	amorphous	$[\alpha]_D^{23} - 7$ (EtOH)	*Liparis keitaoensis* Hay	Lindström and Lüning, 1972
nervosine (10)	130–131 (picrate)	$[\alpha]_D^{20} + 12.8$ (MeOH) as HCl salt	*Liparis nervosa* Lindl.	Nishikawa and Hirata, 1967
kuramerine (11)	105–107 (picrate)	$[\alpha]_D^{20} - 19.7$ (MeOH) as HCl salt	*Liparis kurameri* French et Sav	Nishikawa, Miyamura, and Hirata, 1967
kumokirine (12)	100–102 (picrate)	$[\alpha]_D^{20} - 23.4$ (MeOH) as HCl salt	*Liparis kumokiri* F. Maekawa	Nishikawa, Miyamura, and 1967
auriculine (13)	amorphous	$[\alpha]_D^{20} - 19.1$ (MeOH) as picrate	*Liparis auriculata* Blume	Nishikawa, Miyamura, and Hirata, 1969
paludosine (14)	amorphous	$[\alpha]_D^{23} + 9$ (EtOH)	*Hammarbya paludosa* (L.) O.K.	Lindström and Lüning, 1971
grandilfoline (15)	amorphous	$[\alpha]_D^{23} - 7$ (EtOH)	*Malaxis grandifolia* Schltr.	Lindström, Lüning, and Siirala-Hansen, 1971
phalaenopsine T (16)	104.5–105	$[\alpha]_D^{20} - 15$ (EtOH)	*Phalaenopsis amabilis* Bl.	Brandänge and Lüning, 1969
phalaenopsine La (17)	—	$[\alpha]_D^{22} - 42$ (EtOH)	*Phalaenopsis equestris* Rchb. f.	Brandänge, Lüning, Moberg, and Sjöstrand, 1972
phalaenopsine Is (18)	125–135	$[\alpha]_D^{20} + 10$ (EtOH)	*Phalaenopsis mannii* Rchb. f.	Brandänge and Lüning, 1969
cornucervine (19)	oil	$[\alpha]_D^{22} - 4.3$ (EtOH)	*Phalaenopsis corn-cervi* Rchb. f.	Brandänge, Moberg, and Sjöstrand, 1971
chysin A (20)	oil	$[\alpha]_D^{25} + 64$ ($CHCl_3$)	*Chysis bractescens* Lindl.	Lüning and Tränkner, 1968
chysin B (21)	—	—	*Chysis bractescens* Lindl.	Lüning and Tränkner, 1965

Table 4-3. Physical properties and first reported occurrence of dendrobine-type alkaloids from Dendrobium

Structure	R_1	R_2	R_3	R_4	Alkaloid
	H	H	H	H	dendrobine (22)
	H	H	OH	H	2-hydroxydendrobine (23)
	H	OH	H	H	6-hydroxydendrobine (dendramine) (24)
	H	H	H	O	dendrobine N-oxide (25)
	H	H	H	CH_3	N-methyldendrobinium iodide (26)
	H	H	H	$(CH_3)_2C = CH—CH_2$	N-isopentenyl-dendrobinium bromide (27)
	CH_2COOCH_3	H	H	H	dendrine (28)
	H	—	—	—	nobilonine (nobiline; 29)
	OH	—	—	—	6-hydroxynobilonine (30)
	H	H	H	—	dendroxine (31)
	H	H	OH	—	4-hydroxydendroxine (32)
	H	OH	—	—	6-hydroxydendroxine (33)
	$(CH_3)_2C = CH—CH_2$	H	H	—	N-isopentenylden-droxine (34)
	$(CH_3)_2C = CH—CH_2$	OH	OH	—	N-isopentenyl 6-hydroxydendroxine (35)
					dendrowardine (36)

Melting point (°C)	$[\alpha]_D$ (solvent)	Plant source	Reference
134	$[\alpha]_D^{16} - 51.5$ (EtOH)	Chin-Shih-Hu	Suzuki, Keimatsu, and Ito, 1932
103–105	$[\alpha]_D^{26} - 45$ (CHCl$_3$)	D. findlayanum Par. et Rchb. f	Granelli, Leander, and Lüning, 1969
178–180	$[\alpha]_D - 18.6$ (EtOH)	D. nobile Lindl.	Okamoto et al., 1966b
186–188	$[\alpha]_D - 27$ (CHCl$_3$)	D. nobile Lindl.	Inubushi, Ishii, Yasui, Konita, and Harayama, 1964
160–180	$[\alpha]_D^{23} - 34$ (MeOH)	D. nobile Lindl.	Hedman and Leander, 1972
245–246	$[\alpha]_D^{23} - 29$ (MeOH)	D. nobile Lindl.	Hedman and Leander, 1972
—	$[\alpha]_D^{23} - 33$ (MeOH)	D. nobile Lindl.	Hedman and Leander,, 1972
191–192	$[\alpha]_D - 114$ (CHCl$_3$)	D. nobile Lindl.	Inubushi and Nakano, 1965
87–88	ORDØ$_{320}^D$ + 10.4 10^2 (MeOH)	D. nobile Lindl.	Yamamura and Hirata, 1964
158–159.5	$[\alpha]_D^{23} + 62$ (CHCl$_3$)	D. hildebrandi Rolfe	Elander and Leander, 1971
114–115	$[\alpha]_D - 30.1$ (EtOH)	D. nobile Lindl.	Okamoto et al., 1966a
208–210	—	D. nobile Lindl.	Okamoto et al., 1972
amorphous	—	D. nobile Lindl.	Okamoto et al., 1966b
108–120	$[\alpha]_D^{22} - 48$ (MeOH)	D. friedricksianum Lindl.	Hedman, Leander, and Lüning, 1971
144–156	$[\alpha]_D^{22} - 30$ (MeOH)	D. friedricksianum Lindl.	Hedman, Leander, and Lüning, 1971
168–172	$[\alpha]_D^{25} - 28$ (MeOH)	D. wardianum Wr.	Blomqvist et al., 1973

The structure and physical properties of the dendrobine-type alkaloids are listed in Table 4-3.

Miscellaneous *Dendrobium* Alkaloids

Dendrodium lohohense Tang *et* Wang is another *Dendrobium* species used medicinally and employed in the form of a drug known as "Chukanso" in Japanese. It produces the phthalide-pyrrolidine alkaloid, shihunine (37; Inubishi, Tsuda, Konita, and Matsumoto, 1964, 1968). Shihunine is also found in *D. pierardii* Roxb. together with the structurally related alkaloid (−)-pierardine (38; Elander, Leander, and Lüning, 1969; Elander, Gawell, and Leander, 1971). Shihunine is rapidly and virtually completely converted into the betaine (39) in water or methanol solutions, suggesting that shihunine occurs as the betaine in the plant.

Shihunine (betaine form; 39)

Dendrobium primulinum Lindl. produces a 5,7-dimethyloctahydroindolizine (Lüning and Leander, 1965). The relative configuration of the naturally occurring isomer is 5,7-*cis*-9-*trans* (40; Lüning and Lundin, 1967). The absolute configuration of this alkaloid, called dendroprimine, is (5R,7S,9R)-5,7-dimethyloctahydroindolizine (Blomqvist, Leander, Lüning, and Rosenblom, 1972).

Dendrobium anosmum Lindl. and *D. parishii* Rchb. f. contain an interesting imidazolium compound first isolated as the bromide. Its structure, octahydrodipyrido [1,2-a; 1′,2′-c] imidazol-10-ium bromide (41) was confirmed by synthesis (Leander and Lüning, 1968a).

Three alkaloids are now known to occur in *Dendrobium crepidatum*. They have been named crepidine (42; Kierkegaard, Pilotti, and Leander, 1970), crepidamine (43), and dendrocrepine (44; Elander, Leander, Rosenblom, and Ruusa, 1973). The first of these papers reported the iolation of five alkaloids from this plant. However, on the basis of a careful acidic extraction the second paper reports that isocrepidamine (45) and isodendrocrepine (46) are artifacts formed during the isolation process. Both crepidamine (43) and dendrocrepine (44) are readily isomerized to the iso forms (45 and 46) by boiling in ethanol. The relative and absolute configurations of crepidine (42) has been determined by X-ray diffraction studies of crepidine methiodide (Pilotti, 1971).

isocrepidamine (45)

isodendrocrepine (46)

Dendrobium chrysanthum Wall. produces three pyrrolidine alkaloids, hygrine (Lüning and Leander, 1965) and N-*cis*- and N-*trans*-cinnamoylnorcuskhygrine (47; Ekevag *et al.*, 1973). The latter two, named *cis*- and *trans*-dendrochrysine (47 and 48, respectively), are unique to this orchid. Their structures were elucidated by physical methods and confirmed by the synthesis of ($\pm$) *trans*-dendrochrysine. The absolute configuration of the N-cinnamoyl pyrrolidinyl group was established by comparing the CD curve of *cis*-dendrochrysine with those of N-*cis*-cinnamoyl-L-prolinol and N-*cis*-cinnamoyl-L-2-methyl pyrrolidine.

1-Phenyl Tetrahydroisoquinolines

Three substituted 1-phenyl tetrahydroisoquinolines, S(+)-cryptostyline I (49), S(+)-cryptostyline II (50), and S(+)-cryptostyline III (51), have been isolated from *Cryptostylis fulva* Schltr. (Leander and Lüning, 1968b; Leander, Lüning, and Ruusa, 1969). Their R(−) isomers (52, 53, 54) have been found in *C. erythroglossa* Hayata (Agurell, Granelli, Leander, Lüning, and Rosenblom, 1974). Two related quaternary salts were also isolated from *C. erythroglossa*. These are 1-(3,4-methylenedioxyphenyl)-6,7-dimethoxy-2-methyl-3,4-dihydroisoquinolinium iodide (55) and its fully aromatic derivative (56) isolated as the chloride.

These alkaloids are of interest as they are the first of their type to have been isolated. The absolute configuration of S(+)-cryptostyline I (49), S(+)-cryptostyline II (50), and S(+)-cryptostyline III (51), determined by circular dichroism (Brossi and Teitel, 1971), indicates that the alkaloids have the S-configuration. This is supported by X-ray diffraction studies on the methiodide of (+)-cryptostyline I (49; Leander, Lüning, and Westin, 1973; Westin, 1972) but is not in agreement with the R-configuration assigned to (+)-cryptostyline III on the basis of optical rotatory dispersion and circular dichroism spectra (Kametani, Sugi, and Shibuya, 1971). The biosynthesis of R(−)-cryptostyline I has been studied in *Cryptostylis erythroglossa*. As with the mescaline-type alkaloids, the large number of oxidations and methylations involved in the biosynthesis make it difficult to determine the order of the reactions with the tetrahydroisoquinolines. The cyclization step is a further complication. Not unexpectedly, the preliminary results (Agurell, Granelli, Leander, Lüning, and Rosenblom, 1974) showed that tyrosine and dopamine are specifically incorporated. 3-Hydroxy-4-methoxyphenethylamine is incorporated better than the isomeric 4-hydroxy-3-methoxyphenethylamine. This is consistent with the predicted facilitation of the cyclization by a *para*-hydroxy group. A further paper (Agurell, Granelli, Leander, and Rosenblom, 1974) describes the specific incorporation of 3,4-dimethoxyphene-thylamine, N-(3-hydroxy-4-methoxybenzyl)-3-hydroxy-4-methoxyphenethylamine (57) and 1-(methylenedioxyphenyl)6,7-dimethoxy-2-methyl-3,4-dihydroisoquinoli-nium bromide (58).

N-(3-hydroxy-4-methoxybenzyl)-
3-hydroxy-4-methoxyphenethylamine (57)

1-(methylenedioxyphenyl)6,7-dimethoxy-
2-methyl-3,4-dihydroisoquinolinium bromide (58)

Preliminary results also indicate that dopamine is a precursor of the 1-phenyl group and the C-1 carbon atom while vanillin is better incorporated than isovanillin. The results from both papers do not allow an unambiguous pathway to be proposed and must be regarded as preliminary. N-methylpiperidine N-oxide, as the hydrobromide, and N-methylpyridinium ion, as the iodide, have been isolated from *Vandopsis longi-caulis* Schltr. (Brandänge and Lüning, 1970).

The structures and physical properties of the miscellaneous alkaloids from Orchid-aceae are listed in Table 4-4.

Phenethylamines

Simple phenethylamines have been found in *Eria jarensis* Zoll *et* Mor. (Hedman, Leander, and Lüning, 1969). They are N-methyl phenethylamine, N,N-dimethyl-phenethylamine, and the major alkaloid, a N,N,N-trimethylphenethylammonium salt, isolated as the iodide.

Finally there are several well-known alkaloids and simple bases which have been reported in Orchidaceae. Hygrine has been found in *Dendrobium primulinum* and *D. chrysanthum* (Lüning and Leander, 1965), as well as in *Vandopsis parishii* (Brandänge and Granelli, 1973). Choline occurs in *Eria jarensis* (Hedman, Leander, and Lüning, 1969). Guanadine has been isolated from *Liparis bicallosa* and *Liparis hachijoensis* (Nishikawa, Miyamura, and Hirata, 1969). Ethanolamine and γ-aminobutyric acid

Table 4-4. Physical properties and first reported occurrence of miscellaneous Orchidaceae alkaloids

Structure	Alkaloid	Melting point (°C)	$[\alpha]_D$ (solvent)	Plant source	Reference
	shihunine (37)	78.5–79	—	*Dendrobium lohohense* Tang et Wang	Inubushi, Tsuda, Konita, and Matsumoto, 1964
	pierardine (38)	viscous oil	$[\alpha]_D^{23} - 69°$ (CHCl$_3$)	*Dendrobium pierardii* Roxb.	Elander, Leander, and Lüning, 1969
	dendroprimine (40)	oil	$[\alpha]_D - 38°$ (CHCl$_3$)	*Dendrobium primulinum* Lindl.	Lüning and Leander, 1965
	octahydrodipyrido [1,2-a; 1′, 2′-c] imidazol-10-ium bromide (41)	164–165	—	*Dendrobium anosmum* Lindl. and *Dendrobium parishii* Rchb. f.	Leander and Lüning, 1968a
	crepidine (42)	221–222	$[\alpha]_D^{24} - 78°$ (CHCl$_3$)	*Dendrobium crepidatum* Lindl.	Kierkegaard, Pilotti, and Leander, 1970

Table 4-4 *(Continued)*

Structure	Alkaloid	Melting point (°C)	$[\alpha]_D$ (solvent)	Plant source	Reference
	crepidamine (43)	107.5–109	$[\phi]^{125}_{200-600}\ 0°$ (MeOH)	*Dendrobium crepidatum* Lindl.	Elander, Leander, Rosenblom, and Ruusa, 1973
	dendrocrepine (44)	158–163	$[\phi]^{20}_{200-600}\ 0°$ (MeOH)	*Dendrobium crepidatum* Lindl.	Elander, Leander, Rosenblom, and Ruusa, 1973
	cis-dendrochrysine (47) R = *cis*-cinnamoyl	viscous oil	$[\alpha]^{22}_D - 11°$ (CHCl$_3$)	*Dendrobium chrysanthum* Wall.	Ekevag *et al.*, 1973
	trans-dendrochrysine (48) R = *trans*-cinnamoyl	viscous oil	$[\alpha]^{22}_D - 19°$ (CHCl$_3$)	*Dendrobium chrysanthum* Wall.	Ekevag *et al.*, 1973
	S(+)-cryptostyline I (49) R$_1$ = H, R$_2$ = R$_3$ = OCH$_2$O	101–102	$[\alpha]^{20}_D + 56°$ (CHCl$_3$)	*Cryptostylis fulva* Schltr	Leander, Lüning, and Ruusa, 1969
	S(+)-cryptostyline II (50) R$_1$ = H, R$_2$ = R$_3$ = OCH$_3$	117–118	$[\alpha]^{25}_D + 58°$ (CHCl$_3$)	*Cryptostylis fulva* Schltr	Leander, Lüning, and Ruusa, 1969
	S(+)-cryptostyline III (51) R$_1$ = R$_2$ = R$_3$ = OCH$_3$	126–129	$[\alpha]^{25}_D + 51°$ (CHCl$_3$)	*Cryptostylis fulva* Schltr.	Leander, Lüning, and Ruusa, 1969

Structure	Compound	m.p. (°C)	$[\alpha]_D$	Source	Reference
	R(−)-cryptostyline I (52) $R_1 = H, R_2 = R_3 = OCH_2-O$	101–102	$[\alpha]_D^{22}$ − 56° (CHCl$_3$)	*Cryptostylis erythroglossa* Hayata	Agurell *et al.*, 1974
	R(−)-cryptostyline II (53) $R_1 = H, R_2 = R_3 = OCH_3$	116–117	$[\alpha]_D^{22}$ − 58° (CHCl$_3$)	*Cryptostylis erythroglossa* Hayata	Agurell *et al.*, 1974
	R(−)-cryptostyline III (54)	128–130	$[\alpha]_D^{22}$ − 52° (CHCl$_3$)	*Cryptostylis erythroglossa* Hayata	Agurell *et al.*, 1974
	1-(3,4-methylenedioxyphenyl)-6,7-dimethoxy-2-methyl-3,4-dihydroisoquinolinium iodide (55)	208–209		*Cryptostylis erythroglossa* Hayata	Agurell *et al.*, 1974
	1-(3,4-methylenedioxyphenyl)-6,7-dimethoxy-2-methylisoquinolinium picrate (56) R = picrate	218–223		*Cryptostylia erythroglossa* Hayata	Agurell *et al.*, 1974
	N-methyl piperidine N-oxide hydrobromide	175–190		*Vandopsis longicaulis* Schltr.	Brandänge and Lüning, 1970
	N-methyl pyridinium iodide	114–116		*Vandopsis longicaulis* Schltr.	Brandänge and Lüning, 1970

appear to be widespread and have been detected in 80 Australian species (Lawler, Slaytor, and Done, 1971).

Conclusions

(1) Structures of about 60 alkaloids from the Orchidaceae have now been published. Considering the enormous size of the family, chemotaxonomic conclusions must be speculative. (2) The number of alkaloids also to be found in other families is very small and these are of widespread distribution. (3) Very few alkaloids are derived from aromatic amino acids and none from tryptophan. (4) The majority of alkaloids containing an aromatic nucleus are C_6-C_1 compounds, including those from Liparidinae and *Cryptostylis* spp., or C_6-C_3 derivatives, which are found in the phalaenopsine alkaloids.

Literature Cited

Agurell, S., I. Granelli, K. Leander, B. Lüning, and J. Rosenblom. 1974. Studies on Orchidaceae alkaloids. XXXIX. Isolation of (−)-cryptostyline I, II, III and two quaternary salts from *Cryptostylis erythroglossa* Hayata. Biosynthetic studies of (−)-cryptostyline I. Acta Chem. Scand. B28:239–243.

Agurell, S., I. Granelli, K. Leander, and J. Rosenblom. 1974. Studies on Orchidaceae alkaloids. XL. Biosynthetic studies on (−)-cryptostyline I in *Cryptostylis erythroglossa* Hayata. Acta Chem. Scand. B28:1175–1179.

Behr, D., and K. Leander. 1972. Studies on Orchidaceae alkaloids. XXVIII. The absolute configuration of the dendrobine alkaloids. Acta Chem. Scand. 26:3196–3202.

Blomqvist, L., K. Leander, B. Lüning, and J. Rosenblom. 1972. Studies on Orchidaceae alkaloids. XXIX. The absolute configuration of dendroprimine, an alkaloid from *Dendrobium primulinum* Lindl. Acta Chem. Scand. 26:3203–3206.

Brandänge, S., L. Gawell, K. Leander, and B. Lüning. 1973. Studies on Orchidaceae alkaloids. XXXVII. Dendrowardine, a quaternary alkaloid from *Dendrobium wardianum* Wr. Acta Chem. Scand. 27:1439–1441.

Brandänge, S., and I. Granelli. 1973. Studies on Orchidaceae alkaloids. XXXVI. Alkaloids from some *Vanda* and *Vandopsis* species. Acta Chem. Scand. 27:1096–1097.

Brandänge. S., I. Granelli, and B. Lüning. 1970. Studies on Orchidaceae alkaloids. XVIII. Isolation of Phalaenopsine La from *Kingiella taenialis* Lindl. Rolfe. Acta Chem. Scand. 24:354.

Brandänge, S., Josephson, and S. Vallén. 1973. Studies on Orchidaceae alkaloids. XXXVIII. Asymmetric synthesis of 2-isobutylmalic acid and 2-cyclohexylmethyl malic acid. Acta Chem. Scand. 27:3668–3672.

Brandänge, S., and B. Lüning. 1969. Studies on Orchidaceae alkaloids. XII. Pyrrolizidine alkaloids from *Phalaenopsis amabilis* Bl. and *Ph. mannii* Rchb. f. Acta Chem. Scand. 23:1151–1153.

——. 1970. Studies on Orchidaceae alkaloids. XVII. Alkaloids from *Vandopsis longicaulis* Schltr. Acta Chem. Scand. 24:353–354.

Brandänge, S., B. Lüning, and C. Lundin. 1973. Studies on Orchidaceae alkaloids. XXXI. Synthesis of I-ethoxycarbonyl-Δ-^{1,8}-dehydropyrrolizidine and some other pyrrolizidine derivatives. Acta Chem. Scand. 27:433–438.

Brandänge, S., B. Lüning, C. Moberg, and E. Sjöstrand. 1971. Studies on Orchidaceae alkaloids. XXIV. A pyrrolizidine alkaloid from *Phalaenopsis cornu-cervi* Rchb. f. Acta Chem. Scand. 25:349–350.

——. 1972. Studies on Orchidaceae alkaloids. XXX. Investigation of fourteen Phalaenopsis species. A new pyrrolizidine alkaloid from *Phalaenopsis equestris* Rchb. f. Acta Chem. Scand. 26:2558–2560.

Brossi, A., and S. Teitel. 1971. Synthesis and absolute configuration of cryptostylines I, II and III. Helv. Chim. Acta 54:1564–1571.

Ekevag, U., M. Elander, L. Gawell, K. Leander, and B. Lüning. 1973. Studies on Orchidaceae alkaloids. XXXIII. Two new alkaloids, *N-cis-* and *N-trans-*cinnamoylnorcuskhygrine from *Dendrobium chrysanthum* Wall. Acta Chem. Scand. 27:1982–1986.

Elander, M., L. Gawell, and K. Leander. 1971. Studies on Orchidaceae alkaloids. XXII. Synthesis and absolute configuration of pierardine-lactone-betaine isomeration of shihunine. Acta Chem. Scand. 25:721–724.

Elander, M., and K. Leander. 1971. Studies on Orchidaceae alkaloids. XXI. 6-hydroxynobiline, a new alkaloid from *Dendrobium hildebrandii* Rolfe. Acta Chem. Scand. 25:717–720.

Elander, M., K. Leander, and B. Lüning. 1969. Studies on Orchidaceae alkaloids. XIV. A phthalide alkaloid from *Dendrobium pierardii* Roxb. Acta Chem. Scand. 23:2177–2178.

Elander, M., K. Leander, J. Rosenblom, and E. Ruusa. 1973. Studies on Orchidaceae alkaloids. XXXII. Crepidine, crepidamine and dendrocrepine, three new alkaloids from *Dendrobium crepidatum* Lindl. Acta Chem. Scand. 27:1907–1913.

Garay, L. A. 1972. On the origin of the Orchidaceae. II. J. Arnold Arb. 53:202–215.

Granelli, I., and K. Leander. 1970. Studies on Orchidaceae alkaloids. XIX. Synthesis and absolute configuration of dendrine. Acta Chem. Scand. 24:1108–1109.

Granelli, I., K. Leander, and B. Lüning. 1970. Studies on Orchidaceae alkaloids. XVI. A new alkaloid, 2-hydroxydendrobine, from *Dendrobium findlayanum* Par. *et* Rchb. f. Acta Chem. Scand. 24:1209–1212.

Hartley, T. G., E. A. Dunstone, J. S. Fitzgerald, S. R. Johns, and J. A. Lamberton. 1973. A survey of New Guinea plants for alkaloids. Lloydia 36:217–319.

Hawkes, A. D. 1961. Orchids: their botany and culture, p. 263–273. Harper and Row, New York.

Hedman, K., and K. Leander. 1972. Studies on Orchidaceae alkaloids. XXVII. Quaternary salts of the dendrobine type from *Dendrobium nobile* Lindl. Acta Chem. Scand. 26:3177–3180.

Hedman, K., K. Leander, and B. Lüning. 1969. Studies on Orchidaceae alkaloids. XV. Phenethylamines from *Eria jarensis* Ames. Acta Chem. Scand. 23:3261.

——. 1971. Studies on Orchidaceae alkaloids. XXV. N-isopentenyl derivatives of dendroxine and 6-hydroxydendroxine from *Dendrobium friedricksianum* Lindl. and *Dendrobium hildebrandii* Rolfe. Acta Chem. Scand. 25:1142–1144.

Inubushi, Y., H. Ishii, B. Yasui, T. Konita, and T. Harayama. 1964. Isolation and characterization of alkaloids of the Chinese drug "Chin-Shih-Hu." Chem. Pharm. Bull. 12:1175–1180.

Inubushi, Y., E. Katarao, Y. Tsuda, and B. Yasui. 1964. Absolute configuration of dendrobine. Chem. Ind.: 1689–1690.

Inubushi, Y., and J. Nakano. 1965. Structure of dendrine. Tetrahedron Letters: 2723–2728.

Inubushi, Y., Y. Sasaki, Y. Tsuda, and J. Nakano. 1965. Structure of dendrobine (supplement). Tetrahedron Letters: 1519–1523.

Inubushi, Y., Y. Sasaki, Y. Tsuda, B. Yasui, T. Konita, I. Matsumoto, E. Katarao, and J. Nakano. 1964. Structure of dendrobine. Tetrahedron 20:2007–2023.

Inubushi, Y., Y. Tsuda, and E. Katarao, 1965. A reversible rearrangement of dendrobinic acid to a lactam derivative. Chem. Pharm. Bull. 13:1482–1483.

——. 1966. The structure of dendramine. Chem. Pharm. Bull. 14:668–671.

Inubushi, Y., Y. Tsuda, T. Konita, and S. Matsumoto. 1964. Shihunine. A new phthalide-pyrrolidine alkaloid. Chem. Pharm. Bull. 12:749–750.

——. 1968. The structure of shihunine, a new phthalide-pyrrolidine alkaloid. Chem. Pharm. Bull. 16:1014–1018.

Kametani, T., H. Sugi, and S. Shibuya. 1971. The absolute configuration of cryptostyline. III. Studies on the synthesis of heterocyclic compounds. CCCXCVII. Tetrahedron 27:2409–2414.

Kierkegaard, P., A. Pilotti, and K. Leander. 1970. Studies on Orchidaceae alkaloids. XX. The constitution and relative configuration of crepidine, an alkaloid from *Dendrobium crepidatum* Lindl. Acta Chem. Scand. 24:3757–3759.

Lawler, L. J., and M. Slaytor. 1969. The distribution of alkaloids in New South Wales and Queensland Orchidaceae. Phytochemistry 8:1959–1962.

——. 1970. The distribution of alkaloids in orchids from the Territory of Papua and New Guinea. Proc. Linn. Soc. N.S.W. 94:237–241.

Lawler, L. J., M. Slaytor, and J. Done. 1971. Biochemical investigations of Australian Orchidaceae. Proc. 6th World Orchid Conf. Sydney (1969), p. 51–54.

Leander, K., and B. Lüning. 1967. Studies on Orchidaceae alkaloids. VII. Structure of a glucosidic alkaloid from *Malaxis congesta* comb. nov. (Rchb. f.). Tetrahedron Letters: 3477–3478.

——. 1968a. Studies on Orchidaceae alkaloids. VIII. An imidazolium salt from *Dendrobium anosmum* Lindl. and *Dendrobium parishii* Rchb. f. Tetrahedron Letters: 905–908.

——. 1968b. Studies on Orchidaceae alkaloids. IX. A 1-phenyltetrahydroisoquinoline alkaloid from *Cryptostylis fulva* Schltr. Tetrahedron Letters: 1393–1394.

Leander, K., B. Luning, and E. Ruusa. 1969. Studies on Orchidaceae alkaloids. XI. Three 1-phenyl-1,2,3,4-tetrahydroisoquinolines from *Cryptostylis fulva* Schltr. Acta Chem. Scand. 23:244–248.

Leander, K., B. Lüning, and L. Westin. 1973. Studies on Orchidaceae alkaloids. XXXIV. The absolute configuration of cryptostyline I, II and III, three 1-phenyl-1,2,3,4-tetrahydroisoquinolines from *Cryptostylis fulva* Schltr. Acta Chem. Scand. 27:710.

Lindström, B., and B. Lüning. 1969. Studies on Orchidaceae alkaloids. XIII. A new alkaloid, laburnine acetate from *Vanda cristata* Lindl. Acta Chem. Scand. 23:5–6.

——. 1971. Studies on Orchidaceae alkaloids. XXIII. Alkaloids from *Liparis loeselii* (L.) L. C. Rich and *Hammarbya paludosa* (L.) O.K. Acta Chem. Scand. 25:895–897.

——. 1972. Studies on Orchidaceae alkaloids. XXXV. Alkaloids from *Hammarbya paludosa* (L.) O.K. and *Liparis keitaoensis* Hay. Acta Chem. Scand. 26:2963–2965.

Lindström, B., B. Lüning, and K. Siirala-Hansen. 1971. Studies on Orchidaceae alkaloids. XXVI. A new glycosidic alkaloid from *Malaxis grandifolia* Schltr. Acta Chem. Scand. 25:1900–1903.

Lüning, B. 1964. Studies on Orchidaceae alkaloids. I. Screening of species for alkaloids 1. Acta Chem. Scand. 18:1507–1516.

——. 1966. Chemotaxonomy in a *Dendrobium* complex. Proc. 5th World Orchid Conf., Long Beach, p. 211–215.

——. 1967. Studies on Orchidaceae alkaloids. IV. Screening of species for alkaloids 2. Phytochemistry 6:857–861.

Luning, B., and K. Leander. 1965. Studies on Orchidaceae alkaloids. III. The alkaloids in *Dendrobium primulinum* Lindl. and *Dendrobium chrysanthum* Wall. Acta Chem. Scand. 19:1607–1611.

Lüning, B., and C. Lundin. 1967. Studies on Orchidaceae alkaloids. VI. Synthesis and relative configuration of 5,7-dimethyloctahydroindolizines. Acta Chem. Scand. 21:2136–2142.

Lüning, B., and H. Tränkner. 1965. Studies on Orchidaceae alkaloids. II. Structure of alkaloids in *Chysis bractescens* Lindl. Tetrahedron Letters: 921–922.

——. 1968. Studies on Orchidaceae alkaloids. X. A pyrrolizidine alkaloid from *Chysis bractescens* Lindl. Acta Chem. Scand. 22:2324–2328.

Lüning, B., H. Tränkner, and S. Brandänge. 1966. Studies on Orchidaceae alkaloids. V. A new alkaloid from *Phalaenopsis amabilis* Bl. Acta Chem. Scand. 20:2011.

Nishikawa, K., and Y. Hirata. 1967. Chemotaxonomical alkaloid studies. I. Structure of nervosine. Tetrahedron Letters: 2591–2596.

——. 1968. Chemotaxonomical alkaloid studies. III. Further studies of Liparis alkaloids. Tetrahedron Letters: 6289–6291.

Nishikawa, K., M. Miyamura, and Y. Hirata. 1967. Chemotaxonomical alkaloid studies. II. Structures of kuramerine and kumokirine. Tetrahedron Letters: 2597–2600.

——. 1969. Chemotaxonomical alkaloid studies. Structures of Liparis alkaloids. Tetrahedron 25:2723–2741.

Okamoto, T., M. Natsume, T. Onaka, F. Uchimaru, and M. Shimizu. 1966a. The structure of dendroxine. The third alkaloid from *Dendrobium nobile*. Chem. Pharm. Bull. 14:672–675.

——. The structure of dendramine (6-oxydendrobine) and 6-oxydendroxine. The fourth and fifth alkaloid from *Dendrobium nobile*. Chem. Pharm. Bull. 14:676–680.

——. 1972. Further studies on the alkaloidal constituents of *Dendrobium nobile* (Orchidaceae). Structure determination of 4-hydroxydendroxine and nobilomethylene. Chem. Pharm. Bull. 20:418–421.

Onaka, T., S. Kamata, T. Maeda, Y. Kawazoe, M. Natsume, T. Okamoto, F. Uchimaru, and M. Shimizu. 1964. The structure of dendrobine. Chem. Pharm. Bull. 12:506–512.

——. 1965. The structure of nobilonine. The second alkaloid from *Dendrobium nobile*. Chem. Pharm. Bull. 13:745–747.

Pfitzer, E. 1889. Orchidaceae. *In* Die natürlichen Pflanzenfamilien. Vol. 2, Part 6. Engler and Prantl, Leipzig.

Pilotti, A. 1971. The crystal structure of 2-acetyl-3,6-dihydroxy-3,7-dimethyl-6-phenyl-12-azatricyclo-[7,2,1,0^{5,12}] dodecane methiodide. Acta Cryst. 27:887–892.

Porter, L. A. 1967. Picrotoxin and related substances. Chem. Rev. 67:441–464.

Schweinfurth, C. 1959. Classification of orchids, p. 15–43. *In* C. L. Withner (ed.), The orchids: a scientific survey. Ronald Press, New York.

Suzuki, H., I. Keimatsu, and M. Ito. 1932b. Alkaloid of the Chinese drug "Chin-Shih-Hu." II. Dendrobine. J. Pharm. Soc. Japan 52:1049–1060.

——. 1934a. Alkaloids of the Chinese drug "Chin-Shih-Hu." III. Dendrobine. J. Pharm. Soc. Japan 54:802–819.

———. 1934b. Supplement to the study of "Chin-Shih-Hu." J. Pharm. Soc. Japan 54:820–823.

Westin, L. 1972. The crystal structure and absolute configuration of the methiodide of the alkaloid cryptostyline. I. Acta Chem. Scand. 26:2305–2314.

Yamamura, S., and Y. Hirata. 1964. Structures of nobiline and dendrobine. Tetrahedron Letters: 79–87.

Yamazaki, M., M. Matsuo, and K. Arai. 1966. Biosynthesis of dendrobine. Chem. Pharm. Bull. 14:1058–1059.

5

Anthocyanins of the Orchidaceae: Distribution, Heredity, Functions, Synthesis, and Localization*

JOSEPH ARDITTI and MICHAEL H. FISCH

* The survey of literature pertaining to this review was concluded in November, 1974.

Introduction

Few plants surpass the orchids in distribution throughout the world, variability of growth habits, and the magnificent spectrum of colors produced by their flowers and leaves (Arditti, 1967; Arditti and Ernst, 1971; Strauss and Arditti, 1972). To a very large extent, this wealth of colors is due to anthocyanins. Singly or in combinations with other pigments (Figs. 1, 2, 3), they contribute to delicate pastels, dazzling yellows, brilliant reds, dull browns, and exciting purples. All of these colors may be found in seedlings from the same capsule (Cutak, 1949). Not surprisingly, color variations have also been used by orchidologists in describing a number of species and varieties (Dunn, 1949; Northen, 1949, 1953, 1962, 1970). Unfortunately, interest in the anthocyanins of orchids among phytochemists has been limited and information about them has been slow to accumulate (Shibata, Shibata, and Kasiwagi, 1921; Ball, 1938; Soysa, 1938, 1943; Blumenschein, 1960; Sanford *et al.*, 1964; Tosello, 1969, 1970; Arditti and Ernst, 1969, 1971; Harper, 1972a,b; George *et al.*, 1973; Lowry and Keong, 1973; Withner, 1974). Data on their distribution and function is spotty and inadequate to establish patterns of function or levels of significance. However, by relating the available information to what is known about other plants (Harborne, 1967; J. W. McClure, Miami University, Oxford, Ohio, personal communication), it becomes possible to draw certain conclusions about anthocyanins in orchids.

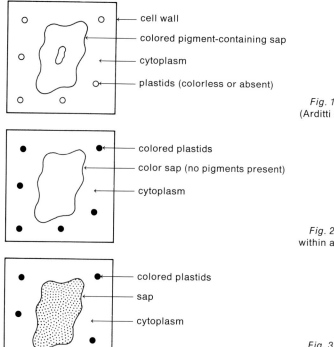

cell wall

colored pigment-containing sap

cytoplasm

plastids (colorless or absent)

Fig. 1. Location of anthocyanins within a cell (Arditti and Dunn, 1969).

colored plastids

color sap (no pigments present)

cytoplasm

Fig. 2. Location of carotenes or chlorophyll within a cell (Arditti and Dunn, 1969).

colored plastids

sap

cytoplasm

Fig. 3. Location of anthocyanins and carotenes or chlorophyll within a cell (Arditti and Dunn, 1969).

Chemistry of the Anthocyanins

Anthocyanins are flavonoids (Latin: *flavus*, yellow) derived from 2-phenylbenzo-pyran (Fig. 4; Bate-Smith, 1949). Their parent skeleton is a flavone (Table 5-1, VI). Anthocyanins are also acetogenins, and thus belong to the most numerous and varied class of natural pigments. They consist of an aglyconic chromophore (the anthocyanidin) linked to sugar(s) and sometimes to an organic acid as well. The sugar may be a hexose (six-carbon sugar such as glucose), pentose (five-carbon sugar, e.g., xylose), a deoxy-sugar (rhamnose), or a number of di- and trisaccharides (Harborne, 1962).

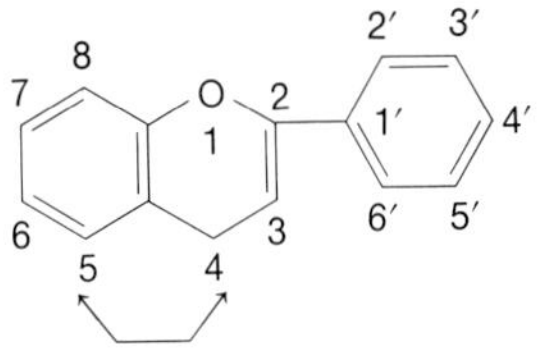

Benzopyran

Fig. 4. 2-Phenyl benzopyran.

To date, sixteen naturally occurring anthocyanidins have been isolated from plants (Harborne, 1967). The six most common—pelargonidin (Table 5-1, X), cyanidin (Table 5-1, IV), delphinidin (Table 5-1, V), peonidin (Table 5-1, XI), malvidin (Table 5-1, IX), and petunidin (Table 5-1, XII)—possess hydroxy ($-OH$) substituents in the 3, 5, 7, and 4 positions. This basic substitution pattern is that of pelargonidin; the other five common anthocyanidins differ only in that additional hydroxyl and/or methoxyl ($-OCH_3$) substitution is present in the B ring, *ortho* to the first hydroxyl function. Less common anthocyanins are known in which there is no hydroxyl group at C-3 (3-deoxy-anthocyanins) or in which additional phenolic functions are present at C-6 or C-8. In some of these compounds, C-5 or C-7 (but never both) are methoxyl substituted. Single glycosylation occurs at the 3 position except in the deoxyanthocyanidins, where 3-glycosidation is not possible, and condensation usually occurs at C-5. Apigeninidin (Table 5-1, II), luteolinidin (Table 5-1, VIII), and tricetinidin (Table 5-1, XIV) are such pigments. As a further variant, several dozen 3, 5 and 3, 7 diglycosides are also known, all but a very few being of the former class. The characteristic substitution patterns of the anthocyanins have been taken as evidence of their biosynthetic origin, ring A arising from polyacetyl cyclization and ring B deriving from shikimic acid (Richards and Hendrickson, 1964). Detailed studies of the pathway indicate that a chalcone or a flavone may be the primary C-5 intermediate (Barz and Griesebach, 1971).

Anthocyanins range in color from yellow to red and magenta. Generally, introduction of hydroxyl groups at the 3 position or in the B ring bathochromically shifts the visible spectrum, yielding bluer hues. In contrast, OH substitution at the 6 or 8 position does not displace the absorption maximum in any consistent way. When existing hydroxyl groups are methylated, the result is invariably a hypsochromic shift of the visible spectrum (bluer hues), but the effect is small. Solvent effects are also important, bathochromic shifts being observed as solvent polarity is decreased. For

Table 5-1. Spectra, structural formulas, color, chemistry, and R_f values of some anthocyanidins[a]

Name	Spectral characteristics				Structural Formula (ϵ_{max})	Colors		Substitution	R_f values, paper chromatography		
	In MeOH-HCl	In Ethanolic HCl	$\epsilon_{440}/\epsilon_{max}$ as %	AlCl$_3$ $\Delta\lambda$(mμ)		Visible light	Ultraviolet light		Forestal[b]	Formic[c]	BAW[d]
Anthocyanidin I											
Apigeninidin II	276 476	483	55	0		orange-yellow	yellow-brown	5,7,4' trihydroxy	0.75	0.44	0.74
Capensinidin III	273 538		12	0		purple		delphinidin 5,3',5' Tri-o-methyl-ether	0.88		0.79
Cyanidin IV	277 535	545	19	18		bluish red or magenta	pink	3,5,7,3',4' pentahydroxy	0.49	0.22	0.68
Delphinidin V	277 546	557	16	23		purple-blue	mauve	3,5,7,3',4',5' hexahydroxy	0.32	0.13	0.42

Table 5.1 (continued)

Name	Spectral characteristics				Structural Formula	Colors		Substitution	R' values, paper chromatography		
	In MeOH-HCl	In Ethanolic HCl	$\varepsilon_{440}/\varepsilon_{max}$ as %	$AlCl_3$ $\Delta\lambda(m\mu)$	ε_{max}	Visible light	Ultraviolet light		Forestal	Formic	BAW
Flavone VI	330–350 250–270										
Hirsutidin VII	536	545	23	0		bluish red o magenta	mauve	delphinidin 7,3',5'-tri-o-methyl-ether	0.78	0.36	0.66
Luteolinidin VIII	279 493	503	45	52		orange	red-brown	5,7,3',4'-tetrahydroxy	0.61	0.35	0.56
Malvidin IX	275 542	554	19	0		purple	mauve	delphinidin 3',5'-di-o-methyl-ether	0.60	0.27	0.58
Pelargonidin X	270 520	530	39	0		scarlet-red	orange-red	3,5,7,4'-tetrahydroxy	0.68	0.33	0.80

Compound					Structure	Color	Color	Name			
Peonidin XI	532	542	25	0		bluish red or magenta	pink	cyanidin-3'-o-methyl-ether	0.63	0.30	0.71
Petunidin XII	276 543	558	17	14		purple-blue	mauve	delphinidin-3'-o-methyl-ether	0.46	0.20	0.52
Rosinidin XIII	524	534	—	0		bluish red or magenta	pink	cyanidin-7,3'-di-o-methyl-ether	0.76	0.39	0.77
Tricetinidin XIV	281 513		22	40		orange		5,7,3',4',5'-pentahydroxy	0.46	0.28	0.38

[a] Adapted from Harborne, 1967a; Reproduced with changes from Arditti and Dunn, 1967.
[b] Forestal, acetic acid : conc. HCl : water (30:3:6).
[c] Formic, formic acid : conc. HCl : water (5:2:3).
[d] BAW, n-butanol : acetic acid : water (4:1:5).

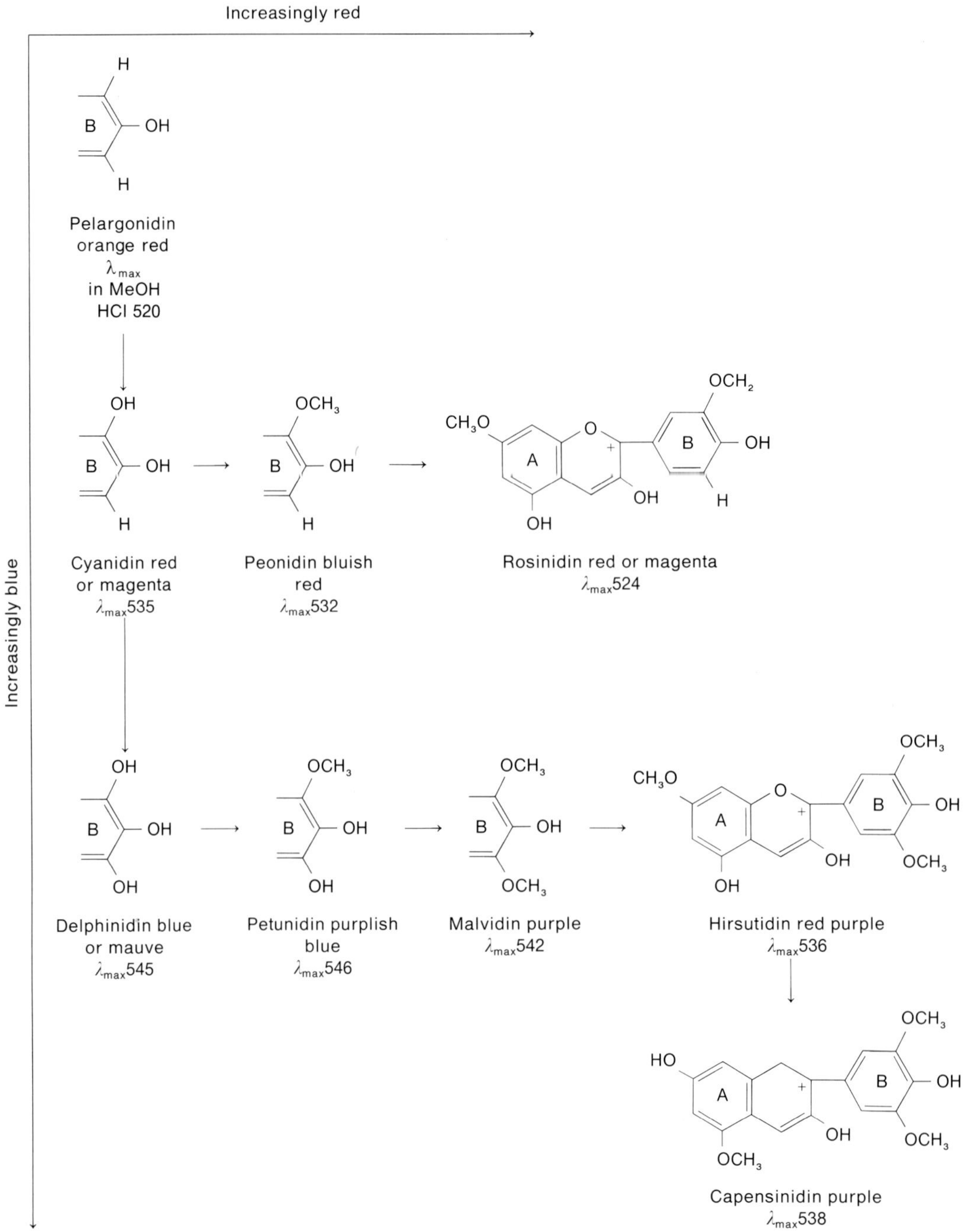

Fig. 5. Coloration in respect to hydroxylation and methylation in anthocyanidins (after Hess, 1964; from Arditti and Dunn, 1969).

purposes of tabulation and comparison, spectra are recorded in methanol containing 0.01% HCl. Other factors affecting color are the type of substituent (ether or hydroxyl), the presence of other flavonoids or metallic ions, and the pH (Table 5-1, Fig. 5). Hypsochromic shifts result from additional glycosylation in the 5 position of 3-glycosides; bathochromic shifts result from chelation with iron or aluminum. Because the cationic center is scavenged by addition of nucleophilic hydroxide ions and regenerated in acid, the anthocyanin pigments are indicators (a fact noted by Robert Boyle in 1664), turning red under acid conditions (low pH) and blue in alkali (high pH). These characteristic variations in spectra are central to current techniques of identification (Harborne, 1958a,b, 1962, 1963, 1967; Akiyoshi, Webb, and Kepner, 1963; Albach, Kepner, and Webb, 1965).

Anthocyanins possess all the necessary characteristics of chemotaxonomic agents: chemical complexity, structural variability, physiological stability, widespread distribution, comparative ease of isolation, and relative speed of identification (Harborne, 1967). They have been used in a number of taxonomic studies including those of *Linum* (Giannasi and Rogers, 1970), *Vitis vinifera* (Akiyoshi, Webb, and Kepner, 1963), *Petunia* (Muszynski, 1964), *Mimulus cardinalis* (Pollock, Vickery, and Wilson, 1967) and Poaceae (Clifford and Harborne, 1967). Although alkaloids (Lüning, 1966; Lawler and Slaytor, 1969, 1970), fragrances (Dodson and Hills, 1966; Dodson, 1967; Hills, Williams, and Dodson, 1968), and sugar content of floral and extrafloral exudates (Jeffrey and Arditti, 1968, 1969; Baskin and Bliss, 1969; Jeffrey, Arditti, and Koopowitz, 1970) have been used in orchid taxonomy, there are at present few published reports dealing with the utilization of anthocyanins to this end (Blumenschein, 1960; Sanford *et al.*, 1964; Tosello, 1969, 1970; Arditti, 1969a,b; Arditti and Ernst, 1969, 1971; George *et al.*, 1973; Lowry and Keong, 1973). Since surveys of anthocyanins have proved useful to better understanding of systematic relationships among other plants (Alston, Mabry, and Turner, 1963; Alston and Turner, 1963, 1966; Harborne, 1967), analogous investigations may be expected to find wider use in the chemotaxonomic study of orchids. In addition, presently available information suggests that novel anthocyanins may be discovered in the Orchidaceae (Lowry and Keong, 1973).

Nature and Distribution of Anthocyanins in Orchids

It is ironic that so little is known about the nature and distribution of anthocyanins in the Orchidaceae since the considerable popularity of this family is primarily due to the colors of many of its flowers (Arditti, 1966a, 1967). Much empirical and practical information has accumulated during the last century on the colors of orchid flowers (Matsumoto, 1966; Arditti and Dueker, 1968; Dueker and Arditti, 1968; Arditti and Ernst, 1969, 1971; Strauss and Arditti, 1972). Unfortunately however, very few biochemical and chemotaxonomic studies have been attempted, perhaps because orchids are largely ignored as experimental organisms by biochemists, geneticists, physiologists, and chemotaxonomists. This situation is especially regrettable since the great variety of orchids, the well-kept breeding records (Sander's, 1946; Sander and

Table 5-2. Anthocyanins of the Orchidaceae

Species	Organ	Identity or color and R_f of anthocyanin	Is identification chemically definite?	Reference
Acianthus fornicatus	flower	cyanidin bioside	no	Gascoigne *et al.*, 1949
Anacamptis pyramid-alis	flower	cyanidin-3,5-diglucoside	yes	Harborne, 1963
Appendicula undulata	leaf	*Vanda* DA[a]	no	Lowry and Keong, 1973
Aranda xWendy Scott	flower	*Vanda* A[b]	no	Lowry and Keong, 1973
A. xNancy Storei	flower	*Vanda* A[b]	no	Lowry and Keong, 1973
Arundina bambusifolia	flower	*Vanda* A[b]	no	Lowry and Keong, 1973
Ascocenda xDarcey Starr (*Vanda* xEisen-hower × *Asco-centrum curvifolium*)	flower	*Vanda* A[b]	no	Lowry and Keong, 1973
xMeda Arnold (Color Plate V)	flower	*Vanda* A[b]	no	Lowry and Keong, 1973
Bletilla striata	flower	red-violet	no	Shibata *et al.*, 1949
Brassavola glauca	root	gray, 0.16[c]	no	Sanford *et al.*, 1964
		rosy-purple, 0.22[c]	no	
B. nodosa	flower	cyanidin 3-sophoroside 5-glucoside acylated with *p*-coumaric acid (Raphanusin C)	yes	Arditti, 1969a
Brassocattleya	root	blue-purple, 0.22[c]	no	Sanford *et al.*, 1964
xAndes 'Baldwin Paradise'	root	purple, 0.29[c]	no	
		rose-purple, 0.16, 0.23[c]	no	Sanford *et al.*, 1964
xWindover 'Adm. Semmes'	root	rose-purple, 0.23[c]	no	Sanford *et al.*, 1964
Bromhaedia finlayso-niana	young leaf	cyanidin glycoside cf *Vanda* DA[a]	no	Lowry and Keong, 1973
Broughtonia domin-gensis	flower, label-lum	pelargonidin glucoside[d]	no	Arditti, 1969a
	SPOC[e]	pelargonidin-3-rutinoside, 5-glucoside	yes	
		acylated with *p*-coumaric acid (Pelanin)	yes	
B. negrilensis	flower, label-lum	pelargonidin 3,5-diglucoside (Pelar-gonin)	yes	Arditti, 1969a
		pelargonidin 3-glucoside (Callistephin)	yes	
	SPOC[e]	pelargonidin 3,5-diglucoside (Pelar-gonin)	yes	
		pelargonidin 3-rutinoside, 5-glucoside acylated with *p*-coumaric acid (Pelanin)	yes	
B. sanguinea	flower, label-lum	cyanidin 3-sophoroside, 5-glucoside acylated with ferulic acid (Raphanusin D)	yes	Arditti, 1969a

Table 5-2 (continued)

Species	Organ	Identity or color and R_f of anthocyanin	Is identification chemically definite?	Reference
	SPOC[e]	petunidin 3-glucoside	yes	
		pelargonidin 3-sophoroside, 5-glucoside pelargonidin 3-sophoroside, 5-glucoside acylated with ferulic acid (Raphanusin B)	yes	
Brassotonia xJohn Miller	flower, labellum	pelargonidin 3-gentiotrioside	yes	Arditti, 1969a
		pelargonidin 3-sophoroside	yes	
		pelargonidin 5-glucoside acylated with ferulic acid (Raphanusin B)	yes	
		pelargonidin 3,5-diglucoside (Pelargonin)	yes	
		pelargonidin 3-sophoside, 5-glucoside	yes	
	SPOC[e]	pelargonidin 3-sambubioside (?) probably acylated with caffeic acid	yes	
		pelargonidin 3-sophoside, 5-glucoside acylated with ferulic acid (Raphanusin B)	yes	
		pelargonidin 3-glucoside (Callistephin)	yes	
		pelargonidin 3-sophoroside, 5-glucoside	yes	
Caladenia carnea	flower	cyanidin and some malvidin bioside	no	Gascoigne et al., 1964
C. patersonii	flower	malvidin bioside	no	Gascoigne et al., 1964
Caleana major	flower	cyanidin, acylated sugar	no	Gascoigne et al., 1964
Cattleya				
xBow Bells var. Honolulu, selfed	root	blue 0.11[c]	no	Sanford et al., 1964
		rose-purple, 0.23[c]	no	
	leaf tip	rose, 0.09[c]	no	
xEdithae	root	mauve, 0.23[c]	no	Sanford et al., 1964
xEvamay Patterson Wright's	root	rose-purple, 0.16[c]	no	Sanford et al., 1964
		blue, 0.11[c]	no	
xJane Sander × xBow Bells	root	blue-purple, 0.16[c]	no	Sanford et al., 1964
		blue, 0.11[c]	no	
xJulie Lawrence var. Cadillac	root	blue, 0.15[c]	no	Sanford et al., 1964
C. labiata	flower	cyanidin-3,5 dimonoside	yes	Robinson and Robinson, 1932
xLittle Angel × C. labiata alba	root	blue, 0.08[c]	no	Sanford et al., 1964

Table 5-2 (continued)

Species	Organ	Identity or color and R_f of anthocyanin	Is identification chemically definite?	Reference
xNational Velvet × C. xRosette Warland	root	blue, 0.08[c], 0.11[c]	no	Sanford et al., 1964
xSandiana	root	blue, 0.08[c]	no	Sanford et al., 1964
		purple, 0.16[c]	no	
		rosy-mauve, 0.29[c]	no	
		blue-mauve, 0.15[c]	no	
C. skinneri	flower	cyanidin-3,5 dimonoside	yes	Lawrence et al., 1939
C. skinner var. autumnalis	root	rose-purple, 0.16[c]	no	Sanford et al., 1964
		rose, 0.29[c]	no	
	leaf tip	rose, 0.29[c]	no	
Cattleyopsis lindenii	flower	pelargonidin 3-sophoroside, 5 glucoside acylated with p-coumaric acid (Raphanusin A)	yes	Arditti, 1969a
Cattleytonia xRosy Jewell	flower	pelargonidin 3-gentiotrioside	yes	Arditti, 1969a
		pelargonidin 3-sophoroside, 5-glucoside acylated with p-coumaric acid (Raphanusin A)	yes	
Cymbidium finlaysonianum	flower	cyanidin-3-glycoside	yes	Lowry and Keong, 1973
		cyanidin-3-rutinoside	yes	
Dendrobium xCaesar	flower	Vanda A[b]	no	Lowry and Keong, 1973
D. cornutum	flower	cyanidin glycoside cf Vanda DA[a]	no	Lowry and Keong, 1973
D. crocatum	flower-column	cyanidin-3-glucoside	yes	Lowry and Keong, 1973
D. nobile	flower	light violet-red with Al$_2$(SO$_4$)		Shibata et al., 1921
D. xRose Marie × D. Anouk	flower	rosy, 0.34[c]	no	Sanford et al., 1973
Diabroughtonia	flower	cyanidin 3-sophoroside, 5 glucoside acylated with ferulic acid (Raphanusin D)	yes	Arditti, 1969a
Dipodium punctatum	flower	cyanidin, acylated with sugar	no	Gascoigne et al., 1949
Diuris aurea	flower	cyanidin dimonoside	no	Gascoigne et al., 1949
D. elongata	flower	malvidin bioside	no	Gascoigne et al., 1949
D. sulphurea	flower	malvidin dimonoside	no	Gascoigne et al., 1949
Elythranthera brunonis	flower	cyanidin-3-glucoside, delphinidin-3-glucoside	yes	George et al., 1973; Strauss et al., 1974
E. emarginata (Color Plate VI)	flower	cyanidin-3-glucoside, delphinidin-3-glucoside	yes	George et al., 1973; Strauss et al., 1974

Table 5-2 (continued)

Species	Organ	Identity or color and R_f of anthocyanin	Is identification chemically definite?	Reference
Epidendrum radicans	root	rose, 0.13[c]	no	Sanford et al., 1964
		rose-blue, 0.16[c]	no	
Glossodia major (New South Wales, Australia)	flower	delphinidin dimonoside	no	Gascoigne et al., 1949
G. major (Victoria, Australia)	flower	delphinidin bioside	no	Gascoigne et al., 1949
G. minor	flower	petunidin dimonoside	no	Gascoigne et al., 1949
Grammatophyllum speciosum	flower	cyanidin-3-glucoside	yes	Lowry and Keong, 1973
Gymnadenia conopsea	sepal	cyanidin-dihexoside	no	Ueno et al., 1969
Habenaria	flower	cyanidin based	no	Forsyth and Simmonds, 1954
Laelia purpurata	root, flower, labellum	rose-purple, 0.23[c]	no	Sanford et al., 1964
		violet, 0.18[c]		
Laeliocattleya				
xAconagua, selfed	root	purple, 0.16[c]	no	Sanford et al., 1964
		blue, 0.11[c]	no	
xArdmore × Lc. xH. Wickwire	root	blue-mauve, 0.19[c]	no	Sanford et al., 1964
Cattleya intermedia var. amethystima × Laelia purpurata Werckhauserii	root	rose-purple, 0.19[c] blue, 0.11[c] rose, 0.16[c]	no no no	Sanford et al., 1964
C. xKanoa × Lc. xSargon 'Magnifica'		blue, 0.15[c]	no	Sanford et al., 1964
xRosemary Sander × Lc. xAreca 'Model Wilmoss'	root	blue, 0.08[c], 0.11[c]	no	Sanford et al., 1964
Masdevallia harryana purpurea	flower	cyanidin diglucoside	yes	Robinson and Robinson, 1934
Nephalophyllum pulchrum	leaf	acylated cyanidin glycoside of Vanda A,[b] probably monoacylated	no	Lowry and Keong, 1973
Oncidium cebolleta	flower	rose, 0.45[c]	no	Sanford et al., 1964
O. pulchellum	flower	rose "fading" to violet, 0.60–0.70[c]	no	Sanford et al., 1964
O. sphacelatum	flower-column	cyanidin-3-glucoside	yes	Lowry and Keong, 1973
		cyanidin-3-rutinoside	yes	
		cyanidin-3-arabinoside	yes	
Orchis aristata	sepal	cyanidin-dihexoside	no	Ueno et al., 1969
O. mascula	flower	cyanidin-3,5-dimonoside	no	Robinson and Robinson, 1932
		cyanidin-3,5-dimonoside	no	Harborne, 1967a
Pogonia japonica	sepal	cyanidin-3-glucoxyloside	yes	Ueno et al., 1969
		cyanidin-monoglucoside	no	
Prasophyllum elatum (?)	flower	cyanidin dimonoside	no	Gascoigne et al., 1949
Renanthera xLena Rowell	flower	Vanda A[b]	no	Lowry and Keong, 1973

Table 5-2 (continued)

Species	Organ	Identity or color and R_f of anthocyanin	Is identification chemically definite?	Reference
R. xOricil	flower	*Vanda* A[b]	no	Lowry and Keong, 1973
Rodricidium xTahiti	flower	rose "fading" to violet, 0.60–0.70[c]	no	Sanford *et al.,* 1964
		rose, 0.79[c]	no	
Sophrolaeliocattleya	root	blue-violet, 0.11[c]	no	Sanford *et al.,* 1964
		rose-purple, 0.16[c]	no	
	flower	violet, 0.19–0.24[c]	no	
	labellum	rose, 0.35–0.43[c]	no	
	FSP[f]	rose, 0.23[c]	no	
		rose, 0.12[c]	no	
Sophronitis grandiflora (Color Plate VII)	flower	pelargonidin-3-bioside	yes	Robinson and Robinson, 1932
Spathoglottis plicata	flower	cyanidin-based anthocyanin	no	Forsyth and Simmonds, 1954
	flower	acylated cyanidin glycoside, R_f values similar to *Vanda* A[b]	no	Lowry and Keong, 1973
Spiranthes amoena	flower	red anthocyanin	no	Shibata *et al.,* 1949
Thelymitra ixioides	flower	cyanidin dimonoside	no	Gascoigne *et al.,* 1949
T. venosa	flower	cyanidin monoside	no	Gascoigne *et al.,* 1949
Vanda xBella Tew	flower	*Vanda* A[b]	no	Lowry and Keong, 1973
V. coerulea	root, leaf	mauve, 0.12[c]	no	Sanford *et al.,* 1964
V. xEisenhower	root	blue-mauve, 0.12[c]	no	
V. xMiss Joaquim (Color Plate VIII)	flower	cyanidin-based anthocyanin	no	Forsyth and Simmonds, 1954
		Vanda A[b]	no	Lowry and Keong, 1973
V. xMok Sand	flower	*Vanda* A[b]	no	Lowry and Keong, 1973
V. xNellie Morley	flower	blue, 0.19[c]	no	Sanford *et al.,* 1964
V. xProfusion	flower	*Vanda* A[b]	no	Lowry and Keong, 1973
V. xRothshildiana × *V. suavis*	flower	rose-purple, 0.15[c]	no	Sanford *et al.,* 1964
V. xTan Chay Yan	flower	*Vanda* A[b]	no	Lowry and Keong, 1973

[a] *Vanda* DA is a cyanidin glycoside containing "one complex sugar residue attached at the 3 position" (Lowry and Keong, 1973).

[b] *Vanda* A is a newly isolated anthocyanin from *Vanda* xMiss Joaquim. It "is a cyanidin-3-(p-coumaroyl, feruloyl) arabinosylglucoside, the actual number of sugar residues and their mode of linkage being unknown" (Lowry and Keong, 1973).

[c] R_f values are for Whatman No. 1 paper developed with n-butanol:acetic acid:water (4:1:5).

[d] Identity uncertain due to the very small amount of anthocyanin or its components available for analysis.

[e] Sepals, petals, ovary, and column.

[f] Flowers, sepals, and petals.

Wreford, 1961; Wreford, 1963, 1966), and the multitude of intra- and intergeneric hybrids present unequaled opportunities for basic research into plant biochemistry, metabolism, genetics, and chemotaxonomy.

Presently available information on orchid anthocyanins (Table 5-2) comes to a large extent from surveys of regional floras (Gascoigne, Ritchie, and White, 1949; Forsyth and Simmonds, 1954), isolation of anthocyanins from occasional plants (Robinson and Robinson, 1932, 1934; Lawrence *et al.*, 1939; Shibata, Hayashi, and Isaka, 1949), and four systematic surveys (Sanford *et al.*, 1973; Arditti, 1969a; George *et al.*, 1973; Lowry and Keong, 1973). Anthocyanins occur in the flowers, but not the roots (Table 5-2), of certain orchids (e.g., *Oncidium*, *Rhyncholaelia digbyana*, Mexican *Laelia*). In others (*Cattleya* and Brazilian *Laelia*, for example), they may be found in both. When present in both flowers and roots, the anthocyanins in each of the two organs may be the same or different. There are also orchids which contain anthocyanins in all organs. *Haemaria* and many of the so-called "jewel orchids" have excited interest largely because of their leaf coloration, which is undoubtedly due at least in part to anthocyanins. Leaves of the Spiranthinae, Erythrodinae, and Physurinae are spotted due to the presence of anthocyanin-containing cells in certain areas. Some of them are, therefore, cultivated as house plants (Schlechter, 1970).

Taxonomic Significance of Orchid Anthocyanins

Anthocyanin distribution and content between or within taxa as well as parts of individual plants can, if properly applied, be of considerable chemotaxonomic value. Due to the absence of information, it is not possible at this time to engage in wide-ranging discussions regarding the exact nature of orchid anthocyanins. Nor is it possible to do more than speculate about the relationship of specific, generic, tribal, or subfamily affinities. Clearly, much more work is needed; yet, several interesting, albeit tentative, conclusions may be drawn from presently available information (Table 5-2).

The available data regarding anthocyanin distribution within plants suggests that Brazilian *Laelia* species, which contain anthocyanins in their roots, may be more closely related to *Cattleya* than to the Mexican *Laelia* group, whose roots are anthocyanin-free. Also, it is possible that some affinity may exist between *Rhyncholaelia* (*Brassavola*) *glauca*, *Cattleya*, and Brazilian *Laelia*, all of which contain anthocyanins in their roots. *Rhyncholaelia* (*Brassavola*) *digbyana* and *R. (B.) glauca* are similar, but both differ considerably from *Brassavola nodosa* and *B. cucullata* (Table 5-1). Yet anthocyanins can be found only in the roots of *R. (B.) glauca* (Table 5-1). This may suggest a closer relationship between this species and the other non-*Laelia*-like *Brassavola* species, *B. cordata*, *B. nodosa*, *B. perinii*, and *B. cucullata*.

One existing report of a systematic study of orchid anthocyanins (Sanford *et al.*, 1964) identifies them only by R_f values in one system (Whatman No. 1 paper and butanol:acetic acid:water, 4:1:5) and colors under visible light (Table 5-2). It provides some interesting information and a basis for speculation, but caution is necessary. The R_f values of anthocyanins are generally reproducible (Harborne,

1967) but may vary as indicated by a number of reports (Bate-Smith, 1949; Halevy and Asen, 1959).

A rose-purple anthocyanin extracted from *Vanda* xProfusion (Table 5-2) may be similar to a rose-purple one found in *Cattleya* and x*Laeliocattleya* (Sanford *et al.*, 1964). Both genera belong to the subfamily Epidendroideae, but to different series (Schultes and Pease, 1963). Thus, unless some parallelism exists between distantly related species, these pigments should prove different even if based on the same aglycone.

A rosy-purple pigment R_f 0.22 in *Rhyncholaelia* (*Brassavola*) *glauca* is suggested as being the same as a mauve pigment, R_f 0.23 from the *Cattleya* complex (Sanford *et al.*, 1964). Since these genera are closely related (Fig. 6), it is possible that the two pigments may be identical.

The rose anthocyanin, R_f 0.29 from *Cattleya skinneri* var. *autumnalis*, is close enough in color, origin, and R_f value to cyanidin-3,5-diglucoside (Harborne, 1967), which is found in *Cattleya skinneri* (Lawrence *et al.*, 1939), to suggest that the two may be identical (Table 5-2).

A blue-mauve anthocyanin, R_f 0.12 from *Vanda coerulea* (Sanford *et al.*, 1964), may be similar to the blue-violet pigment, R_f 0.11 from the *Cattleya* group (Table 5-2). A grey-blue anthocyanin, R_f 0.16 from *Rhyncholaelia* (*Brassavola*) *glauca*, may resemble the blue one, R_f 0.15 from *Cattleya*, in view of the close relationship between the two genera.

x*Rodricium* Tahiti is a hybrid between *Oncidium flexuosum* and *Rodriguezia secunda* (Sander and Wreford, 1961). The presence of the same rose "fading" to violet pigment (R_f 0.60–0.70) in both the hybrid and the closely related *Oncidium pulchellum* (Table 5-2) is, therefore, not surprising. *Oncidium cebolleta* is not closely related to *O. flexuosum*, *O. pulchellum*, or x*Rodricidium* Tahiti. It is, therefore, not unexpected that its rosy pigment, R_f 0.45, is different from the one found in x*R.* Tahiti.

Anthocyanins of *Broughtonia* (Plate 5-1-**A-G**), *Brassavola nodosa* (Plate 5-2) and *Cattleyopsis lindenii* (Plate 5-1-**H** and Fig. 7) have been identified (Arditti, 1969a) by well-established techniques (Harborne, 1958a, b, 1962, 1967; Albach, Kepner, and Webb, 1965; Halevy and Asen, 1965). Therefore, they are suitable for chemotaxonomic application to the vexing classification problem of *Broughtonia* (Lindley and Paxton, 1853; Fowlie, 1961, 1966, 1967).

The four pollinia in *Broughtonia* (Table 5-3) distinguish it from *Cattleyopsis*, which has eight (Lindley and Paxton, 1853; Correll, 1941; Dressler, 1961; Fowlie, 1961, 1966, 1967). In addition, a controversial long sepaline tube, if it exists at all in *Broughtonia* (Table 5-3), is absent in *Cattleyopsis* (Correll, 1941). Geographically, the two genera overlap only in Jamaica. *Broughtonia* may be found also on Hispaniola, whereas *Cattleyopsis* has been collected on the Bahama Islands and Cuba (Correll, 1941; Fowlie, 1961). Furthermore, *Broughtonia* is apparently hummingbird-pollinated (Table 5-3), whereas *Cattleyopsis* depends on bees. *Cattleyopsis lindenii* has been transferred to *Broughtonia* as *B. lindenii* (Dressler, 1966) because of certain floral similarities. The absence of anthocyanins common to *Broughtonia* and *Cattleyopsis lindenii* as well as the morphological and pollination differences (Table 5-3) may be interpreted to suggest that the transfer should not have been made. However, it is also possible that

Table 5-3. Comparison between *Broughtonia* and *Cattleyopsis*[a]

Character	*Broughtonia*	*Cattleyopsis*
Sepaline tube	present[b]	absent[b]
Pollinia	4	8
Leaves	coriaceous	fleshy, thick, rigid
Margin	entire	serrate
Pollinator	birds[c]	bees[c]

[a] Correll, 1941; Dressler, 1966; Fowlie, 1967; Dodson, 1968; Arditti, 1969a.
[b] This has been questioned (Dressler, 1969).
[c] Difference is not certain (Dressler, 1969).

the chemical differences are not as significant as one might wish (Fig. 7), since they represent only a change in acylating agents (Table 5-2). In addition, a question may also be raised regarding pollinators (Table 5-3). The difference could well be probable rather than certain. Both *Broughtonia domingensis* and *B. negrilensis* have purple flowers with trumpet-shaped lips much like those of *Cattleyopsis lindenii*, suggesting that all three are bee-pollinated. The existence of a sepaline tube or spur (Table 5-3) in *Broughtonia sanguinea* is also in question. Nectaries in *B. sanguinea*, *B. domingensis*, *Cattleyopsis lindenii*, and *C. ortgiesiana*, though they may vary in size, are similar to each other and those of *Brassavola*. Thus, the chemotaxonomic evidence must be weighed together with other characters by systematists, who must, in the final analysis, make appropriate determinations.

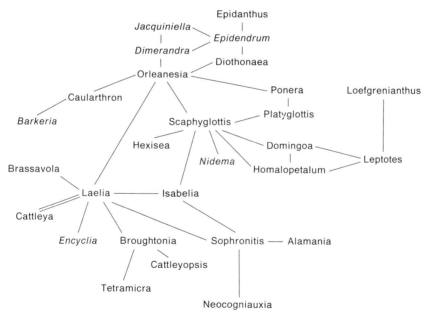

Fig. 6. Phylogenetic relationships in the *Epidendrum* alliance. Italicized genera have been included (entirely or in part) in genus *Epidendrum* by some authors. The double line connecting *Cattleya* and *Laelia* indicates that these genera are artificial as presently used (Dressler, 1961). *Cattleyopsis* has been placed arbitrarily (Arditti, 1969a).

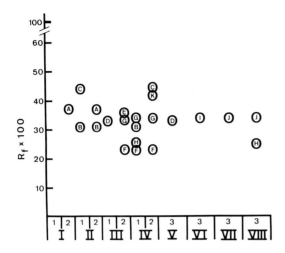

Fig. 7. Anthocyanins present in the flowers of Broughtonia domingensis (I), B. negrilensis (II), B. sanguinea (III), × Brassotonia 'John Miller' (IV), × Diabroughtonia (V), Brassavola nodosa (VI), Cattleyopsis lindenii (VII), and × Cattleytonia 'Rosy Jewell' (VIII). 1, labellum; 2, sepals, petals, ovary, and column; 3, whole flower. **A**, pelanin; **B**, pelargonidin-3,5-diglucoside; **C**, pelargonidin-3-glucoside; **D**, raphanusin D; **E**, petunidin-3-glucoside; **F**, pelargonidin-3-sophoroside, 5-glucoside; **G**, raphanusin B; **H**, pelargonidin-3-gentiotrioside; **I**, raphanusin C; **J**, raphanusin A; **K**, pelargonidin-3-xyloglucoside, probably acylated with caffeic acid (Arditti, 1969a).

There is no general agreement regarding the exact number of species within *Broughtonia*. *B. sanguinea* (Plate 5-1-**D**), which has yellow (Plate 5-1-**C**) and white varieties (Plate 5-1-**F**) occurring naturally (Fowlie, 1967), has been listed as the only species of this genus (Correll, 1941). Others have distinguished two species in Jamaica, *B. sanguinea* (Plate 5-1-**D**) and *B. domingensis* (Plate 5-1-**G**), on the basis of flower color and shape, form of the labellum, appearance of sepals, and column length (Fawcett and Rendle, 1910). A third species, *B. negrilensis* (Plate 5-1-**B**) has been described from the Negril Hill area in Jamaica (Fowlie, 1961). But, it has also been suggested that instead of a new species, the plant from Negril Hill may actually be a natural hybrid between *B. sanguinea* and *B. domingensis*. Still, a "glazed effect" on the leaves of *B. negrilensis* which is not present either in *B. sanguinea* or *B. domingensis*, as well as breeding experiments with the new species in which no segregation of cross characters was observed, tend to argue against the possibility that *B. negrilensis* may be a natural hybrid (Fowlie, 1967).

As can be expected from their different colors, the *Broughtonia* species analyzed do not have the same anthocyanin complements, although similarities do exist (Table 5-2). These would seem to suggest that *B. negrilensis* is not a hybrid of *B. sanguinea* and *B. domingensis*. Thus, though anthocyanin analysis tends to support the suggestions obtained from the breeding experiments, these suggestions also imply that *B. negrilensis* and *B. domingensis* are more closely related to each other than to *B. sanguinea*.

Brassavola nodosa (Plate 5-2) flowers contain an anthocyanin (Table 5-2; Fig. 7) not present in any of the other taxa studied. This is in line with current ideas regarding relationships within the *Epidendrum* alliance (Fig. 6) which includes *Broughtonia*, *Brassavola*, and *Cattleyopsis* (Dressler, 1961). *Brassavola*, *Broughtonia*, and probably *Cattleyopsis* are related to one another through *Laelia* and, therefore, *Cattleya* (Fig. 6), rather than directly.

A remarkable feature of the *Vanda-Aranda-Renanthera* group of cultivated hybrids is the occurrence of only a single anthocyanin (Lowry and Keong, 1973).

Plate 5-1.
Broughtonia and *Cattleyopsis*. **A-H**, Photographs by Dr. J. A. Fowlie (reproduced from Fowlie, 1966, 1967).
A, *Broughtonia negrilensis* × *B. sanguinea*; **B**, *B. negrilensis*; **C**, *B. sanguinea* var. *flava* 'Carmen Gauntlett'
(yellow); **D**, *B. sanguinea*; **E**, *B. sanguinea* × *B. negrilensis*; **F**, *B. sanguinea* var. *alba* (white); **G**, *B. domingensis*;
H, *Cattleyopsis lindenii*.

Plate 5-2.
Brassavola nodosa; drawing by Gordon W. Dillon (from Ames and Correll, 1953); reproduced with the permission of the Field Museum of Natural History, Chicago.

The foregoing examples show how anthocyanins may serve as chemotaxonomic agents in orchids, especially when several pigments have been found in species of one genus (Table 5-2; Fig. 7; Gascoigne *et al.*, 1949). When combined with morphological evidence, pollinators, and other chemotaxonomical data, anthocyanins will undoubtedly be instrumental in the resolution of unclear taxonomic situations.

A general concern among taxonomists interested in the application of biochemicals to phylogeny and/or taxonomy is that secondary metabolites, including anthocyanins, are less precise indicators than proteins. It is entirely possible that the significance of anthocyanins as chemotaxonomic agents may be weakened by parallelism in distantly related types and diversity within closely related taxa or even within one species. Presently available evidence, although scant, suggests that anthocyanins, alkaloids, and fragrances, singly or in combination, may indeed prove to be powerful chemotaxonomic agents on levels ranging from orchid species to subtribes and possibly tribes. Further studies will establish the chemotaxonomic value of anthocyanins, and make possible comparison between their alkaloids (Lüning, 1966, and many other papers not cited here; Lawler and Slaytor, 1969, 1970) and fragrances (Dodson and Hills, 1966, van der Pijl and Dodson, 1966; Hills *et al.*, 1968; Dodson *et al.*, 1969) within a single family. This will provide a basis for further comparative studies involving amino acids, proteins, and genetic material.

Chemotaxonomy alone, based as it may be on anthocyanins, alkaloids, scents, protein, or any other group of compounds, cannot be expected to provide all the necessary information required to establish systematic relationships among the orchids. Therefore, data obtained from chemotaxonomic studies must be correlated with available information on the anatomy, cytology, embryology, morphology, physiology, fungal associates, pollination, pollen morphology, nectar composition, geographical distribution, stomatal structure, requirements for seed germination, and other aspects of the species to be studied.

Inheritance of Color in the Orchids

Very little direct information is available on the actual inheritance of anthocyanins in orchids. And, at best, the available information is sketchy. *Brassocattleya* hybrids contain a blue pigment R_f 0.15 similar to the blue pigment R_f 0.16 isolated from *Rhyncholaelia (Brassavola) glauca* (Table 5-2). This may be their common heritage from the *Brassavola* parent. If so, this pigment may be dominant in its inheritance. But at the moment we do not have information on the nature or identity(ies) of the pigment(s). Anthocyanins present in *Broughtonia sanguinea* were also detected in its hybrids, but *Cattleytonia* xRosy Jewell contained additional pigments (Table 5-2; Fig. 7). The latter may represent its *Cattleya* parent and indicate that anthocyanins may be inherited across generic lines. It is also interesting to note that *Vanda coerulea* contains a blue-mauve anthocyanin R_f 0.12 which may be similar to the one from *Vanda* xProfusion (Sanford *et al.*, 1964). This is interesting since *Vanda* xRothschildiana, the seed parent of *V.* xProfusion, is a hybrid of *V. coerulea*. Thus, the pigment may have been inherited through two hybrids.

Despite a scarcity of information, a discussion of the inheritance of anthocyanins in orchids is possible. Present evidence that most, if not all, reds, purples, blues, pinks, mauves, and rose colors are due to anthocyanins is fairly conclusive. Thus, a selective review of color inheritance in orchids does, in fact, deal with anthocyanins.

The inheritance patterns of flower colors in orchids have received considerable attention and have been the concern of many orchid breeders. In 1862, Henri Lecoq (cited by Fenton, 1951), possibly foreshadowing Mendel but probably speaking in terms of "blending" inheritance, suggested that crosses between white and red orchids will produce hybrids of a more dilute color. He also suggested that if such hybrids were selfed, the brilliant colors would reappear in the progeny.

Charles Chamberlain Hurst was probably the first to study flower-color inheritance in orchids (Lenz and Wimber, 1959). Following a series of early experiments (Hurst, 1898), he became aware of Mendel's principles and applied them to orchid breeding (Hurst, 1912, 1913, 1925). Most of Hurst's findings have been substantiated by others (Lenz and Wimber, 1959).

In particular, he investigated the genetics of albinism, a matter of much interest (Anonymous, 1911, 1912, 1913a,b, 1914a,b,c,d,e, 1915; Foote, 1938), in several *alba* forms of *Paphiopedilum*, *Cattleya*, *Dendrobium*, and *Laelia* (Hurst, 1913, 1925). Inheritance of albinism has since been also investigated by others in *Dendrobium* and *Laelia* (Thwaites, 1912), *Laeliocattleya* (Anonymous, 1911, 1914c), *Dendrobium nobile virginale* (Anonymous, 1912), a peloric form of *Cattleya labiata* a hybrid between *Cattleya gaskelliana alba* and *C. labiata* xPurity (Anonymous, 1914a), *Cypripedium insigne* xSanderae (Anonymous, 1914b), *Lycaste skinneri* (Twiss, 1914), and *Paphiopedilum* (Rolfe, 1908; Wilson, 1923, 1927; Black, 1933; McQuade, 1949; Lenz and Wimber, 1959).

The general question of flower-color inheritance in *Sophronitis*, *Cattleya*, *Laelia*, and *Brassavola* hybrids has received wide attention (Curtis and Duncan, 1942; Storey, 1946; Northen, 1949, 1953, 1962, 1970; Fenton, 1951; Mehlquist, 1958; Storey and Kamemoto, 1960; Sweet, Beckner, and Livingston, 1960; Woodward, 1964, 1965; Bennet, 1965; Sauleda, 1966; Withlow, 1966a,b, 1967a,b). Color inheritance in *Spathoglottis* has also been studied extensively (Storey, 1950, 1958; Lenz and Wimber, 1959; Fig. 11). The available information on each genus is summarized in the alphabetical listing below.

Cattleya

Flower-color inheritance in this, perhaps the most popular of all orchid genera, has received more attention than in any other member of the Orchidaceae. Early *Cattleya* breeders must have been somewhat baffled to discover that crosses between two white flowers often resulted in colored hybrids (Lenz and Wimber, 1959). Observations of several white clones suggested that "there can be little doubt that the rosy-purple color in the various species of *Cattleya* and *Cypripedium* is due to the simultaneous presence of two complimentary color factors, which we call C and R. If one or both of these factors is absent, the result is a true albino with no trace of purple sap. . . . This purple color can only be produced when the two factors C and R are both present"

Table 5-4. Genetic constitution of albino *Cattleya* species and hybrids[a]

Group I, *ccRR*

C. gaskelliana var. *alba*	*C.* xObrieniana 'Alba' (*C. dolosa* × *C. loddigesii*)
C. intermedia var. *alba*	*C. skinneri* var. *alba*
C. labiata var. *alba*	*C. speciosissima* var. *alba*
C. labiata 'Harefield Hall'	*C. trianae* var. *alba*[b]
C. loddigesii var. *alba*	*C. trianae* 'Broomhills'
C. loddigesii 'Stanley'	*C. trianae* 'Verdonck'
C. lueddemanniana var. *alba*	*C. warneri* var. *alba*[b]
C. mossiae var. *wageneri*	

Group II, *CCrr*

C. xEldorado var. *alba*	*C. schroederae* var. *alba*
C. harrisoniana var. *alba*	*C. trianae* var. *alba*[b]
C. mendelii var. *alba*	*C. warneri* var. *alba*[b]
C. percivaliana var. *alba*	*C. warscewiczii* 'Firmin Lambeau'

[a] Hurst, 1925; Curtis and Duncan, 1942; Storey, 1946; Mehlquist, 1958; Lenz and Wimber, 1959.

[b] This species appears to contain both genetic types.

(Hurst, 1913). The purple sap or rosy-purple color are most probably anthocyanins. C_-R_- would, therefore, be colored whereas ccR_- and C_-rr would be white. It is easy to see why the cross $ccR_- \times C_-rr$ will produce some colored offspring despite the fact that each parent, if selfed, would produce white offspring only. The *C* and *R* hypothesis is now generally accepted as being valid by all orchid breeders and geneticists (Storey and Kamemoto, 1960) and a number of white *Cattleya* have been classified as being either *CCrr* or *ccRR* albinos (Table 5-4).

Caution is necessary in making assumptions regarding the genotype of any white *Cattleya* since the information (Table 5-4) pertains to specific clones (Lenz and Wimber, 1959). However, when appropriate clones are used in breeding, white hybrids can be produced, as, for example, *Cattleya* xSnowdon (Fig. 8). *Cattleya warscewiczii* var. Firmin Lambeau (a *CCrr* white) when crossed with a *ccRR* white produced only colored progeny, presumably of the *CcRr* genotype (Fig. 9; Storey and Kamemoto, 1960).

Some *Cattleya* forms produce flowers with white sepals and petals, but colored lips. The term "semi-alba" is used to describe these combinations (Mehlquist, 1958). Observation of several hybrids and especially the cross between *Laeliocattleya* xMount Shasta (a semi-alba) and *Cattleya schroederae alba*, whose progeny segregated as 1.

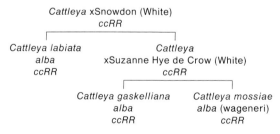

Fig. 8. The pedigree of *Cattleya* xSnowdon (Anonymous, 1914c; Sander's, 1946).

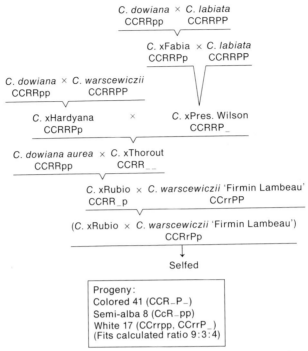

Fig. 9. Pedigree of the progeny of *Cattleya* xRubio × *C. warscewiczii* 'Firmin Lambeau' selfed, with assigned hypothetical genotypes (Storey and Kamemoto, 1960).

alba, 2 semi-alba, 1 colored, led to the postulation of a gene *p* (Mehlquist, 1958; Storey and Kamemoto, 1960). Proof of its existence was obtained from progeny of *Cattleya* xRubio (dark lavender) × *Cattleya warscewiczii* var. Firmin Lambeau (*CCrr* white). The progeny segregated into 9 colored, 3 semi-alba, and 4 white (Fig. 9), clearly indicating the existence of gene *p* and its effects (Storey and Kamemoto, 1960). From this information, the genotypes of the relevant plants were deduced (Fig. 9).

Yellow coloration in *Cattleya* (which is probably not due to anthocyanins) is controlled by genes Y_1, Y_2, y_1, and y_2 (Fig. 10), but is recessive to purple (Northen, 1962). This suggests several possibilities. First, it may be that when present, the anthocyanins simply "cover up" the yellow. Second, it is possible that genes in the Y and y series both shut off yellow pigment production, and turn on anthocyanin synthesis. And, third, production of yellow pigments and anthocyanins may be competitive, the genes favoring the latter only.

Cymbidium

Flower color in this genus may be due to chlorophyll (Arditti, 1966b; Matsumoto, 1966), anthocyanins, and other pigments (Lenz and Wimber, 1959). Green, chlorophyll-containing flowers are actually capable of photosynthesis (Dueker and Arditti, 1968). The presence of anthocyanins is apparently due to a single dominant gene (Lenz and Wimber, 1959; Strauss and Arditti, 1972). In some species, such as the white *Cymbidium lowianum* var. 'Concolor', *C. insigne album*, *C. eburneum*, and green

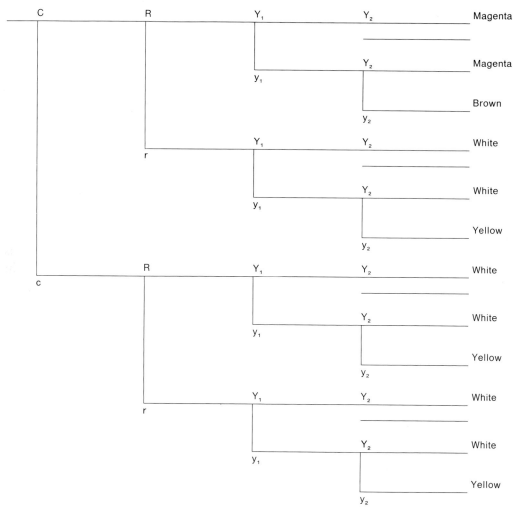

Fig. 10. Flower-color inheritance in *Cattleya* (Curtis and Duncan, 1942; Storey, 1946; Paris, Haney, and Wilson, 1960).

species like *C. sinense* and *C. ensifolium*, anthocyanins may be absent. Concolor and other pure-white varieties are apparently of related genetic constitution (Lenz and Wimber, 1959) and when intercrossed will produce similarly colored hybrids. However, concolors have also been obtained from crosses involving one colored parent such as *C.* xEsmeralda 'Concolor' (*C.* xVenus 'Dione' × *C. lowianum* var. 'Concolor') and even two colored parents as in the cross *C.* xCeres × *C.* xWheateater, which produced *C.* xFrivolity 'Alba' (Lenz and Wimber, 1959). The cross between *C.* xBlue Smoke and *C.* xVale of Cashmir produced 38 colored and 9 concolor hybrids, essentially a 3:1 ratio (Lenz and Wimber, 1959). Color and marking pattern variations on the labellum of *Cymbidium* flowers are probably under some sort of genetic control, the elucidation of which is complicated by the existence of intraclonal variations (Lenz, Wimber, and Dodson, 1955; Wimber, Lenz, and Dodson, 1956).

Dendrobium

The evidence, although meager, suggests that flower-color inheritance in this genus follows the *Cattleya* pattern. *Dendrobium nobile* var. *virginale*, when selfed, yielded only white offspring (Anonymous, 1912; Lenz and Wimber, 1959) as did the cross *D. nobile* var. virginale × *D. findlayanum* var. *album* (Lenz and Wimber, 1959). Both must, therefore, have the same genotype and be either *CCrr*, *ccRR*, or *ccrr*.

On the other hand, the cross *D. wardianum* var. *album* × *D. nobile* var. *album* produced only colored offspring (Lenz and Wimber, 1959). This suggests that one of the white parents was *ccRR* and the other *CCrr*.

Some evidence is available to suggest that yellow is dominant over purple in this genus (Lenz and Wimber, 1959). If so, the system is probably different from that in *Cattleya*.

Laelia

Yellow and orange pigmentation appears to be dominant over purple in this genus (Northen, 1949; Lenz and Wimber, 1959).

Paphiopedilum

Flower color and albinism in this genus are inherited in the same fashion as in *Cattleya* (Rolfe, 1908; Hurst, 1898, 1913, 1925; Wilson, 1923, 1927; Black, 1933; McQuade, 1949; Lenz and Wimber, 1959). Forms of *Paphiopedilum* species which lack anthocyanin type colors, although rare (Table 5-5), have contributed much to present-day hybrids. These plants are all green-flowered forms of otherwise colored species, except for *P. bellatulum* var. *album*, which is pure white, and *P. insigne* var. *sanderianum*, which is yellow.

Crosses between *Paphiopedilum callosum*, *P. lawrenceanum* var. *hyeanum*, *P. insigne* var. *sanderianum*, and *P. curtisii* (all *ccRR*) produce white progeny, whereas hybrids between these species and *P. bellatulum* var. *album* (*CCrr*) result in all colored progeny only (Lenz and Wimber, 1959). The inheritance and pattern markings on the dorsal sepal of *P. insigne*, *P. spicerianum*, and *P. boxallii* are somewhat complex. They depend on two factors: first, a base or ground color and markings on it; second, median color band on the dorsal sepal and a similar one on the lateral petals.

Each of these characteristics is apparently governed by an incompletely dominant allelomorph (Hurst, 1925; Lenz and Wimber, 1959).

Table 5-5. Genetic constitution of *Paphiopedilum* lacking anthocyanin-type pigmentation[a]

P. callosum var. *sanderae*	*ccRR*
P. lawrenceanum var. *hyeanum*	*ccRR*
P. insigne var. *sanderianum*	*ccRR*
P. bellatulum var. *album*	*CCrr* (?)
P. curtisii 'Sanderae'	*ccRR*
P. charlesworthii 'Bromilowiae'	*ccRR* (?)
P. charlesworthii 'Bromilowianum'	*ccRR* (?)

[a] Lenz and Wimber, 1959.

Sophronitis

This genus has contributed red coloration to many modern *Sophrolaeliocattleya* and *Potinara* ("*Brassosophrolaeliocattleya*") hybrids. The gene for red is reportedly dominant. It gives beautiful red when homozygous (Northen, 1949; Lenz and Wimber, 1959). Still, truly red hybrids are hard to obtain (Ilsley, 1961). Pelargonidin-3-bioside has been identified in *Sophronitis grandiflora* (Table 5-2) and is probably responsible at least in part for its red-orange-red color. It appears safe to assume that the red color of *Sophronitis* hybrids is also due to this pigment. The lack of truly red *Sophrolaeliocattleya* and *Potinara* hybrids is probably due to the inheritance of additional anthocyanins from the other parents.

Rosy or red-violet tones can be obtained from crosses between *Sophrocattleya* and *Cattleya* and *Laeliocattleya* (Northen, 1962; Sauleda, 1966). Identification of individual anthocyanins from a series of *Sophrocattleya*, *Sophrolaeliocattleya*, *Potinara*, and related hybrids and their parents will undoubtedly provide much valuable information on qualitative and quantitative aspects of the inheritance of individual anthocyanins.

Spathoglottis

Several observations on flower-color inheritance (Lowson, 1944; Kerns, 1946; Quisumbing, 1948; Putnam, 1953) and two genetic studies (Storey, 1950, 1958) have

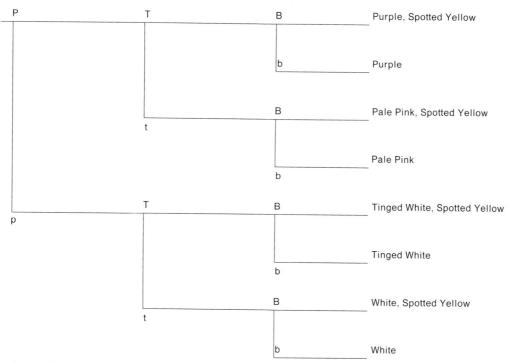

P gives pink.
T gives purple.
B gives yellow calli and yellow spotted labellum base.

Fig. 11. Genetics of flower color in a *Spathoglottis* cross (Storey, 1950, 1958; Paris, Haney, and Wilson, 1960).

produced much information on the subject. Three independent gene pairs control flower color (Storey, 1950, 1958; Fig. 11):

P—Dominant allele for pink coloring of sepals and petals and red spots on calli and base of labellum.

p—Recessive allele. No color or spots.

T—Dominant allele for pale pink or purple tinge of sepals and petals.

t—Recessive allele. No color or pale tinging.

B—Dominant allele for bright lemon-yellow color on calli and base of labellum.

b—Recessive allele producing only pale sulfur-yellow color.

Many of the orchid hybrids and plants utilized for the early genetic studies can still be obtained. Much information on the biochemical aspects of flower color and anthocyanin inheritance as well as orchid genetics could be obtained from a study of their anthocyanins.

Anthocyanins and Orchid Pollination

Scents (Dodson and Hills, 1966; Hills, Williams, and Dodson, 1968; Dodson et al., 1969) and morphology (Dodson and Frymire, 1961; van der Pijl and Dodson, 1966) play important roles in the attraction of orchid pollinators. Sugar content of nectars, if it plays any role at all, is of minor importance (Jeffrey and Arditti, 1968, 1969; Baskin and Blis, 1969; Jeffrey, Arditti, and Koopowitz, 1970; Arditti et al., 1973). Colors play important roles in animal-pollinated plants, as, for example, in the Gesneriaceae and Plumbaginaceae (Clifford and Harborne, 1967). The human nose, at least, seems to suggest that not all orchids rely on scents for attracting pollinators. If so, it seems reasonable to suppose that coloration plays an important role in some species. In such cases, selection may have favored colors attractive to pollen vectors. A single gene mutation, if perpetuated, may, in these instances, have a profound effect on the survival of species or populations. The very color of flowers may determine the nature of their pollinators.

Because birds see red well, many flowers of this color are pollinated by them. The same is also true of orchids as exemplified by Cochlioda vulcanica, Comparetia falcata, Eleanthus capitatus, Masdevalia rosea, and others (van der Pijl and Dodson, 1966). Fly vision is especially acute in the blue region and they often pollinate flowers of such a color. Indeed, several fly-pollinated orchids are blue or have blotches of this color (George et al., 1973). Bees are attracted by scents and prefer red flowers. In cases where pollinators are attracted by the total image of a flower, Oncidium planilabre, for example (van der Pijl and Dodson, 1966), coloration undoubtedly plays an important role. Since anthocyanins are major contributors to such coloration, they are undoubtedly of considerable importance in attracting the pollinator.

Post-pollination phenomena in orchid flowers are an exceedingly interesting but not fully appreciated aspect of the Orchidaceae (Knauft, Arditti, and Flick, 1970). Pollination not only considerably shortens the life of flowers, but also induces numerous and remarkable changes in morphology and coloration (Anonymous, 1899). In Cymbidium, for example, pollination induces anthocyanin formation (Arditti, 1969c;

Arditti and Knauft, 1969; Arditti, Flick, and Jeffrey, 1971; Arditti, Jeffrey, and Flick, 1971; Arditti, Hogan, and Chadwick, 1973; Arditti and Flick, 1974). Anthocyanin spots on labella of *Brassotonia* diffuse and disappear following pollination, eventually suffusing the entire lip with a pale magenta color. Yellow trichomes on the labellum of pollinated *Bifrenaria harrisoniae* flowers become red, whereas blossoms of *Schomburgkia tibicinis* turn a darker color after pollination. *Vanda* flowers, on the other hand, lose their anthocyanins (Burg and Dijkman, 1967; Dijkman and Burg, 1970). Although opposite in nature (production vs. destruction), both phenomena probably render the flowers less attractive or unattractive to pollinators by obliterating visible or UV light patterns. A series of spectacular photographs (Thien, 1971) do indeed indicate changes in ultraviolet light (UV) reflection. These changes in visible coloration and UV reflection may discourage visits by vectors to already-pollinated flowers. In a family which depends very closely on one specific pollinator, and whose flowers are pollinated relatively rarely, this may be an important survival and adaptation feature.

Orchid Anthocyanins and the Environment

Despite numerous investigations, the ecological roles of anthocyanins are as yet not entirely clear. Due to their absorption of ultraviolet light in solution, it has been suggested that anthocyanins may prevent damage due to such irradiation. This may be the case with *Lycaste* in Colombia (Fowlie, 1970). Plants from higher elevations, where UV of solar origin is not as effectively filtered out, contain more anthocyanin and, if transplanted to lower elevations, survive. On the other hand, less intensely colored plants from lower areas perish if moved to higher elevations (Fowlie, 1970). It is, of course, not clear at present whether this is entirely due to a screening effect by the anthocyanins. Still, the possibility cannot be fully discounted.

Leaf temperature measurements indicate that red leaves attain higher temperatures than "a white or pale leaf of the same thickness or texture" (Smith, 1909). This can but does not have to be interpreted as supporting either the screening function of anthocyanins or the notion that the anthocyanin promotes transpiration and translocation by raising the temperature of the leaf (Smith, 1909; Blank, 1947). About half of the sun's energy output is in the infrared. UV amounts to only 4% of the whole, and the region below 300 nm (where the λ max. of anthocyanins lies) accounts for only $\frac{1}{2}\%$ of the total ultraviolet energy (Leighton, 1961). It seems probable that the rise in leaf temperature, occasioned by anthocyanin absorption of solar radiation, if it exists, should be in major part attributed to high extinction coefficients in the mid-visible range. It is not at all clear whether raised floral (sepals, petals, and/or labella) temperatures may be ecologically advantageous or deleterious in orchids. One possible speculation is that raised temperatures may promote volatilization of scents which would serve to attract pollinators.

Many plants respond to changes in temperature or light intensity with modifications in their anthocyanin content. This is also true of orchids. *Phalaenopsis* leaves, for example, turn redder when night temperatures are suboptimal.

Anthocyanins and Disease Resistance in Orchids

On the whole, the roles of anthocyanins in plants are not entirely clear despite many theories (Buscalioni and Pollacci, 1904; Harborne, 1967). One suggestion is that flavonoids may have a protective function, but the evidence regarding antho-cyanins in this respect is very tenuous (Harborne, 1967). Saturated cyanidin solutions inhibit the germination of apple fruit-rot fungus, *Gloesporium perenans* (Harborne, 1967). Pelargonidin-3-glucoside (P3G) and delphinidin-3-glucoside (D3G) inhibit the growth of *E. coli*, as does malvidin-3-glucoside (M3G) in some stages (Powers *et al.*, 1960). *Staphylococcus aureus* was inhibited by a number of anthocyanins, but D3G, M3G, malvidin-3, 5-diglucoside (M3, 5DG), and delphidinidin increased growth (Powers *et al.*, 1960). At a concentration of 10 mg per test disk, M3,5DG inhibited the growth of *Lactobacillus casei* for which P3G was also inhibitory (Powers *et al.*, 1960). A number of other anthocyanins also have bactericidal activity (for reviews, see Powers *et al.*, 1960; Harborne, 1967). Synthetic anthocyanins at concentrations ranging from 3×10^{-7} M to 10^{-4} M enhance root growth and reverse IAA-induced inhibition in wheat seedlings (Stenlid, 1962). The same is true of cyanidin diglucoside (Harborne, 1967). In orchids, as in other plants (Blank, 1947), certain types of injury to flowers or leaves may cause anthocyanin formation around the injured area. Thus, it is possible that anthocyanins may have certain protective repair functions in orchids. Reports that certain flavonoids inhibit the activity of bovine pancreatic ribonuclease (Mori and Noguchi, 1970) would seem to lend general support to this idea. However, in the absence of specific evidence, this suggestion, like several others pertaining to the functions of anthocyanins, must be considered speculative.

Control of Anthocyanin Production in Orchids

A large, although inconclusive, amount of information is available regarding the factors which generally control anthocyanin production. All plant hormones have been implicated, often with contradictory results. In orchids, auxins, gibberellin (GA), abscisic acid (ABA), and ethylene induce anthocyanin synthesis (Arditti, 1969c; Arditti and Knauft, 1969; Knauft, Arditti, and Flick, 1971; Arditti, Hogan, and Chadwick, 1973). Auxin and apparently ethylene also cause disappearance of anthocyanins (Burg and Dijkman, 1967; Dijkman and Burg, 1970). Cytokinins seem to have no influence but may counteract the effects of other hormones (Arditti and Knauft, 1969; Arditti, Flick, and Jeffrey, 1971).

Early indications that auxin may effect flower anthocyanins came from investigations of post-pollination phenomena in orchid flowers (Anonymous, 1899; Fitting, 1909a,b, 1910; Hubert and Maton, 1939; Hsiang, 1951a,b; Arditti, 1969c, 1971; Arditti and Knauft, 1969; Arditti, Flick, and Jeffrey, 1971). Application of actinomycin D, ethionine, puromycin, ABA, GA, and kinetin following auxin treatments inhibits production of anthocyanins. Actinomycin D, ethionine, and puromycin must be applied within 1–2 hours of the auxin in order to inhibit anthocyanin synthesis. This time period is similar to that required for the onset of post-pollination phenomena following disturbance of the rostellum. And removal of the tip of the column or the rostellum 30 or 60 minutes after pollination had more pronounced effects than excision after 150 minutes (Arditti and Flick, 1974). The inhibitors have a lesser effect or do not prevent other post-pollination phenomena. This may be interpreted to suggest that post-pollination anthocyanin synthesis requires *de novo* DNA-dependent RNA and/or protein synthesis (Arditti and Knauft, 1969). Support for this suggestion comes from the finding that in pollinated *Nicotiana alata* flowers, rRNA and DNA content increased 30% and 16% respectively (Tupy and Rangaswamy, 1973).

ABA accumulates in colored autumn leaves which depend in part on anthocyanin for their coloration (Brian, Petty, and Richmond, 1959; Cornforth *et al.*, 1965; Milborrow, 1967). Application of ABA to *Cymbidium* cv Samarkand flowers induced anthocyanin formation in petals, sepals, labella, and columns, but not other post-pollination phenomena (Arditti, Flick, and Jeffrey, 1971). However, simultaneous treatment with ABA, NAA, GA, or kinetin reduces pigment levels considerably.

Gibberellins enhance anthocyanin content in *Impatiens* hypocotyl segments (Arnold and Albert, 1964), in *Spirodela intermedia* grown with only 45 minutes illumination per 24 hours (McClure, 1970; Norman, 1968), and in autumn leaves of *Taxodium distichum* (Brian, Petty, and Richmond, 1959). Content is also promoted slightly in 7–10 day-old cultures of *Spirodela oligorrhiza* (Furuya and Thimann, 1964), but the reverse is true for older *S. oligorrhiza* cultures (Furuya and Thimann, 1964), or red maple seedlings (Bachelard, 1965) and probably parthenocarpic figs (Crane, 1965; Hirai, 1966). Light-induced increases of kaempferol triglucoside content in peas (Russell and Galston, 1969), synthesis of cyanidin-3-glucoside in *Spirodela intermedia* (McClure, 1970) as well as production of delphinidin-3-glucoside and cyanidin-3-glucoside in *Dimorphotheca* tissue cultures (Ball, Harborne, and Arditti, 1973) are also inhibited by GA. Thus, there is no agreement in the literature regarding the effects of GA on anthocyanin synthesis. Application of GA in the range of 0.001–100 μmoles/flower to *Cymbidium* cv Samarkand induce anthocyanin synthesis (Arditti, Flick, and Jeffrey, 1971). However, anthocyanin content following GA treatments is reduced by simultaneous application of NAA, ABA, or kinetin.

Kinetin in concentrations of 0.1 and 1 mg/flower brings about a slight enhancement of anthocyanin content in *Cymbidium* cv Samarkand labella (Arditti, Flick, and Jeffrey, 1971; Arditti, Jeffrey, and Flick, 1971). This is in line with some previous reports regarding the effects of cytokinins on anthocyanin production. Cytokinins increase the purple coloration of the rachis in grapes (Crane, 1964) and anthocyanin levels in cultured petals of *Impatiens balsamina* (Klein and Hagen, 1961), but inhibit it in *Spirodela* (Thimann and Radner, 1962) and parthenocarpic figs (Crane, 1965; Crane and van Overbeek, 1965; Hirai, 1966).

Ethylene, 10 μl/liter for up to 78 hours, induces anthocyanin formation in both gynostemia (columns) and labella (lips). After that, pigment levels decrease. During 24-hour exposures, ethylene concentrations of 0.1, 1, and 10 μl/liter raise anthocyanin levels in both columns and lips (Arditti, Hogan, and Chadwick, 1973). Such ethylene-mediated increases in anthocyanin content have also been reported in ripening fruits and sorghum (Biale, 1950; Cracker, 1971; Cracker, Standley, and Starbuck, 1971). On the other hand, ethylene can cause fading (i.e., apparent destruction of anthocyanins) in *Vanda* (Burg and Dijkman, 1967; Dijkman and Burg, 1970).

Emasculation or even slight disturbance of the rostellum-viscidium interface can induce some post-pollination phenomena in orchids. In *Cymbidium*, this includes anthocyanin formation and in *Vanda*, disappearance. The rostellum seems to play a major role in anthocyanin production by pollinated *Cymbidium* flowers (Arditti and Flick, 1974). Excision of the rostellum and/or removal of the column tip 30 and 60 minutes after pollination reduce anthocyanin levels.

Auxin, gibberellin, ABA, pollination, emasculation, and damage can initiate ethylene evolution in orchid flowers and other plants (Davidson, 1946; Lindner, 1946; Fischer, 1950; Akamine and Sakamoto, 1951; Akamine, 1963; Addicott and Lyon, 1969; Pratt and Goeschl, 1969; Dijkman and Burg, 1970). Ethylene, in turn, seems to control anthocyanin production (*Cymbidium*) or destruction (*Vanda*). Thus, it is not clear at present whether anthocyanin synthesis or degradation in orchid flowers following hormonal treatments or pollination is a direct or ethylene-mediated phenomenon.

Anthocyanin synthesis by orchid flowers, being controlled as it is by ABA, ethylene, auxins, GA, and cytokinins, may be activated by a "multitarget" trigger. It is possible to speculate that there may be several starting points, each activated by a different hormone. NAA may initiate the formation of new specific RNA(s) or stabilize the existing one(s) (Gayler and Glasziou, 1969). ABA, on the other hand, could act by inhibiting the production of specific ribonuclease(s) which destroy(s) RNA required for anthocyanin synthesis. GA may affect an early step (Furuya and Thimann, 1964) or possibly function indirectly through increased production of hydrolytic enzymes which raise the concentration of monosaccharides in columns and labella (Gessner, 1948; Oertli and Kohl, 1960), thereby enhancing anthocyanin synthesis (Thimann, Edmondson, and Radner, 1951; Thimann and Radner, 1962; Harborne, 1967). Cytokinins have no appreciable effects by themselves but perhaps counteract the influence of other hormones through their well-known ability to delay senescence (assuming that anthocyanin production in pollinated or hormone-treated flowers is one aspect of aging). The mode of action of ethylene remains unclear although it, too, probably functions at the nucleic acid or protein synthesis levels.

The destruction of anthocyanins in *Vanda* (Burg and Dijkman, 1967; Dijkman and Burg, 1970) is a particularly interesting phenomenon since it is one of the very few well-described instances where anthocyanin destruction in plants can be initiated by a hormone. *Vanda* anthocyanins are cyanidin-based (Table 5-2). And, interestingly, only the young seedlings of some nonorchidaceous plants contain cyanidin (Barz and Griesebach, 1971). Therefore, since feeding experiments indicated that cyanidin is subject to metabolic turnover (Barz and Griesebach, 1971), it is possible to ask whether its destruction may be indicative of aging in these cases. In the same vein, it can be asked whether anthocyanin production by pollinated *Cymbidium* flowers is also a symptom of aging in a manner similar to that in some ripening fruits (apples, for example).

The physiological and biochemical events which may be operative in fading *Vanda* flowers are unclear. It is possible that: (1) anthocyanidin production ceases while destruction does not and continues at unmodified or even increased rates or (2) synthesis remains unmodified while degradation is greatly increased. Answers to these questions could be obtained with relative ease from feeding experiments as well as from time-course determinations of degradation products.

That light is required for anthocyanin formation in *Orchis ustulata* was noted during an experiment which came to a tragic end. Flowers of *Orchis ustulata* had the usual shape but "in contrast to the ones grown in the field where the pointed ends of the upper perigon which form the helmet are colored brown-red, those growing in the dark were completely white" (Askenasy, 1876). In the field the brown-red coloration on the helmet and the red dots on the lip disappear in older flowers. Continues the report: "I could not determine how this works in the dark since my *O. ustulata* died by accident" (Askenasy, 1876).

Localization of Anthocyanins in Orchid Cells

Cursory examinations indicate that anthocyanins are found in the cell sap (Fig. 1). Within individual cells, they may be present alone (Fig. 1) or in conjunction with colored plastids (Fig. 3). In flower parts of *Cypripedium aucale*, large quantities of anthocyanidins appear bound in a massive colloidal "albuminous body" (Van Fleet, 1969). At the same time, water-soluble anthocyanins develop in low quantities. Large mitochondrial swarms develop in these cells and after they divide "there is conversion of insoluble anthocyanidins to water-soluble glucosidal anthocyanins that diffuse in the vacuole" (Van Fleet, 1969). Proteinaceous anthocyanin-containing bodies have also been noted in *Laelia anceps* (Politis, 1911a,b, 1914a,b). In mottled-leaf orchids like *Orchis latifolia* and *O. maculata*, anthocyanins are stored in parts of the epidermis (Blank, 1947).

Concluding Remarks

As with most aspects of the Orchidaceae, information regarding their anthocyanins is scant. Little has accumulated through the years despite much concern with their coloration. Even today, few investigators are concerned with this, the largest, plant family. The information or science "explosion" of the last two decades has scarcely touched the orchids. We find this regrettable in view of the scientific wealth orchids hold in store for investigators.

Acknowledgments

Our research in this area is supported in part by grants from Mrs. Emma D. Menninger; the American Orchid Society; the Orchid Digest Corporation; the Population Council; the National Science Foundation (GB-13417 and GB-40685); the Textilana Corporation; U.C.I. Industrial Associates; Peninsula Orchid Society; and the Office of Naval Research (contract NR 1008-796). We thank Michael S. Strauss for assisting with certain phases of this manuscript and many discussions as well as Robert Ernst, Chris Gonzales, and Brigitta H. Flick for being generally helpful.

Literature Cited

Addicott, F. T., and J. L. Lyon. 1969. Physiology of abscisic acid and related substances. Ann. Rev. Plant Physiol. 20:139–164.

Akamine, E. M. 1963. Ethylene production in fading *Vanda* orchid blossoms. Science 140:1217–1218.

Akamine, E. K., and H. I. Sakamoto. 1951. Brominated charcoal to prevent fading of Vanda orchid flowers. Amer. Orchid Soc. Bull. 20:149–152.

Akiyoshi, M., A. D. Webb, and R. E. Kepner. 1963. The major anthocyanin pigments of *Vitis vinifera* varieties Flarue, Tokay, Emperor and Red Malaga. J. Food Sci. 28:177–181.

Albach, R. F., R. E. Kepner, and A. D. Webb. 1965. Structures of acylated anthocyanin pigments in *Vitis vinifera* variety Tinta Pinheira. Identification of anthocyanidin, sugar and acid moities. J. Food Sci. 30:69–76.

Alston, R. E., T. J. Mabry, and B. L. Turner. 1963 Perspective in chemotaxonomy. Science 142:545–552.

Alston, R. E., and B. L. Turner. 1963a. Biochemical systematics. Prentice-Hall, Englewood Cliffs, N.J.

——. 1963b. Biochemical methods in systematics, p. 92–113. *In* W. A. Jensen and G. Kavaljian (eds.), Plant biology today. Wadsworth, Belmont. Calif.

Ames, O., and D. S. Correll. 1953. Orchids of Guatemala. Fieldiana (Bot.) 26:424.

Anonymous. 1899. Change of colour after fertilization. Orchid Rev. 7:165–166. (Probably by R. A. Rolfe.)

——. 1911. Notes. Orchid World 1:73. (Probably by G. Wilson.)

——. 1912. Albino hybrids. Orchid World 2:122. (Probably by G. Wilson.)

——. 1913a. Albinism in orchids. Orchid World 3:74. (Probably by G. Wilson.)

——. 1913b. Albinism. Orchid World 3:125. (Probably by G. Wilson.)

——. 1914a. An albino result. Orchid World 4:73. (Probably by G. Wilson.)

——. 1914b. Albinism. Orchid World 4:97. (Probably by G. Wilson.)

——. 1914c. An albino result. Orchid World 4:194. (Probably by G. Wilson.)

——. 1914d. An albino result. Orchid World 5:1. (Probably by G. Wilson.)

——. 1914e. An albino result. Orchid World 5:25. (Probably by G. Wilson.)

——. 1915. Unexpected albinism. Orchid World 5:121. (Probably by G. Wilson.)

Arditti, J. 1966a. Orchids. Sci. Amer. 214(1):70–78.

——. 1966b. The green color of cymbidiums. What is it? Cymbidium Soc. News 20:10–11.

——. 1967. Factors affecting the germination of orchid seeds. Bot. Rev. 33:1–97.

——. 1969a. Floral anthocyanins in species and hybrids of Broughtonia, Brassavola and Cattleyopsis (Orchidaceae). Amer. J. Bot. 56:59–68.

——. 1969b. Floral anthocyanins in some orchids. Amer. Orchid Soc. Bull. 38:407–413.

——. 1969c. Post-pollination phenomena in orchid flowers. Aust. Orchid Rev. 34:155–158.

——. 1971. Orchids and the discovery of auxin. Amer. Orchid Soc. Bull. 40:211–214.

Arditti, J., and J. Dueker. 1968. Photosynthesis by various organs of orchid plants. Amer. Orchid Soc. Bull. 37:862–866.

Arditti, J., and A. S. Dunn. 1969. Experimental plant physiology. Holt, Rinehart and Winston. New York.

Arditti, J., and R. Ernst. 1969. Floral pigments in orchids. Orchid Dig. 33:129–131.

——. 1971. Anthocyanins in the chemotaxonomy of orchids. Proc. 6th World Orchid Conf., Sydney (1969), p. 202–217.

Arditti, J., and B. H. Flick. 1974. Post-pollination phenomena in orchid flowers. V. Participation by the rostellum and gynostemium tip. Amer. J. Bot. 61:643–651.

Arditti, J., B. H. Flick, and D. C. Jeffrey. 1971. Post-pollination phenomena in orchid flowers. II. Effects of abscisic acid and its interactions with auxin, gibberellic acid and kinetin. New Phytol. 70:333–341.

Arditti, J., N. M. Hogan, and A. V. Chadwick. 1973. Post-pollination phenomena in orchid flowers. IV. Effects of ethylene. Amer. J. Bot. 60:883–888.

Arditti, J., D. C. Jeffrey, and B. H. Flick. 1971. Post-pollination phenomena in orchid flowers. III. Effects and interactions of auxin, kinetin or gibberellin. New Phytol. 70:1125–1141.

Arditti, J., and R. L. Knauft. 1969. The effects of auxin, actinomycin D, ethionine and puromycin on post-pollination behavior in orchid flowers. Amer. J. Bot. 56:620–628.

Arditti, J., H. Koopowitz, D. C. Jeffrey, and B. H. Flick. 1973. Der Zuckergehalt in Orchideennektaren. Die Orchidee 24:24–25.

Arnold, A. W., and L. S. Albert. 1964. Chemical factors affecting anthocyanin formation and morphogenesis in cultured hypocotyl segments of Impatiens balsamina. Plant Physiol. 39:307–311.

Askenasy, E. 1876. Ueber den Einfluss des Lichtes auf die Farbe der Blüten. Bot. Zeitung 34:1–8.

Bachelard, E. P. 1965. The interrelations between root formation and anthocyanin synthesis in red maple cuttings: effects of gibberellic acid, CCC and 8 azaguanine. Aust. J. Biol. Sci. 18:699–702.

Ball, E. A., J. B. Harborne, and J. Arditti. 1972. Anthocyanins of Dimorphotheca (Compositae). I. Identity of pigments in flowers, stems and callus cultures. Amer. J. Bot. 59:924–930.

Ball, N. G. 1938. The pigmentation of orchid flowers. Orchideologia Zeylanica 5:137–138.

Barz, W., and H. Grisebach. 1971. Enzymology of flavonoids biosynthesis and metabolism. Newsletter Phytochem. Sec. Bot. Soc. Amer. 3:4–28.

Baskin, S. I., and C. A. Blis. 1969. Sugar content of extrafloral exudates in orchids. Phytochemistry 8:1139–1145.

Bate-Smith, E. C. 1949. Anthocyanins, flavones and other phenolic compounds. Symposia Biochem. Soc. London 3:62–73.

Bennet, F. N. 1965. Orchids and genetics. Amer. Orchid Soc. Bull. 34:100–105.

Biale, J. B. 1950. Post harvest physiology and biochemistry of fruits. Ann. Rev. Plant Physiol. 1:183–206.

Black, J. M. 1933. Albinism in cypripediums. Orchid Rev. 41:69–72.

Blank, F. 1947. The anthocyanin pigments of plants. Bot. Rev. 13:241–317.

Blumenschein, A. 1960. Cromatografia em papel de filtro de pigmentos de flores de Laelinae. Pub. Cientifica, Inst. de Genetica, Escole Superior Agric. "Luiz de Queiros," Univ. Piracicaba São Paulo 1: 51–55.

Brian, P. W., J. H. Petty, and P. T. Richmond. 1953. Effects of gibberellic acid on development of autumn color and leaf fall of deciduous woody plants. Nature 183:58–59.

Burg, S. P., and M. J. Dijkman. 1967. Ethylene and auxin participation in pollen induced fading of Vanda orchid blossoms. Plant Physiol. 42:1648–1650.

Buscalioni, L., and G. Pollacci. 1904. Le antocianine e il loro significato biologico nelle piante. Atti Inst. Bot. Univ. Pavia, N.S. 8:135–136.

Clifford, H. T., and J. B. Harborne. 1967. Anthocyanin composition of and distribution in the Poaceae (Gramineae). Proc. Linn. Soc. London 178:125–127.

Cornforth, J. W., B. V. Milborrow, G. Ryback, and P. F. Wareing. 1965. Chemistry and physiology of "dormins" in sycamore. Identity of sycamore "dormin" with abscisin II. Nature 205:1269–1270.

Correll, D. S. 1941. Notes concerning some West Indian orchids. Bot. Mus. Lflts. Harvard Univ. 10:41–51.

Cracker, L. E. 1971. Post harvest color promotion in cranberry with ethylene. Hort. Sci. 6:137–139.

Cracker, L. E., A. Standley, and M. J. Starbuck. 1971. Ethylene control of anthocyanin synthesis in sorghum. Plant Physiol. 48:349–352.

Crane, J. C. 1964. Growth substances in fruit setting and development. Ann. Rev. Plant Physiol. 15:303–326.

———. 1965. The chemical induction of parthenocarpy in Calimyrna fig and its physiological significance. Plant Physiol. 40:606–610.

Crane, J. C., and J. van Overbeek. 1965. Kinin-induced parthenocarpy in the fig, Ficus carica L. Science 147:1468–1469.

Curtis, J. T., and R. E. Duncan. 1942. The inheritance of flower color in Cattleya. Amer. Orchid Soc. Bull. 10:283–286, 304–307.

Cutak, L. 1949. Color variation in orchids (a photograph). Amer. Orchid Soc. Bull. 18:282.

Davidson, O. W. 1949. Effects of ethylene on orchid flowers. Proc. Amer. Soc. Hort. Sci. 53:440–446.

Dijkman, M. J., and S. P. Burg. 1970. Auxin-induced spoiling in Vanda blossoms. Amer. Orchid. Soc. Bull. 39:799–804.

Dodson, C. H. 1967. Relationships between pollinators and orchid flowers. Atlas do Simposio sobre a Biota Amazonica. Vol. 5 (Zoologia): 1–72.

Dodson, C. H., R. L. Dressler, H. G. Hills, R. M. Adams, and N. H. Williams. 1969. Biologically active compounds in orchid fragrances. Science 164:1243–1249.

Dodson, C. H., and G. P. Frymire. 1961. Natural pollination of orchids. Missouri Bot. Gard. Bull. 49:133–152.

Dodson, C. H., and H. G. Hills. 1966. Gas chromatography of orchid fragrances. Amer. Orchid Soc. Bull. 35:720–825.

Dressler, R. L. 1961. A reconsideration of Encyclia (Orchidaceae). Brittonia 13:253–266.

——. 1966. Nomenclatural notes on the Orchidaceae. III. Taxon 15:241–243.

Dueker, J., and J. Arditti. 1968. Photosynthetic $^{14}CO_2$ fixation by green Cymbidium (Orchidaceae) flowers. Plant Physiol. 43:130–132.

Dunn, H. A. 1949. Panama's only Cattleya, Cattleya skinneri var. autumnalis. Amer. Orchid Soc. Bull. 18:364–365.

Fawcett, W., and A. B. Rendle. 1910. Flora of Jamaica. Vol. 5. Orchidaceae. British Museum. Reprint, 1963. G. Hart, Kingston, Jamaica.

Fenton, K. J. 1951. Color inheritance in orchids. Amer. Orchid Soc. Bull. 20:519–523, 587–591.

Fischer, C. W., Jr. 1950. Ethylene gas as a problem in cut-flower storage. Bull. N.Y. State Flower Growers 61:1, 4.

Fitting, H. 1909a. Die Beinflussung der Orchideenblüten durch die Bestäubung und durch andere Umstände. Ztsch. für Bot. 1:1–86.

——. 1909b. Entwicklungsphysiologische Probleme der Fruchtbildung. Biol. Centralblatt 29:193–206.

——. 1910. Weitere entwicklungsphysiologische Untersuchungen an Orchideenblüten. Zeitschr. für Bot. 2:225–267.

Foote, G. B. 1938. White orchids. Orchideologia Zeylanica 5:145–146.

Forsyth, W. G. C., and N. W. Simmonds. 1954. A survey of anthocyanins of some tropical plants. Proc. Roy. Soc. London, Ser. B, 142:549–564.

Fowlie, J. A. 1961. Obscure species. Broughtonia species compared. Orchid Dig. 25:416–418.

——. 1966. The enigmatic broughtonias of Jamaica. Lasca Leaves 16:3–8.

——. 1967. The enigmatic broughtonias of Jamaica. Orchid Dig. 31:69–72.

——. 1970. The genus Lycaste. Azul Quinta Press, La Canada, Calif.

Furuya, M., and K. V. Thimann. 1964. The biogenesis of anthocyanins. XI. Effects of gibberellic acid in two species of Spirodela. Arch. Biochem. Biophys. 108:109–116.

Gascoigne, R. M., C. Ritchie, and D. E. White. 1949. A survey of anthocyanins in the Australian flora. J. and Proc. Roy. Soc. N.S.W. 82:44–70.

Gayler, K. R., and K. T. Glasziou. 1969. Plant enzyme synthesis: Hormonal regulation of invertase and peroxidase synthesis in sugar cane. Planta 84:185.

George, A., C. Gonzales, M. S. Strauss, and J. Arditti. 1973. Chemotaxonomic and ecological implications of anthocyanins in Elythranthera. Biochem. Syst. 1:45–49.

Gessner, F. 1948. Stoffwanderungen in bestäubten Orchideenblüten. Biol. Centralblatt 67:457–479.

Giannasi, D. E. and G. M. Rogers. 1970. Taxonomic significance of floral pigment in Linum (Linaceae). Brittonia 22:163–174.

Halevy, A. H., and S. Asen. 1959. Identification of the anthocyanins in petals of tulip varieties, Smiling Queen and Pride of Haarlem. Plant Physiol. 34:494–499.

Harborne, J. B. 1958a. Spectral methods of characterizing anthocyanins. Biochem. J. 70:22–28.

——. 1958b. The chromatographic identification of anthocyanin pigments. J. Chrom. 1:473–488.

——. 1962. Anthocyanins and their sugar components. Fortschr. Organ. Naturst. 20:165–199.

——. 1963. Distribution of anthocyanins in higher plants, p. 359–388. In T. Swain (ed.), Chemical plant taxonomy. Academic Press, New York.

——. 1967. Comparative biochemistry of the flavonoids. Academic Press, New York.

Harper, W. J. 1972a. Orchid pigments. 1. Chemical nature of pigments. Orchid Rev. 80:36–38.

——. 1972b. Orchid pigments. 2. Concepts of inheritance. Orchid Rev. 80:57–58.

Hess, D. 1964. Blütenfarbstoffe als Modell für die Wirkungsweise von Genen. Umschau 64:758–762; 65:49–53, 140–143, 160.

Hills, H. G., N. H. Williams, and C. H. Dodson. 1968. Identification of some orchid fragrance components. Amer. Orchid Soc. Bull. 37:967–971.

Hirai, J. 1966. Anatomical, physiological and biochemical studies of the fig fruit. Bull. Univ. Osaka Pref. Univ., Ser. B, 169–218.

Hsiang, T. H. T. 1951a. Physiological and biochemical changes accompanying pollination in orchid flowers. I. General observations and water relations. Plant Physiol. 26:441–455.

——. 1951b. Physiological and biochemical changes accompanying pollination in orchid flowers. II. Respiration, catalase activity and chemical constituents. Plant Physiol. 26:708–721.

Hubert, B., and J. Maton. 1939. The influence of synthetic growth-controlling substances and other chemicals on post-floral phenomena in tropical orchids. Biol. Jaarboek 6:244–285.

Hurst, C. C. 1898. Notes on some curiosities of orchid breeding. J. Roy. Hort. Soc. 21:442–486.

——. 1912. The application of genetics to orchid breeding. Orchid World 3:57–64, 83–86. (Reprinted in Orchid J. 3:122–124, 184–187.)

——. 1913. The application of genetics to orchid breeding. Orchid Conf. Rept. J. Roy. Hort. Soc. 38:412–429.

——. 1925. Experiments in genetics. Cambridge Univ. Press, Cambridge.

Ilsley, P. 1961. The breeding of red cattleyas. Proc. 4th Hawaiian Orchid Conf., p. 43–45.

Jeffrey, D. C., and J. Arditti. 1968. Sugar content of orchid nectars. Orchid Rev. 76:315–316.

——. 1969. The separation of sugars in orchid nectars by thin-layer chromatography. Amer. Orchid Soc. Bull. 38:866–868.

Jeffrey, D. C., J. Arditti, and H. Koopowitz. 1970. Sugar content in floral and extrafloral exudates of orchids. Pollination, myrmecology and chemotaxonomy implications. New Phytol. 69:187–195.

Kerns, K. R. 1946. A color variation in the wild Spathoglottis plicata. Bull. Pacific Orchid Soc. Hawaii 4:no pagination.

Klein, A. O., and C. W. Hagen. 1961. Anthocyanin production in detached petals of Impatiens balsamina L. Plant. Physiol. 36:1–9.

Knauft, R. L., J. Arditti, and B. H. Flick. 1970. Postpollinationsphänomene an Orchideenblüten. Die Orchidee 21:132–135.

Lawler, L. J., and M. Slaytor. 1969. The distribution of alkaloids in New South Wales and Queensland Orchidaceae. Phytochemistry 8:1959–1962.

——. 1970. A simple method for screening plants for antibacterial activity. Aust. J. Pharm. 51:no pagination.

Lawrence, W. J. C., Jr., J. R. Price, G. M. Robinson, and R. Robinson. 1939. The distribution of anthocyanins in flowers, fruits and leaves. Philosophical Trans. Roy. Soc. London, Ser. B, Biol. Sci. 230:149–178.

Leighton, P. A. 1961. Photochemistry of air pollution. Academic Press, New York.

Lenz, L. W., and D. E. Wimber. 1959. Hybridization and inheritance in orchids, p. 261–314. In C. L. Withner (ed.), The orchids: a Scientific survey. Ronald Press, New York.

Lenz, L. W., D. Wimber, and C. H. Dodson. 1955. Intraclonal lip pattern variation in Cymbidiums. Cymbidium Soc. News 10:17–20.

Lindley, J., and J. Paxton. 1853. The Haytian Laeliops. Paxton's Flower Garden 3:155–156, pl. 105.

Lindner, R. E. 1946. Studies on packaging and storage of Vanda (Joacquim) flowers. Hawaii Agric. Exp. Sta. Progress Notes 49:1–5.

Lowry, J. C., and S. C. Keong. 1973. A preliminary study of Malaysian orchid pigments. Malaysia J. Sci. 2:115–121.

Lowson, J. M. 1944. One of our garden orchids. Bull. Pacific Orchid Soc. Hawaii 3:no pagination.

Lüning, B. 1966. Chemotaxonomy in a Dendrobium complex. Proc. 5th World Orchid Conf., Long Beach, p. 211–215.

Matsumoto, K. 1966. Determination of the chlorophyll content of Cymbidium blooms. Cymbidium Soc. News 29:11–14.

McClure, J. W. 1970. Secondary constituents of aquatic angiosperms, p. 233–268. In J. B. Harborne (ed.), Phytochemical phylogeny. Academic Press, New York.

McQuade, H. A. 1949. The cytology of Paphiopedilum maudiae Hort. Ann. Missouri Bot. Gard. 36:433–472.

Mehlquist, G. A. L. 1958. Genetics and orchid breeding. Proc. 2d World Orchid Conf., Honolulu (1957), p. 200–209.

Milborrow, B. V. 1967. The identification of (+)-abscisin II (+)-dormin in plants and measurement of its concentrations. Planta 76:93–113.

Mori, S., and I. Noguchi. 1970. Effects of flavonoid compounds on enzyme activites. I. Inhibitory action on bovine pancreatic ribonuclease. I. Arch. Biochem. Biophys. 139:444–446.

Muszynski, S. 1964. A survey of anthocyanidins in Petunia. Physiol. Plant. 17:975–979.

Norman, A. M. 1968. The influence of light and growth factors on flavonoid production in Spirodela intermedia. M.S. thesis. Miami Univ., Oxford, Ohio.

Northen, R. T. 1949. Home orchid growing. Van Nostrand, New York.

——. 1953. Cattleya mossiae. Amer. Orchid Soc. Bull. 22:256–259.

——. 1962. Home orchid growing. 2d ed. Van Nostrand Reinhold, New York.

——. 1970. Home orchid growing. 3d ed. Van Nostrand Reinhold, New York.

Oertli, J. O., and H. C. Kohl. 1960. Der Einfluss der Bestäubung auf die Stoffbewegungen in Cymbidiumblüten. Die Gartenbauwiss. 25:107–114.

Paris, C. D., W. J. Haney, and G. B. Wilson. 1960. A survey of the interactions of genes for flower color. Tech. Bull. 281, Mich. State Univ. Agric. Exp. Sta., East Lansing, Mich.

Pijl, L. Van der, and C. H. Dodson. 1966. Orchid flowers: their pollination and evolution. Univ. of Miami Press, Coral Gables, Fla.

Politis, I. 1911a. Sopra uno speciale corpo cellulare trovato in due orchidee. Atti Reale Acad. Lincei, Redincoti Ser. 5, 20:343–349.

——. 1911b. Sopra speciali corpi cellulari che formano antocianine. Atti. Reale Acad. Lincei, Redincoti Ser. 5, 20:828–834.

——. 1914a. Sopra speciali cellulare che formano antocianine. Atti Inst. Bot. Univ. Pavia, Ser. II, 14:363–376.

——. 1914b. Sopra uno speciale corpi cellulare trovato in due orchidee. Atti Inst. Bot. Univ. Pavia, Ser. II, 14:377–383.

Pollock, H. G., R. K. Vickery, Jr., and K. G. Wilson. 1967. Flavonoid pigments in Mimulus cardinalis and its related species. I. Anthocyanins. Amer. J. Bot. 54:695–701.

Powers, J. J., D. Somaatmadja, D. E. Pratt, and M. K. Hamdy. 1960. Anthocyanins. II. Action of anthocyanin pigments and related compounds on the growth of certain microorganisms. Food Technol. 14:626–632.

Pratt, H. K., and J. D. Goeschl. 1969. Physiological roles of ethylene in plants. Ann. Rev. Plant Physiol. 20:541–584.

Putnam, G. S. 1953. More about Spathoglottis flower color. Bull. Pacific Orchid Soc. Hawaii 11:54.

Quisumbing, E. 1948. The genus Spathoglottis in the Philippines. Bull. Pacific Orchid Soc. Hawaii 7:45 50. (Reprinted from Philippine Orchid Rev. 1.)

Richards, J. H., and J. B. Hendrickson. 1964. Biosynthesis of terpenes, steroids and acetogenins. Benjamin Press, New York.

Robinson, G. M., and R. Robinson. 1932. A survey of anthocyanins. II. Biochem. J. 26:1647–1664.

——. 1934. A survey of anthocyanins. Biochem. J. 28:1712–1723.

Rolfe, R. A. 1908. Inheritance of albinism in orchids. Orchid Rev. 16:265–268.

Russell, D. W., and A. W. Galston. 1969. Blockage by gibberellic acid of phytochromic effects on growth, auxin responses and flavonoid synthesis in etiolated pea internodes. Plant Physiol. 44:1211–1216.

Sander, D. F., and W. J. Wreford. 1961. One table list of orchid hybrids. Vol. 1. David Sander's Orchids, Selsfield, England.

Sander's. 1946. Sander's complete list of orchid hybrids. Sander's, St. Albans, England.

Sanford, W. W., A. Krallis, A. Xanthakis, E. Fourakis, and K. Kapri. 1964. Anthocyanins in orchids. Orchid Dig. 28:362–367.

Sauleda, R. P. 1966. Current breeding trends in red cattleyas. Amer. Orchid Soc. Bull. 35:630–632.

Schlechter, R. 1970. Die Orchideen. 3d ed. by F. G. Brieger, R. M. Maatsch, and K. Senghas. Verlag Paul Parey. Berlin.

Schultes, R. E., and A. S. Pease. 1963. Generic names of orchids. Academic Press, New York.

Shibata, K., K. Hayashi, and T. Isaka. 1949. Studien über Anthocyane. XIV. Uber Wasserstoffionen-konzentration des Pressaftes von den Anthocyan-führenden Pflanzenorganen: Versuch zu einer Erklärung der Farbenvariation der Blüten. I. Acta Phytochim. 15:17–33.

Shibata, K., Y. Shibata, and I. Kasiwagi. 1921. Studies on anthocyanins: color variation in anthocyanins. J. Amer. Chem. Soc. 41:208–220.

Smith, A. M. 1909. On the internal temperature of leaves in tropical isolation, with special reference to the effect of their colour on the temperature; also observations on the periodicity of the appearance of young colored leaves of trees growing in Peradeniya gardens. Ann. Roy. Bot. Gard. Peradeniya 4:229–248.

Soysa, E. 1938. The floral tints of the orchid family. Orchideologia Zeylanica 5:140–144.

——. 1943. The floral tints of orchids, p. 114. In E. Soysa (ed.), Orchid culture in Ceylon. Caxton Press, Colombo, Ceylon.

Stenlid, G. 1962. The effect of some synthetic anthocyanidins on growth and iron absorption by roots. Physiol. Plant. 15:598–605.

Storey, W. B. 1946. Inheritance of flower color in Cattleya. Bull. Pacific Orchid Soc. Hawaii 4:1–10.

——. 1950. Genetics of flower color in a Spathoglottis cross. Bull. Pacific Orchid Soc. Hawaii 8:327–331.

——. 1958. Additional observations on the genetics of flower color in Spathoglottis. Bull. Pacific Orchid Soc. Hawaii 16:7–13.

Storey, W. B., and H. Kamemoto. 1960. Inheritance of semialba in a Cattleya pedigree. Amer. Orchid Soc. Bull. 29:24–29.

Strauss, M. S., and J. Arditti. 1972. Floral pigments in Cymbidium. Cymbidium Soc. News 7:170–171.

Strauss. M. S., C. Gonzales, J. Arditti, and A. George. 1974. Anthocyanins of the enamel orchids. Orchid Rev. 82:198–199.

Sweet, J. S., J. Beckner, and R. Livingston. 1960. Hereditary influences of the Cattleya alliance. Amer. Orchid Soc. Bull. 29:14–15.

Thien, L. B. 1971. Orchids viewed with ultraviolet light. Amer. Orchid Soc. Bull. 40:877–880.

Thimann, K. V., Y. H. Edmondson, and B. S. Radner. 1951. The biogenesis of anthocyanins. III. The role of sugars in anthocyanin formation. Arch. Biochem. Biophys. 34:305–323.

Thimann, K. V., and B. S. Radner. 1962. The biogenesis of anthocyanins. VII. The requirement for both purines and pyrimidines. Arch. Biochem. Biophys. 96:270–273.

Thwaites, R. G. 1912. Albinism in orchids. Orchid World 3:52–55.

Tosello, G. 1969. Estudios filogenicos da subtribo Epidendrinae (Orchidaceae) pela analise cromato-grafica do flavonois, pp. 77–81. Relatorio Cientifico, Catedra de Citologia e Genetica, Escola Superior Agric. "Luiz de Queiros," Univ. Piracicaba, São Paulo, Brazil.

———. 1970. Emprego de cromatografia dos flovonois em estudio filogeneticos no genero *Cattleya* Ldl. (Orchidaceae-Epidendrinae), pp. 124–129. Relatorio Cientifico, Catedra de Citologia e Genetica, Escola Superior Agric. "Luis de Queiros," Univ. Piracicaba, São Paulo, Brazil.

Tupy, J., and N. S. Rangaswamy. 1973. The investigation on the effect of pollination on ribosomal RNA, transfer RNA and DNA content in styles of *Nicotiana alata*. Biol. Plant. (Prague) 15:95–101.

Twiss, R. 1914. Permanence of albinism. Orchid World 4:145.

Ueno, N., E.-I. T. Hayashi, and K. Hayashi. 1969. Additional data for the paper chromatographic survey of anthocyanins in the flora of Japan (IV). Studies on anthocyanins. LXI. Bot. Mag. (Tokyo) 82:155–161.

Van Fleet, D. S. 1969. An analysis of the histochemistry and function of anthocyanins. Adv. Frontiers in Plant Sci. 23:65–89.

Wilson, G. 1923. Cypripedium Maudiae. Orchid Rev. 31:299–300.

———. 1927. Albinism in *Cypripedium Charlesworthii*. Orchid Rev. 35:40–41.

Wimber, D. E., L. W. Lenz, and C. H. Dodson. 1956. Further studies in intraclonal lip pattern variation in *Cymbidium*. Amer. Orchid Soc. Bull. 25:153–158.

Withlow, C. E. 1966a. The blue Cattleya and Laelia species. Amer. Orchid Soc. Bull. 35:834–835.

———. 1966b. Blue hybrids of the Cattleya group. Amer. Orchid Soc. Bull. 35:915–916.

———. 1967a. The large blue Cattleya hybrids. Amer. Orchid Soc. Bull. 36:23–24.

———. 1967b. Thoughts on Laeliocattleya Blue Boy type hybridizing. Amer. Orchid Soc. Bull. 36:99–101.

Withner, C. L. 1974. Developments in orchid physiology, p. 129–168. *In* C. L. Withner (ed.), The Orchids: scientific studies. Wiley-Interscience, New York.

Woodward, G. P. 1964. The future of white and white-with-colored lip Cattleya. Amer. Orchid Soc. Bull. 33:569–571.

———. 1965. A review of the genetics and inheritance characteristics of Cattleya and related genera. Amer. Orchid Soc. Bull. 34:116–122.

Wreford, M. 1963. Sander's list of orchid hybrids, 1961–1963. Royal Horticultural Society, London.

———. 1966. Sander's list of orchid hybrids, 1964–1966. Royal Horticultural Society, London.

6

Vitamin Requirements and Metabolism in Orchids*

JOSEPH ARDITTI and CHARLES R. HARRISON

* The survey of literature pertaining to this review was concluded in August, 1974.

Introduction

Perhaps the most interesting adaptive features of the Orchidaceae are those occurring in the physiology of their seed germination. Unfortunately, the evolutionary origins of these features are lost in antiquity and are now merely matters for speculation (Ames, 1948). The subtle complexity of conditions required by germinating orchid seeds may best be appreciated by recalling that more than two thousand years elapsed between the first description by Theophrastus of what Dioscorides assumed to be an orchid (Ames, 1948; Schultes and Pease, 1963) and the first published description of an orchid seedling (Salisbury, 1804). Almost another century elapsed before it was discovered, nearly by accident, that in nature, orchid seeds will germinate only if infected by a fungus (Bernard, 1899). Finally, twenty additional years had to pass before orchid seeds were germinated asymbiotically on a medium containing inorganic salts and sucrose (Knudson, 1921, 1922). At present, great quantities of orchid seeds are easily germinated asymbiotically and yet our knowledge of their physiology is still limited.

Whereas sugars are necessary as energy sources for the germination of orchid seeds, additional organic factors may also be required. The contribution of the mycorrhizal fungus may indeed include such factors (Cappelletti, 1933; Knudson, 1922, 1924, 1925; Melin, 1953). It has been suggested that one or more of these factors may be vitamins (Burgeff, 1959; Costantin, 1935; Harley, 1951, 1969; Schaffstein, 1938, 1941; Schopfer, 1943). These are a heterogeneous group of organic compounds other than fats, carbohydrates, amino acids, proteins, nucleic acids, and minerals that are required for normal health and development. Although vitamins are commonly needed in small quantities only, a deficiency of one or more can lead to abnormalities ranging from subtle to severe. Vitamins have been shown to promote growth of plant tissues and organs *in vitro* (Aberg, 1961; Bonner, 1937; Bonner and Greene, 1938; Schopfer, 1943). The same is true for orchid tissue cultures (Borriss and Hubel, 1968) and seedlings; and, therefore, the addition of vitamins to culture media has been suggested frequently (Anderson, 1967; Arditti, 1963, 1965a,b; Crovetto, 1957a,b; Detert and Thomale, 1957; Ernst, Arditti, and Healey, 1970; Grota, 1965; Ito and Karasawa, 1968; Kano, 1965; Lawrence and Arditti, 1964; Mariat, 1952, 1954; Poddubnaya-Arnoldi and Selezneva, 1961; Rao and Avadhani, 1963; Sadowsky, 1965).

Unfortunately, demonstration of vitamin requirements by orchids *in vitro* has been difficult (Arditti, 1963, 1965a,b, 1967a; Withner, 1959, 1974) since supposedly pure agar (Hawker, 1936, 1939; Robbins, 1939; Robbins and White, 1936) and sugar (Knudson, 1952; Noggle and Wynd, 1943; Withner, 1942) contain a variety of vitamins and other impurities. In addition, not all experiments were performed critically or under the same conditions. Consequently, evaluation and interpretation of the available data are not easy.

Many experiments have yielded contradictory results. In part, this may be due to physiological differences among various genera and species of the Orchidaceae (Burgeff, 1934, 1936; Harley, 1951, 1969). One noteworthy example is the difference in vitamin C content in ovules and pollen of various orchids (Poddubnaya-Arnoldi, 1960, 1964; Poddubnaya-Arnoldi and Selezneva, 1957; Poddubnaya-Arnoldi and

Zinger, 1961). However, it is not entirely clear whether this is reflected in the needs of seedlings.

From a number of investigations concerning the effects of vitamins on germination and growth of orchid seeds (Table 6-1), it appears that certain species may have specific vitamin requirements (Arditti, 1967a). These needs may be due to complete or partial metabolic blocks in the biosynthesis of the vitamins in question, for example, in the case of thiamine (Mariat, 1952) and niacin (Arditti, 1965a, 1967b). However, it should be remembered that general trends in vitamin requirements cannot be demonstrated except for niacin, where a growth-enhancing effect has been reported repeatedly (Table 6-1).

The biosynthetic pathways of vitamins in plants are currently not as well understood as those in animals. Unfortunately, this is especially true for the orchids. Very little is known about the synthesis of most vitamins in this family. What follows is a review of the available literature on the subject with some speculations and conjectures.

Ascorbic Acid

Scurvy, the scourge of sailors, and its alleviation by fresh fruits led to the discovery of vitamin C (L-ascorbic acid). It is found in most plants and animals, but humans require an exogenous supply. Biochemically, vitamin C functions in oxidation-reduction systems. Ascorbic acid, like most vitamins, has been tested for its ability to enhance orchid seed germination and seedling development (Table 6-1). Growth promotion was observed in three instances (Pollacci and Bergamaschi, 1940; Torikata, Sawa, and Sisa, 1965; Ueda and Torikata, 1969).

In the higher plants, ascorbic acid is synthesized from either glucose or galactose (Goodwin, 1963). Whether this is also true of orchids has not yet been ascertained. Certain speculations, however, are possible. Glucose has repeatedly been shown to be a very suitable hexose for seedling cultures (Ernst, 1967), and the overwhelming majority of culture media contain large amounts of this sugar (Arditti, 1967b; Ernst, Arditti, and Healey, 1970; Withner, 1959). Since most culture media currently in use do not include ascorbic acid, it is possible to assume that in the presence of glucose, orchid seedlings can satisfy their vitamin C requirements, if any. Whether glucose is actually utilized by seedlings as a direct precursor of L-ascorbic acid is presently unclear. The same is true of galactose.

The occurrence of vitamin C in various orchid tissues has been studied in a number of instances. Ungerminated pollen of *Paphiopedilum insigne* gives a negative ascorbic acid reaction, but a slight amount is present in the pollen tube following germination (Poddubnaya-Arnoldi *et al.*, 1961). *Phalaenopsis schilleriana* pollen contains very little vitamin C and that of *Calanthe veitchii* is richer although the amount decreases after pollination (Poddubnaya-Arnoldi *et al.*, 1961).

Membranes of the suspensor cells in *Calanthe, Dendrobium, Stanhopea, Phalaenopsis, Cymbidium,* and *Cattleya* embryos give an intensely positive histochemical reaction for vitamin C (Poddubnaya-Arnoldi, 1964). However, the content in ovules varies with the species and time following pollination (Poddubnaya-Arnoldi, 1959, 1964; Poddubnaya-Arnoldi and Zinger, 1961; Zinger and Poddubnaya-Arnoldi, 1959). Ovules

I. *Phalaenopsis amabilis* (plate 1, section on *Phalaenopsis* in *Illustrations of Orchidaceous Plants* by T. Moore, 1857).

II. *Dendrobium mirbelianum* (plate 215, vol. 5 of *Lindenia*, 1889).

III. *Chysis bractescens.*

IV. *Phalaenopsis equestris* (courtesy of Robert Ernst).

of *Paphiopedilum* (*Cypripedium*) *insigne* give negative reactions for ascorbic acid during the first $2\frac{1}{2}$–3 months. But, 3 months after pollination, at the time of fertilization, vitamin C begins to appear (Zinger and Poddubnaya-Arnoldi, 1959). At this time, it is localized primarily in the peripheral areas of the embryo as well as at the micropylar and chalazal ends. As the seed matures, the vitamin disappears from most of the embryo. Two vitamin C "caps" are eventually found, one at each end, and later only the micropylar cap remains. It is possible, then, that fertilization, and not pollination, triggers the synthesis of ascorbic acid in this case. Also, it may be that the ascorbic acid in *P. insigne* embryos may have its origin in a discharge from the pollen tube. Disappearance of the acid during maturation also suggests several metabolic alternatives. One is that unchanged synthesis rates become coupled with increased destruction as the embryo develops. A second possibility is that reduced synthetic rates are coupled with unchanged degradation. Third, it may be that synthesis ceases altogether while utilization or destruction rates remain constant or unchanged. And, fourth, if the ascorbic acid in the embryo has its source in the pollen, it may be that the reduction in the concentration may represent a constant degradation without replenishment.

In *Calanthe veitchii* (Zinger and Poddubnaya-Arnoldi, 1959), ascorbic acid content of the ovule increases until fertilization and then decreases constantly until the mature seed shows a negative reaction. Inner integuments contain no vitamin C, whereas the outer ones do, although they lose it as the embryo matures. The micropylar end is the last to lose its ascorbic acid. Since vitamin C is already present in the ovules of *Calanthe veitchii* at the time of pollination, pollen can be discounted as an only source. In fact, here it appears that fertilization may reduce or stop synthesis while enhancing or not affecting destruction.

Ascorbic acid appears in *Dendrobium nobile* embryos $2\frac{1}{2}$ months after pollination (Zinger and Poddubnaya-Arnoldi, 1959). Since fertilization in this species occurs 75–80 days after pollination (Valmayor and Sagawa, 1967), it appears safe to assume either that production is triggered by fertilization or that ascorbic acid is discharged into ovules by pollen tubes. The vitamin is localized at the ends and peripheries at first. Later, it becomes concentrated at the chalazal and micropylar poles only to be greatly reduced in quantity as the seed matures. A six-month-old embryo retains small quantities of ascorbic acid at the micropylar end. Fully mature *Dendrobium nobile* seeds contain no vitamin C. The increase in ascorbic acid content immediately following pollination and its constant depletion thereafter suggest metabolic events similar to those in *Paphiopedilum insigne*. Thus, we are faced with the interesting fact that when it comes to ascorbic acid metabolism, *Dendrobium* (Monandrae, Orchidaceae) may resemble *Paphiopedilum* (Diandrae, Orchidaceae, or Cyripediaceae) more than it does *Calanthe* (Monandrae, Orchidaceae). Only time and many more investigations will tell whether this may be phytochemically or chemotaxonomically significant.

Biotin

Biotin was first isolated from egg yolk in 1936 and characterized as 2-oxo-3,4-imidazolido-2-tetrahydrothiophane-n-valeric acid (Goodwin, 1963). Functionally, it is associated with fatty-acid metabolism, primarily in carboxylating enzymes (pyruvate carboxylase). Acetyl carboxylase is synthesized by seedlings, leaves, and various plant tissue cultures. Currently available evidence suggests that biotin is transported from the leaves to roots where it may be excreted (Goodwin, 1963). Biotin has been employed in orchid seed cultures with mixed results (Table 6-1). It seems to have no effects on *Cattleya* and *Epidendrum* in some cases (Withner, 1942, 1951). However, it may enhance the growth and green color of *Cattleya* (Mariat, 1952, 1954), *Odontoglossum*, and *Paphiopedilum* (Lucke, 1969, 1971) and rhizome growth of *Cymbidium goeringii* (Ueda and Torikata, 1969). On this basis alone, it is difficult to speculate whether at least some orchid seeds are deficient in biotin. If they are, it stands to reason that their development in its absence would be inferior to that of seedlings which have an adequate supply. Furthermore, the difficulty with which *Paphiopedilum* seeds germinate suggests that standard culture media do not provide all the required substances, one of which may be biotin. Notably, *Paphiopedilum* seeds germinate and grow very well on media enriched with banana homogenates. These fruits contain 4.4 μg biotin/100 g (von Loesecke, 1950), and 10% banana enrichment of a medium would be roughly equivalent to a 0.00000045% solution of the vitamin. This is 50 to 100 times less than the biotin concentration reported as stimulating for *Odontoglossum* and *Paphiopedilum* seedlings (Lucke, 1969, 1971). It appears, therefore, that banana homogenates may contribute more than just biotin.

Folic Acid

Named after a number of early leaf preparations which could cure nutritional anemias in animals, this vitamin was first crystallized from liver in 1943 and in 1947 from yeast. In 1948, it was identified as pteroylglutamic acid or folic acid (FA), but is also known as folacin and vitamin B_c. It functions as derivatives of 5,6,7,8-tetrahydrofolic acid in the transfer of single carbon units. FA is widely distributed in plants. Some embryos lose FA during maturation and synthesize it as they germinate. In other cases, however, it may be lost during germination (Goodwin, 1963). When used in orchid seedling cultures (Table 6-1), FA has been mostly without effect (Downie, 1949; Withner, 1951), although in at least one instance (Mariat, 1948, 1952, 1954), it was found to stimulate germination.

Some mycorrhizal fungi require folic acid or one of its components, *para*-aminobenzoic acid (Hijner and Arditti, 1973; Stephen and Fung, 1971; Vermeulen, 1947). Germinating seeds of *Epidendrum* cv O'Brienianum produce this component and can satisfy all or part of the fungal requirements (Hijner and Arditti, 1973).

Inositol

As a group, vitamins are rather heterogeneous in both structure and function. Hence, certain substances are classified as vitamins for historical reasons, convenience, or subjective considerations. This is the case with inositol, which has been classified by different investigators as a "growth factor," hormone (at times described as cytokinin-like), or vitamin. Inositol, also known as *myo*-inositol, *meso*-inositol, or *i*-inositol, is one of six isomeric hexahydroxycyclohexanes and the only one biologically active (Goodwin, 1963). It was first isolated in 1850 from muscles. Since then it has been reported to be an important component of the natural neutral fraction of coconut milk, immature corn grain extracts, and *Aesculus* fluid (Steward, 1968).

Inositol is required by certain yeast strains and mammalian cells in culture and these have been among the reasons leading to its classification as a vitamin. On the other hand, the fact that rats on inositol-free diets remained normal suggests that this classification may not be entirely correct. In plants it functions in the production of polyuronides. It also is a growth enhancer in carrot callus and cell cultures (Steward, 1968). Phytic acid, the hexaphosphoric ester of inositol, promotes growth in rice cultures (Watanabe *et al.*, 1971). It is very common in higher plants (Goodwin, 1963) and present in high concentrations in seeds. During germination, phytic acid is released from its cotyledonary form by phytase and translocated to the developing embryo (Goodwin, 1963). Inositol has been used as a supplement in orchid seedling cultures (Table 6-1) and has been reported to have no effects on *Cattleya* hybrids or *Epidendrum tampense* (Withner, 1942), and *Goodyera repens* (Downie, 1949). However, it has also been reported to stimulate possibly the germination of *Cattleya* seeds (Mariat, 1952). Thus, it is not certain whether some or all orchid seeds require inositol. *Phalaenopsis* and *Dendrobium* seeds grown on 2% *myo*-inositol as a sole carbon source failed to differentiate and remained low in weight (Ernst, 1967).

Niacin

Niacin or nicotinic acid (in the older literature, it is also referred to as vitamin P or vitamin PP) is of ubiquitous occurrence in living organisms. It acts as a precursor to a number of compounds (Arditti, 1967b), but its only well-understood direct physiological role seems to be that of a component of the coenzymes NAD and NADP where it appears as niacinamide.

In many mammals, some fungi, selected bacteria, and certain birds, niacin (NA) is synthesized via the tryptophan (TRY) catabolic pathway with formylkynurenine (FKY), kynurenine (KY), 3-hydroxykynurenine (3-OHKY), 3-hydroxyanthranilic acid (3-OHAA), and quinolinic acid (QA) as intermediates. The role of TRY as a precursor to indoleacetic acid (IAA) in plants is well known, but its function as a niacin precursor has been questioned for many years (Arditti, 1965a, 1967b). Investigations utilizing a variety of leaves (Gustafson, 1949), pea seedlings (Galston, 1949), and germinating seeds (Nason, 1949, 1950) have suggested that TRY may indeed act as a NA precursor in angiosperms. On the other hand, a number of researchers have obtained data indicating that TRY is not a NA precursor in flowering plants (for reviews see Arditti, 1965a; Henderson *et al.*, 1959). This lack of agreement may be due at least in part to the plant material used in various experiments.

Germinating orchid embryos and young seedlings have consistently responded favorably to exogenous supplies of NA (Table 6-1). In one set of experiments, germination was actually impaired in its absence (Noggle and Wynd, 1943). Orchids, therefore,

Table 6-1. Use of vitamins for orchid cultures *in vitro*

Investigator	Species	Supplement	Remarks
Burgeff, 1934	*Cattleya*	Vitamin preparation from yeast (same fraction found effective in rats)—Vitamins A, B$_1$, and B$_2$	No effect.
Burgeff, 1936	*Vanda* group	"Bios-II-like material"	Present in dead or live fungus. Slow development in its absence.
	Various	Vitamin "Harris"	Limited effect.
Schaffstein, 1938	*Phalaenopsis*	Neither biotin, vitamins B$_1$, B$_2$, A, or D, nor esterone, nor bios, nor lecithin	Enhancement. Obtained from the fractionation of *Vicia faba*, yeast and various seeds.
Bonner and Greene, 1938	Hybrid *Cattleya*	Vitamin B$_1$	Satisfactory effect.
Pollacci and Bergamaschi, 1940	*Cattleya autumnalis*, *Oncidium pulvinatum*	Vitamin C	Increased germination and growth.
Downie, 1940	*Goodyera repens*	Vitamins B$_1$ and C	No germination.
Evers, 1940	*Cattleya mossiae*	Vitamin B$_1$ applied weekly	Young unflowered plants. No outstanding differences between treated and untreated plants. A few of the treated plants may have been somewhat greener.
Schaffstein, 1941	*Dendrobium nobile*, *Vanda, Phalaenopsis*	"Vandophytin"	Favorable effect. Niacin derivative, but not identical with niacin or niacinamide.
	Dendrobium nobile	Vitamins B$_1$, C, niacin, pantothenic acid, Adermin (vitamin B$_6$)	No effect.
	Phalaenopsis hybrids, *Vanda coerulea*	Niacin, niacinamide	Growth-promoting effect.
Withner, 1942	*Cattleya* hybrids, *Epidendrum tampense*	Vitamins C, B$_1$, B$_2$, B$_6$, calcium, pantothenate, biotin, niacin, and inositol	No effects observed.
Downie, 1943	*Corallorhiza innata*	Vitamins B$_1$ and C	Not very successful.
Withner, 1943	*Epidendrum cochleatum*	Vitamins B$_1$, B$_6$, niacin	Used in ovule culture. Good growth of ovules on Knudson's medium.
Meyer, 1943	*Rodriguezia* sp., *Cattleya harrisoniae*	Vitamin B$_1$	Stimulating.
Noggle and Wynd, 1943	*Cattleya* hybrids	Applied the following vitamins in a medium containing purified maltose:	
		Vitamins B$_1$, C, calcium pantothenate	Not effective.
		Vitamin B$_2$	Slightly effective.
		Vitamin B$_6$	Good germination, poor subsequent growth.
		Niacin	Good germination, good subsequent growth.
Schopfer, 1943	Various	Vitamins A, B$_1$, B$_2$, D	No effect.
Magrou and Mariat, 1945	*Cattleya* seedlings	Vitamin B$_1$	No effect on germination. Accelerated differentiation.
Meyer, 1946	*Rodriguezia* sp., *Cattleya harrisoniae*	Thiamine (0.002 g/1000 ml)	Enhancement.
Storey *et al.*, 1947	Various	Vitamins of the B complex	No conclusive results.
Bouriquet, 1948	*Vanilla planifolia*	Vitamin C	Some germination. Protocorms short-lived.
Mariat, 1948	*Cattleya* hybrids	B$_1$ = pyrimidine = pyrimidine plus thiazole	Favored germination and differentiation.
		Thiazole only	Inhibition noted.

Table 6-1 (continued)

Investigator	Species	Supplement	Remarks
Downie, 1949	Goodyera repens	Thiamine, calcium pantothenate, riboflavin, niacin, aminobenzoic acid, inositol, pyridoxine hydrochloride, folic acid—used singly or together	Did not stimulate asymbiotic germination. Germination and growth did not occur in the presence of fungal extract.
Mariat, 1949	Cattleya seedlings	Niacin	Effective.
Bahme, 1949	Cattleya hybrids	Mixture of vitamins B₁, B₆, C, calcium pantothenate, niacin, and B₂	Enhancement.
		Niacin	The only additive shown effective when used singly.
Harley, 1951	Various	Niacin derivative	The growth factor required may be a niacin derivative.
Henriksson, 1951	Thunia marshalliana	Vitamin B₁	Enhancement.
		Vitamin B₆	Good germination, poor subsequent growth.
		Vitamin C	Not effective.
		Niacin	Excellent enhancement.
		Mixture of vitamin B₆ and niacin	Reduced the effect of niacin.
		Mixture of vitamins B₆, C, and niacin	Reduced the effect of niacin.
		Mixture of vitamins B₆, B₁, and C	Inhibitory.
Potes, 1951	Various	Thiamine	Enhancement.
Tenhaeff, 1951–1952	Phalaenopsis	B vitamins	Enhancement.
Withner, 1951	Cattleya	Thiamine, biotin, folic acid, "10 B vitamins," glutathione	No noticeable effect over control.
Mariat, 1952	Cattleya	Vitamin B₁, pyrimidine, niacin	Effect reaffirmed.
		Biotin	Stimulating.
		Vitamin B₆	Favorable in high doses.
		Vitamins B₂ and B₆	Helpful in the differentiation of plants already at the leaf-point stage.
		Calcium pantothenate	Not effective.
		Thiamine	Pyrimidine portion of molecule is as effective as the whole molecule of this vitamin.
		Niacin	Most effective.
		Inositol, folic acid, para-aminobenzoic acid	May stimulate germination.
Young, 1952	Various	Vitamin B₁	Better growth.
Bouriquet, 1954	Vanilla	Vitamin C	No effects.
		Thiamine	Enhancement.
Burgeff, 1954	European terrestrial spp.	Vitamin B₁	Promoted growth.
Mariat, 1954	Cattleya	Vitamin B₁	Enhancement.
		Niacin	Enhancement.
		Biotin	Enhancement, rapid germination, fast growth.
Withner, 1955	Vanilla planifolia ovules	Mixture of vitamins B₁, B₆, niacin, five amino acids, and indolebutyric acid (IBA)	Promoted growth. Inconsistent.
		Vitamin B₁₂ singly	Similar results.
		Vitamins and IBA	Similar results.

Table 6-1 (*continued*)

Investigator	Species	Supplement	Remarks
Hegarty, 1955	*Cypripedium*	Vitamins B_1 and niacin in a mixture with indole-propionic acid (or IBA) and peptone	Stimulated germination.
		"Vitamins"	Did not improve growth of seedlings in the absence of sugar.
Detert and Thomale, 1957	*Vanda teres* *Paphiopedilum*	Polyvitamin concentrate	Enhancement. No effect.
Crovetto, 1957b	Unlisted	Vitamin B_1, niacin	Enhancement.
Boesman, 1958, 1962a,b	*Cattleya, Cymbidium*	Vitamin T	Enhancement.
Burgeff, 1959	*Vanda*	Niacin	Improved germination.
	Phalaenopsis	Niacinamide	Stimulated growth. Suggests that Vandophytin is identical with niacin.
Ito, 1961	*Dendrobium nobile* pollen, ovary *in vitro*	Vitamins B_1, B_6, and E (tocopherol acetate) mixture	Enhanced germination percentage and tube length.
		Vitamin B_1 (0.1 ppm)	Excellent for fruit growth.
		Vitamin B_6 (1 ppm)	Excellent for fruit growth.
		Vitamin E (5 and 100 ppm)	Inhibits fruit growth, improves seed fertility.
		Mixture of all three vitamins	Fruit growth not improved, seed size increased.
Lawrence and Arditti, 1964	*Cattleya*	Niacin mixture with other factors	Stimulated growth and development.
Voth, 1964	*Acampe renschiana, Anthogonium gracile, Neobenthamia gracilis*	"Multivit B"	Germination of seeds.
Arditti, 1965a,b, 1967b; Arditti and Bils, 1965	*Cattleya, Laeliocattleya*	Niacin, niacin plus adenine, niacin plus ribose, niacin plus adenine and ribose	Only niacin, kynurenine, 3-hydroxyanthranilic acid, and quinolinic acid enhanced germination and the growth of seedlings.
		Tryptophan pathway precursors of niacin	Tryptophan was inhibitory to germination and young seedlings. Niacin also enhanced growth alone and in various combinations with ribose and adenine.
Torikata, Sawa, and Sisa, 1965	*Cymbidium*	Vitamins B_2 and C	Promotes embryonic growth.
Lucke, 1966	*Odontoglossum krameri*	Biotin (0.00008%)	Enhancement.
Ito, 1967	*Dendrobium nobile* (*in vitro* culture of ovaries)	Vitamin B_1 (0.1 ppm)	Enhances fruit growth and seed fertility.
		Vitamin B_6 (1 ppm)	Enhances fruit growth and seed fertility.
Harvais, 1972	*Dactylorhiza purpurella*	Niacin	Enhances asymbiotic growth.
Hijner and Arditti, 1973	*Epidendrum* xO'Brienianum	Niacin	The vitamin produced by a *Rhizoctonia* species and released into the medium stimulates germination.

are an excellent, but neglected, system for the investigation of niacin biosynthesis in flowering plants, either by the utilization of radioactively labeled intermediates or by growth rate comparison. Results from an investigation employing growth rates as a parameter (Arditti, 1965a, 1966a,b, 1967a,b) suggest that the tryptophan pathway may be at least partially operative in orchid seedlings. Only KY, 3-OHAA, and QA exhibited a growth-promoting effect, similar to that of NA, on seedlings of all ages. Very young *Cattleya* seedlings were inhibited by TRY concentrations of 40.6 μM, 81.2 μM, and 162.4 μM. Older (130-day-old) plantlets were inhibited only by 162.4 μM, and 190-day old seedlings were not affected (Arditti, 1965a, 1967b). Similar results were obtained with 182-day old *Brassolaeliocattleya* and 156-day old *Dendrobium* seedlings on 10 and 100 μM TRY but both were inhibited by 10×10^{-3} M (Kano, 1965). On the other hand, 10 μM dl-TRY enhanced the growth of *Phalaenopsis* seedlings (R. Ernst, personal communication). Tryptophan also improved the growth of shoot-tip-derived ("meristem cultures") embryos of *Cymbidium goeringii* both in the dark and under illumination (Ueda and Torikata, 1969).

The inhibitory effects of TRY in young seedlings, along with responses to certain vitamins, provide a number of clues as to its possible site of utilization and role as a NA precursor. Noteworthy is the lack of inhibition in older seedlings since these possess small but well-developed leaves. A good correlation exists between the disappearance of TRY inhibition and the appearance of leaves. This suggests that leaves may be a site of tryptophan utilization or metabolism. As pointed out previously, tryptophan may be a precursor to both NA and IAA, and each of these has been reported as being capable of enhancing the growth of orchid seedlings (Arditti, 1967b; Mariat, 1952; Withner, 1959). Thus, in the absence of information regarding actual incorporation of this amino acid into either auxin and/or niacin, it is difficult to decide whether the growth enhancement of older seedlings elicited by tryptophan is due to its conversion into IAA, NA, or both. In etiolated pea seedlings, tryptophan may be converted rapidly into IAA, but slowly into NA, whereas KY and 3-OHAA are readily transformed into NA (Galston, 1949). This is indicative of an inefficient TRY-to-KY step. Possibly, then, the conversion of TRY to either IAA, KY, or both is inefficient or blocked in very young orchid seedlings. Growth inhibition may, therefore, be due to an accumulation of supraoptimal amounts of tryptophan, its conversion to an inhibitory metabolite, or both. The favorable responses of some orchid seedlings to biotin and thiamine (Table 6-1) provide additional support for the conjecture that the conversion of TRY to KY may not be fully operative. These vitamins have been implicated in this reaction (Dalgliesh, 1955; Shanmuga-Sundaram *et al.*, 1954); and in view of the consistent responses of orchid seedlings to NA, it is possible to assume that biotin and thiamine may act by facilitating the conversion of TRY to KY.

With the appearance of leaves, either the IAA or the KY pathway, or both, may become operative for a variety of reasons, with growth enhancement being the natural outcome. It is well known that leaves are the site of production of both auxin and NAA together with a number of other vitamins, including thiamine. Furthermore, QA appears to enhance NA production in young leaf tissue homogenates, but these results require further substantiation (Arditti, 1965a).

In *Mycobacterium tuberculosis*, aspartic and glutamic acids serve as NA precursors (Albertson and Moat, 1965). The possibility of a similar pathway occurring in orchids should, therefore, be examined in light of the effects these acids have on seedling cultures. Aspartic acid, when incorporated in culture media, could not serve as a carbon source (Knudson, 1932) and did not enhance germination of *Cattleya labiata* either in the presence or in the absence of optimal amounts of NH_4NO_3 (Raghavan, 1964). However, it did act as a good nitrogen source for fully mature *Cattleya trianei* seeds (Spoerl, 1948) and enhanced the growth of *Cymbidium insigne*, *C. pumilum*, and *C. goeringii* "meristem" cultures in both light and darkness (Ueda and Torikata, 1968, 1969). Glutamic acid did not affect the growth of *Cattleya trianei* cultures and reduced the germination of *Galeola septentrionalis* by approximately one-half (Nakamura, 1962). However, it caused a 3% increase in the germination of *Cattleya labiata* both in the presence and in the absence of an optimal amount of NH_4NO_3 (Raghavan, 1964). Aspartic acid or glutamic acid, separately, each at a concentration of 10 ppm, also enhanced germination and tube length in *Dendrobium nobile* pollen (Ito, 1961).

These findings contain some food for thought, but they provide no indication that aspartic or glutamic acid may be acting as NA precursors in orchid seedlings. Their mode of action in pollen is unclear, especially due to the lack of comparisons with the effects of NA. Only experiments specifically designed to study the role of these amino acids in NA biosynthesis by orchid seedlings and pollen can be counted upon to produce unequivocal results.

Obviously, the exact nature of the pathway leading to NA in orchid seedlings is not entirely clear as yet. The presently available evidence suggests that the TRY catabolic pathway, or a similar one, is at least partially functional. Other pathway(s) such as that of *Mycobacterium tuberculosis* or related ones may also be operative, but current information does not seem to substantiate or justify such an assumption regarding orchid seedlings. Whether pollen differs in this respect remains to be seen. Future work, preferably utilizing ^{14}C-labeled intermediates, would, no doubt, throw more light not only on niacin biosynthesis in flowering plants, but also on the metabolism of germinating orchid embryos and pollen grains in particular.

A culture of *Rhizoctonia* species isolated from *Cymbidium* has been shown to produce niacin and release it into the medium (Hijner and Arditti, 1973). Thus, it would seem that niacin requirements by orchid seedlings, if they exist, can be satisfied by their mycorrhizal fungi.

Pantothenic Acid

First isolated from liver, the structure of pantothenic acid (PA) was elucidated around 1940. By 1953, it was clear that this water-soluble vitamin was part of the Coenzyme A (CoA) molecule (Goodwin, 1963). As such, it is ubiquitous and instrumental in the metabolism of two-carbon fragments. When incorporated in orchid seedling cultures (Table 6-1), it has been generally ineffective (Bahme, 1949; Downie, 1949; Mariat, 1952; Noggle and Wynd, 1943; Schaffstein, 1941; Withner, 1942). Therefore, it is reasonable to assume that if orchid seeds do not contain reserves of PA or CoA, they can synthesize them.

Pyridoxine

This factor, also known as vitamin B_6, was isolated from a vitamin B complex capable of curing actodynia. The original isolation from rice and yeast in 1938 led to its identification a year later as 3-hydroxy-4,5-dihydroxy-methyl-2-methylpurine. As pyridoxal phosphate, it is important in amino-acid metabolism. When incorporated in orchid culture media (Table 6-1), pyridoxine may enhance germination or growth (Henriksson, 1957; Mariat, 1952, 1954; Withner, 1943; Noggle and Wynd, 1943), have no effects (Bahme, 1949; Withner, 1943), or inhibit seedling development even in the presence of other vitamins (Henriksson, 1957; Noggle and Wynd, 1943). Vitamin B_6 has also been reported to promote pollen germination and tube length as well as the growth *in vitro* of *Dendrobium nobile* fruits (Ito, 1961, 1967). Since germinating seedlings are clearly the site of very active amino-acid metabolism, the inhibitory effects of exogenous vitamin B_6 may perhaps be interpreted as being due to supra-optimal concentrations.

Riboflavin

Vitamin B_2 is a more commonly used name for this factor and lactoflavin an older one. It was originally isolated from eggs and later from kidney, urine, yeast, liver, and muscle as yellow compounds capable of stimulating the growth of rats. Its structure was elucidated in 1935 as 6,7-dimethyl-9-D-ribityl-isoalloxazin (Goodwin, 1963). Riboflavin-5-phosphate (FMN) and flavine adenine dinucleotide (FAD) are electron carriers.

Like all other water-soluble B vitamins, riboflavin is synthesized by plants, especially by germinating seeds (Goodwin, 1963). In orchid seedling culture media (Table 6-1), riboflavin does not seem to stimulate germination (Burgeff, 1934; Downie, 1949; Withner, 1943). It is helpful, however, in enhancing the differentiation of plants already at the leaf-point stage (Mariat, 1952) and may promote embryonic growth in *Cymbidium* (Torikata, Sawa, and Sisa, 1965).

Thiamine

Thiamine, or vitamin B_1 (old name: aneurin), is of universal importance in its major coenzyme form—thiamine pyrophosphate. The vitamin molecule consists of one pyrimidine residue and one thiazole moiety. Each of the two fragments seems to be synthesized separately with the final step of thiamine biosynthesis being their condensation (Goodwin, 1963). Experiments with *in vitro* cultures of tissues, organs, and whole plants have shown that some may require the entire vitamin molecule whereas others may be cultured with either the pyrimidine or the thiazole fragment alone (Goodwin, 1963; Rédei, 1965). Leaves are chiefly responsible for the production of thiamine in plants. Also, studies with tomatoes, wheat, soya, mung beans, and cotyledonectomized pea seeds have demonstrated that light is required for thiamine synthesis during germination (for a review see Goodwin, 1963). Despite several reports on the biosynthesis of each moiety, none of the substances proposed as likely precursors displayed any activity in thiamineless mutants of the angiosperm *Arabidopsis thaliana* (Rédei, 1965).

Several investigators have studied the effects of thiamine on germinating orchid seeds, pollen grains, ovaries *in vitro*, and young seedlings (Table 6-1). Their work suggests that these may be incapable of entirely satisfying their thiamine requirements since growth in thiamine-enriched media is often enhanced. Only two of these investigators, however (Magrou and Mariat, 1945; Mariat, 1944, 1948, 1952), have contributed to our knowledge of thiamine biosynthesis in orchid seedlings. Having noted that thiamine promotes seedling differentiation (Magrou and Mariat, 1945), they tested the effects of the two compounds separately and in combination (Mariat, 1948, 1952). Thiamine itself, the thiazole and pyrimide fractions in combination, and the pyrimidine fraction alone were all capable of enhancing growth equally well (Table 6-1). This may be taken as an indication that orchid seedlings can condense the two fractions but cannot satisfy their own need for the pyrimidine moiety. Under symbiotic conditions, thiamine may be supplied by fungi like *Corticium catonii* (Cappelletti, 1917). A *Rhizoctonia* species isolated from *Cymbidium* seeds capable of producing the missing moiety can make it available to the orchid (Hijner and Arditti, 1973).

Nutritional mutants, or otherwise nutritionally deficient organisms, which are well suited for the elucidation of the vitamin B_1 biogenetic pathways, are comparatively rare among the flowering plants (Rédei, 1965). Therefore, orchid embryos and young seedlings may provide plant physiologists and biochemists with a rare opportunity for studying a biosynthetic pathway and an exciting family of plants simultaneously.

A *Rhizoctonia* isolated from *Cymbidium* which requires the thiazole moiety of thiamine can probably obtain at least some of it from the orchid (Hijner and Additti, 1973). The same is true for another orchid fungus (Stephen and Fung, 1971).

Vitamin T

A complex of growth-promoting substances, also known as tegotin, termitin, torutilin, Temina, factor T, vitamin T Goetsch, and Goetsch's vitamin, vitamin T was originally isolated from termites. It is also obtainable from roaches, yeast, and fungi and may well be a mixture of known vitamins and growth-promoting substances rather than a new compound. Indeed, its beneficial effect on *Cattleya* and *Cymbidium* seedlings (Boesman, 1958, 1962a,b) could be due to the presence of known vitamins in the mixture.

Other Vitamins and Related Compounds

Through the years, vitamins A, B_{12}, D, and E as well as *para*-aminobenzoic acid, glutathione, and other compounds have been used in orchid seed cultures with mixed results (Table 6-1). Since findings have been inconsistent and since there is little information available on these vitamins and others, there is no justification, at present, for further discussion or speculation. In general, orchid seedlings *in vitro* seem capable of satisfying whatever requirements they may have for most of the vitamins. Possibly, then, the metabolic pathways leading to these vitamins may be fully operative in orchid seedlings. Alternately, it may mean that at least the seeds of some species contain sufficient reserves.

Concluding Remarks

If this review tends to be speculative or not detailed enough in spots, it is simply due to available (or more properly, unavailable) information. Very little is known at present about the physiology and biochemistry of orchids. And, worse yet, the proportion of physiologists and biochemists working with orchids seems to be decreasing steadily. Still, we hope that this review and our speculations will not only point to the great suitability of orchids as organisms for this kind of research, but will also generate curiosity and perhaps encourage additional plant scientists to investigate them.

Acknowledgments

Portions of this work were supported by the American Orchid Society, Orchid Society of Southern California, Stanley Smith Horticultural Trust, Society of Sigma Xi, Loeb Foundation, Orchid Digest Corporation, Malahini Orchid Society, Peninsula Orchid Society, Textilana Corporation, National Science Foundation, Office of Naval Research, and UCI Industrial Associates. We thank Robert Ernst, Brigitta H. Flick, Michael S. Strauss, Nanette M. Hogan, and Diane Reisinger for their help.

Literature Cited

Aberg, B. 1961. Vitamins as growth factors in higher plants, p. 418–449. *In* W. Ruhland (ed.), Handbuch der Pflanzenphysiologie. Vol. 14. Springer-Verlag, Berlin.

Albertson, J. N., Jr., and A. G. Moat. 1965. Biosynthesis of nicotinic acid by *Mycobacterium tuberculosis*. J. Bact. 89:540–541.

Ames, O. 1948. Orchids in retrospect. Bot. Mus. Harvard Univ.

Anderson, L. 1967. Literature review of orchid seed germination. Amer. Orchid Soc. Bull. 36:304–308.

Arditti, J. 1963. Vitamins in your orchid cultures. Orchid Soc. So. Calif. Rev. 5:12–13.

——. 1965a. Studies in growth factor requirements and niacin metabolism of germinating orchid seeds and young tissues. Ph.D. diss., Univ. of Southern California.

——. 1965b. Selected additives for Cattleya seedling cultures. Orchid Dig. 29:432–433.

——. 1966a. Orchids. Sci. Amer. 214(1):70–78.

——. 1966b. The effects of niacin, adenine, ribose and niacinamide coenzymes on germinating orchid seeds and young seedlings. Amer. Orchid Soc. Bull. 35:892–898.

——. 1967a. Factors affecting the germination of orchid seeds. Bot. Rev. 33:1–97.

——. 1967b. Niacin biosynthesis in germinating x*Laeliocattleya* orchid embryos and young seedlings. Amer. J. Bot. 54:291–298.

Arditti, J., and R. F. Bils. 1965. The germination of an orchid seed. Orchid Soc. So. Calif. Rev. 7:5–6.

Bahme, R. 1949. Nicotinic acid as a growth factor for certain orchid embryos. Science 109:522–523.

Bernard, N. 1899. Sur la germination du *Neottia nidus-avis*. C. R. Acad. Sci. Paris 128:1253–1255.

Boesman, G. 1958. Problemes concernant le semis et l'amelioration des orchidees. Proc. 15th Int. Hort. Cong., p. 1–8.

——. 1962a. Resultaten van keimproeven met orchideezaad. Mendelingen van de Landbouwhogenschool en de Opzoekings-Stations van de Staat te Gent 27:619–642.

——. 1962b. Problemes concernant le semis et la selection des orchidees, p. 368–373. *In* Advances in horticultural science and application. Vol. II. Pergamon Press, New York.

Bonner, J. 1937. Vitamin B_1 as a growth factor for higher plants. Science 85:183–184.

Bonner, J., and J. Greene. 1938. Vitamin B_1 and the growth of green plants. Bot. Gaz. 100:226–237.

Borriss, H., and M. Hubel. 1968. Die vegetative Vermehrung von Orchideen durch Meristem-Kultur. Der Deutsche Gartenbau 15:22–24.

Bouriquet, G. 1948. Sur la germination des graines de Vanillier (*Vanilla planifolia* And.). L'Agron. Trop. 2:105–164.

——. 1954. Germination des graines, p. 393–438. *In* G. Bouriquet (ed.), Le vanillier et la vanille dans le monde. Paul Lechevalier, Paris.

Burgeff, H. 1934. Pflanzliche Avitaminose and ihre Behebung durch Vitaminzufuhr. Ber. Deutsch. Bot. Ges. 52:384–390.

——. 1936. Samenkeimung der Orchideen. Gustav Fischer Verlag, Jena.

——. 1954. Samenkeimung und Kultur Europäischer Erdorchideen. Gustav Fischer Verlag, Jena.

——. 1959. Mycorrhiza of orchids, pp. 361–395. *In* C. L. Withner (ed.), The orchids: a scientific survey. Ronald Press, New York.

Cappelletti, C. 1933. Osservazioni sulla germinazione asimbiotica dei semi di orchidee del genere Cymbidium. Boll. Soc. Ital. Biol. Sper. 8:288–291.

——. 1947. Ricerche fisiologiche sull simbiosi nella orchidee. Lavori di Botanica 8:57–76.

Costantin, J. 1925. Une vieille culture asymbiotique au museum. C. R. Acad. Sci. Paris 180:1806–1808.

Crovetto, A. 1957a. La semina asymbiotica delle orchidee. Rev. Ortoflorafruitticultura Ital. 41:306–310.

——. 1957b. L'Azione di particolari sostanze nutritive sulla germinazione dei semi di orchidee. Rev. Ortoflorafruitticultura Ital. 41:637–638.

Dalgliesh, C. E. 1955. Metabolism of the aromatic amino acids. Adv. Prot. Chem. 10:33–150.

Detert, E. R., and H. Thomale. 1957. A critical consideration of orchid culture media. Orchid Dig. 21:10–15.

Downie, D. G. 1940. On the germination and growth of *Goodyera repens*. Trans. and Proc. Bot. Soc. Edinburgh 33:36–51.

——. 1943. Notes on the germination of *Corallorhiza innata*. Trans. and Proc. Bot. Soc. Edinburgh 33:380–382.

——. 1949. The germination of *Goodyera repens* (L.) R. Br. in fungal extract. Trans. and Proc. Bot. Soc. Edinburgh 35:120–125.

Ernst, R. 1967. Effect of carbohydrate selection on the growth rate of freshly germinated Phalaenopsis and Dendrobium seed. Amer. Orchid Soc. Bull. 36:1068–1073.

Ernst, R., J. Arditti, and P. L. Healey. 1970. The nutrition of orchid seedlings. Amer. Orchid Soc. Bull. 39:599–605, 691–700.

Evers, O. R. 1940. Nutritional studies with orchids. Amer. Orchid Soc. Bull. 9:163–164, 177–182.

Galston, A. W. 1949. Indoleacetic-nicotinic acid interaction in the etiolated pea plant. Plant Physiol. 24:577–586.

Goodwin, T. W. 1963. The biosynthesis of vitamins and related compounds. Academic Press, New York.

Grota, A. S. 1965. Vitaminas na cultura de orquidaceas. Orquidea 27:148–150.

Gustafson, F. A. 1949. Tryptophane as an intermediate in the synthesis of nicotinic acid by green plants. Science 110:279–280.

Harley, J. L. 1951. Recent progress in the study of endotrophic mycorrhiza (Abstract). Amer. Orchid Soc. Bull. 20:291–293.

——. 1969. The biology of mycorrhiza. Leonard Hill, London.

Harvais, G. 1972. The development and growth requirements of Dactylorhiza purpurella in asymbiotic cultures. Can. J. Bot. 50:1223–1229.

Hawker, L. H. 1936. The effect of certain accessory growth substances on the sporulation of *Melanospora destruens* and of some other fungi. Ann. Bot. 50:699–718.

——. 1939. The nature of the accessory growth factor influencing growth and fruiting of *Melanospora destruens*. Ann. Bot., N.S. 3:657–676.

Hegarty, C. P. 1955. Observations on the germination of orchid seed. Amer. Orchid Soc. Bull. 24:457–464.

Henderson, L. M., J. F. Someroski, D. R. Rao, P. H. L. Wu, T. Grifith, and R. U. Byerrum. 1959. Lack of a tryptophan-niacin relationship in corn and tobacco. J. Biol. Chem. 234:93–95.

Henriksson, L. E. 1951. Asymbiotic germination of orchids and some effects of vitamins on Thunia marshalliana. Svensk. Bot. Tdskrt. 45:447–459.

Hijner, J. A., and J. Arditti. 1973. Orchid mycorrhiza. Vitamin production and requirements by the symbionts. Amer. J. Bot. 60:829–835.

Ito, I. 1961. In vitro culture of ovary and seed in orchids. Mimeo. Olericulture Lab. Fac. Agric., Kyoto Prefectual Univ., Kyoto, Japan.

———. 1967. In vitro culture of ovary in orchids (II). Influence of vitamins upon the growth of ovary of *Dendrobium nobile* and other several problems. Sci. Repts. Kyoto Prefectual Univ., Agric. 19:6–12.

Ito, I., and K. Karasawa. 1968. Seed formation and sterile culture of the orchids. Kyoto. (In Japanese).

Kano, K. 1965. Studies on the media for orchid seed germination. Mem. Fac. Agric. Kagawa Univ., No. 20.

Knudson, L. 1921. La germinacion no simbiotica de las semillas de orquideas. Bol. Real. Soc. Espanola Hist. Nat. 21:250–260.

———. 1922. Nonsymbiotic germination of orchid seeds. Bot. Gaz. 73:1–25.

———. 1924. Further observations on nonsymbiotic germination of orchid seeds. Bot. Gaz. 77:212–219.

———. 1925. Physiological study of the symbiotic germination of orchid seeds. Bot. Gaz. 79:345–379.

———. 1932. Direct absorption and utilization of amino acids by plants. N.Y. (Cornell) Agric. Exp. Sta. Ann. Rept. 45:iii.

———. 1952. Nutrient solutions for orchid seed germination. Amer. Orchid Soc. Bull. 21:94.

Lawrence, G. D., and J. Arditti. 1964. A new medium for the germination of orchid seeds. Orchid Soc. So. Calif. Rev. 6:4–5; Amer. Orchid Soc. Bull. 33:766–768.

Loesecke, H. W. Von. 1950. Bananas. Interscience, New York.

Lucke, E. 1966. Biotin als Wirkstoff bei der Samenkeimung der Orchideen. Die Orchidee 17:322–323.

———. 1969. Biotin bei der Samenkeimung von Paphiopedilum. Die Orchidee 20:270–271.

———. 1971. The effect of biotin on sowing of Paphiopedilum. Amer. Orchid Soc. Bull. 40:24–28.

Magrou, J., and F. Mariat. 1945. Action de l'aneurine sur le developpement des embryons d'orchidees. Ann. Inst. Pasteur 71:49.

Mariat, F. 1944. Influence favorable de la vitamine B_1 sur les germinations de Cattleya. Rev. Hort. 29:68–69.

———. 1948. Influence de facteurs de croissance sur le développement et la differenciation des embryons d'orchidées. Rev. Gen. Bot. 55:229–243.

———. 1949. Action de l'acide nicotinique sur la germination et le développement des embryons de *Cattleya*. C. R. Acad. Sci. Paris 229:1355–1357.

———. 1952. Recherches sur la physiologie des embryons d'orchidées. Rev. Gen. Bot. 59:324–377.

———. 1954. Action des vitamines sur les germinations d'orchidées, p. 428[1]–428[3]. *In* G. Bouriquet (ed.), Le vanillier et la vanille dans le monde. Paul Lechavalier, Paris.

Melin, E. 1953. Physiology of mycorrhizal relations in plants. Ann. Rev. Plant Physiol. 4:325–346.

Meyer, J. R. 1943. Experiencias relativas a acao de thiamina (vitamin B_1) sobre a germinacao e desenvolvimento de sementes de orquideas em meios assimbioticos. O'Biologico 9:401–406.

———. 1946. Experiments showing the action of thiamin (vitamin B_1) on the germination and development of orchid seeds in asymbiotic media. Amer. Orchid Soc. Bull. 14:505–509.

Nakamura, S. I. 1962. Zur Samenkeimung einer Chlorophyllfreien Erdorchidee *Galeola septentrionalis* Reichb. f. Ztsch. für Bot. 50:487–497.

Nason, A. 1949. Existence of a tryprophan-niacin relationship in corn. Science 109:170.

———. 1950. The distribution and biosynthesis of niacin in germinating corn. Amer. J. Bot. 37:612–623.

Noggle, G. R., and F. L. Wynd. 1943. Effects of vitamins on germination and growth of orchids. Bot. Gaz. 104:455–459.

Poddubnaya-Arnoldi, V. A. 1959. Isledovanie embryonalyih prossesa nekotoryih orchidei na jivommateriale (Studies of the embryological process in some orchids using live material). Trudyi Glavnogo Bot. Sada Acad. Sci. U.S.S.R. 6:49–89.

———. 1960. Study of fertilization in the living material of some angiosperms. Phytomorphology 10:185–198.

———. 1964. Obshtaya embryologia pokritosemenih rastentiby (General embryology of the angiosperms). Nauka, Moscow.

Poddubnaya-Arnoldi, V. A., and A. Selezneva. 1957. Orchidei i ih koultoura (Orchids and their culture). Acad. Sci. U.S.S.R., Moscow.

———. 1961. Orchidei iz semyan (Orchids from seeds). Tsvetovodstvo 4:6–7.

Poddubnaya-Arnoldi, V. A., and N. V. Zinger. 1961. Application of histochemical technique to the study of embryonic processes in some orchids. Recent Advances in Botany (Univ. of Toronto), Sect. 8:711–714.

Poddubnaya-Arnoldi, V. A., N. V. Zinger, T. P. Petrovskaya, and N. N. Polunina. 1961. Gistohimit-cheskoe isledovanie piltzi i piltzevyih trubok nekotoryeh pokritosemenyih rastenii (Histochemical investigations of pollen and pollen tubes of several Angiosperms). Trudyi Glavnogo Bot. Sada 8:163–194.

Pollacci, G., and M. Bergamaschi. 1940. Azione delle vitamine sulla germinazione dei semi di orchidee. Boll. Soc. Ital. Biol. Sper. 15:326–327.

Potes, A. F. 1951. La utilidad de la thiamina, las sales minerales y las fitohormonas en el cultivo de orquideas. Acta Agronomica 1:65–69.

Raghavan, V. 1964. Effects of certain organic nitrogen compounds on growth in vitro of seedlings of Cattleya. Bot. Gaz. 125:260–267.

Rao, A. N., and P. N. Avadhani. 1963. Some aspects of in vitro culture of Vanda seeds. Proc. 4th World Orchid Conf., Singapore, p. 194–202.

Rédei, G. P. 1965. Genetic blocks in the thiamine synthesis of the angiosperm Arabidopsis. Amer. J. Bot. 52:834–841.

Robbins, W. J. 1939. Growth substances in agar. Amer. J. Bot. 26:772–778.

Robbins, W. J., and V. B. White. 1936. Limited growth and abnormalities in excised corn root tips. Bot. Gaz. 98:209–242.

Sadowsky, O. 1965. Orchideen im eigenen Garten. BLV Bayerischer Landwirtschafte Verlag, Munich.

Salisbury, R. A. 1804. On the germination of the seeds of Orchidaceae. Trans. Linn. Soc. London 7:29–32.

Schaffstein, G. 1938. Untersuchungen über die Avitaminose der Orchideenkeimlinge. Jahrb. Wiss. Bot. 86:720–752.

——. 1941. Die Avitaminose der Orchideenkeimlinge. Jahrb. Wiss. Bot. 90:141–198.

Schopfer, W. H. 1943. Plants and vitamins (p. 250–253). Chronica Botanica, Waltham, Mass.

Schultes, R. E., and A. S. Pease. 1963. Generic names of orchids. Academic Press, New York.

Shanmuga-Sundaram, E. R. B., M. O. Tirunarayanan, and P. S. Sarma. 1954. The relation between biotin and tryptophan metabolism studies in Neurospora crassa. Biochem. J. 58:460.

Spoerl, E. 1948. Amino acids as sources of nitrogen for orchid embryos. Amer. J. Bot. 35:88–95.

Stephen, R. C., and K. K. Fung. 1971. Vitamin requirements of the fungal endophytes of Arundina chinensis. Can. J. Bot. 49:411–415.

Steward, F. C. 1968. Growth and organization in plants. Addision-Wesley, Reading, Mass.

Storey, W. B., H. W. Kirch, D. J. Pierce, and H. Kamemoto. 1947. Orchidology. Rept. Univ. Hawaii Agric. Exp. Sta. for the Bienn. Ending June, 1946, p. 82–86.

Tenhaeff, E. H. 1951–1952. Het zaaien van Phalaenopsis. Orchideeen 13:92–93; 14:36–37, 78.

Torikata, H., Y. Sawa, and M. Sisa. 1965. Non-symbiotic germination and growth of the orchid seeds. I. Studies on the medium and additive for germination of seed in Cymbidium. J. Japan. Soc. Hort. Sci. 34:63–70.

Ueda, H., and H. Torikata. 1968. Organogenesis in meristem cultures of cymbidiums. I. Studies on the effects of growth substances added to culture media under continuous illumination. J. Japan. Soc. Hort. Sci. 37:56–64. (In Japanese with English summary and tables.)

——. 1969. Organogenesis in the meristem tissue culture of cymbidiums. II. Effects of growth substances on the organogenesis in dark culture. J. Japan. Soc. Hort. Sci. 38:78–83. (In Japanese with English summary and tables.)

Valmayor, H. L., and Y. Sagawa. 1967. Ovule culture in some orchids. Amer. Orchid Soc. Bull. 36:766–769.

Vermeulen, p. 1947. Studies on Dactylorchis. Diss., Univ. of Amsterdam.

Voth, W. 1964. Asymbiotische Aussaat und Jungpflanzenanzucht einiger botanischer Orchideen. Mitteilungen Klosterneuburg, Ser. B. Obst. und Garten 14B:250–258.

Watanabe, K., K. Tanaka, K. Asada, and Z. Kasai. 1971. The growth-promoting effect of phytic acid on callus tissues of rice seed. Plant and Cell Physiol. 12:161–164.

Withner, C. L. 1942. Nutrition experiments with orchid seedlings. Amer. Orchid Soc. Bull. 11:112–114.

——. 1943. Ovule culture: a new method for starting orchid seedlings. Amer. Orchid Soc. Bull. 11:261–263.

——. 1951. Effect of plant hormones and other compounds on the growth of orchids. Amer. Orchid Soc. Bull. 20:276–278.

——. 1955. Ovule culture and growth of Vanilla seedlings. Amer. Orchid Soc. Bull. 24:380–392.

——. 1959. Orchid physiology, p. 315–360. In C. L. Withner (ed.), The orchids: a scientific survey. Ronald Press, New York.

——. 1974. Developments in orchid physiology, p. 129–168. *In* C. L. Withner (ed.), The orchids: scientific studies. Wiley-Interscience, New York.

Young, H. Y. 1952. Introductory plant physiology with some references to the physiology of orchids. Na Pua Okika O Hawaii Nei 2:59–65.

Zinger, N. V., and V. A. Poddubnaya-Arnoldi. 1953. Primeneie gistohimitcheskoi metodiki k izutchenyu embryonalnyih prozesov u orchidei (Application of histochemical technique to the study of embryonic processes in some orchids). Acad. Nauk S.S.S.R. Trudyi Glavnogo Bot. Sada 6:90–169.

7

Variations in Clonal Propagation

THAVORN VAJRABHAYA

Introduction

Clonal propagation is the asexual multiplication of an individual plant. Normally, members of a clone should have identical genomes because each cell within every plant is produced by mitotic cell division. Consequently, every member of a clone must exhibit exactly the same characteristics. Any recognizable variation within a clone should be minor, resulting from environmental changes during development, and should normally disappear in the next growth (Webber, 1903; Stout, 1940; Stearn, 1949).

In orchid culture, clonal propagation is a very common and important practice. It is particularly valuable in perpetuating clones of special merit. Methods of clonal propagation may be simple, e.g., collecting offshoots which normally develop on pseudobulbs or inflorescences as is sometimes the case with *Dendrobium*, *Oncidium*, and *Phalaenopsis*. In sympodial orchids, the division of clumps is a normal practice. In monopodial types, however, the "terminal-cutting" method normally must be used since side shoots occur infrequently. One of the major breakthroughs in orchidology was the method of clonal propagation suggested by the late Dr. Georges M. Morel in 1960. While applying existing tissue culture techniques (White, 1954) to the study of virus transmission in *Cymbidium*, he noted that protocorm-like bodies developed around shoot tips cultured *in vitro*. These eventually produced roots and shoots as in normal seedling. If such a protocorm-like body was cut into sections and transferred to a new medium, additional bodies were produced. By repeating this process, large tissue stocks of any one clone can be obtained within a relatively short time. If the culture is left undisturbed, many plantlets with normal shoots and roots regenerate from the protocorm-like bodies. Since the initial publication (Morel, 1960), this technique and its modifications (Wimber, 1963; Morel, 1964; Sagawa, Shoji, and Shoji, 1966; Reinert and Mohr, 1967; Sagawa and Shoji, 1967; Scully, 1967; Champagnat and Morel, 1969; Champagnat, Morel, and Mounetou, 1970; Kim, Kunisaki, and Sagawa, 1970; Lindemann, Gunkel, and Davidson, 1970; Vajrabhaya and Vajrabhaya, 1970; Churchill, Arditti, and Ball 1971; Kunisaki, Kim, and Sagawa, 1972; Intuwong and Sagawa, 1973; Teo, Kunisaki, and Sagawa, 1973) have become important in the mass propagation of desirable varieties at rates which would have been undreamt of fifteen years ago. *Cymbidium*, *Cattleya*, *Dendrobium*, *Vanda*, and allied genera are being widely propagated by tissue culture throughout the world (see Appendix).

Clonal propagation is particularly important for orchids because their genotypes are highly heterozygous. Furthermore, asexual propagation is essential for plants which may be completely sterile.

Sexual propagation has the advantage of producing gene recombinations which may give rise to new forms. However, perpetuation of a desirable type can be assured only by clonal propagation. But, in addition, a very important point should be borne in mind: Even asexual propagation may produce heritable variations, i.e., new clones. Such clones may be desirable and therefore subject to further clonal propagation.

At times a given genotype may be influenced by varying environmental factors to produce different phenotypes. Such changes are not permanent, however, since the genotype of the plants remains unaffected. In other cases the genotype is affected and the changes are permanent. This article will be confined to the latter.

Variations within a clone in horticultural crops in general are believed to be numerous, but the number of those reported is relatively small. In the case of orchids, however, growers strive for perfection in each individual flower and discover a larger proportion. Orchids also have two characteristics which render them amenable to the study of variations: First, the flowers have large segments which are of four distinct types (dorsal sepal, lateral sepals, petals, and labellum), in contrast to most plants, which have only two (sepals and petals). Second, the cultural conditions under which orchids are grown are very uniform. Under such conditions, variations due to the environment are minimized.

Orchids are inherently slow-growing plants. Consequently, their asexual propagation is also extremely slow. This has limited the study of clonal variations because enough individuals belonging to the same clone could rarely be found in the same general area. Recently, tissue culture has made possible mass clonal propagation and individuals in any clone could reach astronomical numbers. This has greatly facilitated the study of intraclonal variations since plants can be grown under the same environmental conditions in order to produce phenotypic variations which are due only to genetic differences.

In the future, more and more clonal variation in orchids is likely to occur, for at least two reasons. First, many clones have been and will be propagated by tissue culture, and when any population becomes very large, more variation among its individuals is to be expected. Second, the artificial environment during tissue culture may favor the development of certain variants which would not appear otherwise. Therefore, our present knowledge of clonal variation can be used to prevent an excessive number of unwanted variants, especially in award-winning clones. Or it can be employed to induce variation during clonal propagation as a means of producing new clones.

Occurrence of Variations in Orchids

Variations within species are not unusual among orchids since they are usually cross-pollinated plants. Color variation such as alba (entirely white) and semi-alba (colored lip, white sepals and petals) may be found within a single species: For example, *Cattleya warscewiczii* 'Firmin Lambeau' is an alba clone, whereas *Cattleya warscewiczii* 'Frau Melanie Beyrodt' is a semi-alba. Another source of variation (which plays a very important role) in orchid breeding is polyploidy: Ordinary *Cattleya trianaei* is diploid, *Cattleya trianaei* 'Mooreana' is triploid, and *Cattleya trianaei* 'Llewellyn' is tetraploid (Tanaka and Kamemoto, 1963, 1974). Some species in other genera seem to behave in the same manner. Still, the occurrence of minor variations is a rule rather than an exception. Variation occurring in nature must originate from either asexual or sexual reproduction. Triploids may originate from the union of a normal gamete with an unreduced one. The union of one female gamete with two male gametes also results in a triploid. On the other hand, tetraploids are likely to result from somatic doubling rather than the extremely unlikely union of two unreduced gametes.

Variations in flower have been reported frequently by growers, but subsequent observations are made rarely. These variations might have arisen during the development of individual flowers only, and on the next growth, these plants could produce normal flowers. But some of these characteristics (e.g., wide sepals, labellum-like petals, and multiple petals in *Cattleya*) can be transmitted to offspring (Reychler, 1928). Mutations are more likely to occur during asexual phases than during sexual ones because the latter are very much shorter. However, recessive mutations may remain hidden and become apparent after recombination in sexual reproduction.

Chromosomal Aberrations

Changes in chromosome number in individuals of a clone or within a single root have been reported in orchids and can have a definite influence on the development of phenotypes. For example, the occurrence of aneuploidy in the roots of *Paphiopedilum wardii* has been reported (Duncan, 1945). Certain shorter chromosomes with terminal centromere replicated more than others. The result was an increase in chromosome numbers in some root cells. These aneuploid cells were scattered. Tetraploid and octoploid cells, the result of extra replications of all chromosomes, were also found. Irregularities in the distribution of these cells throughout the plant body may explain the characteristic mottling of the leaves in this species, due to differences in number of genes controlling chlorophyll production in each cell. Since offshoots of *Paphiopedilum wardii* could arise from roots (Duncan, 1945), it has been suggested that a new clone may originate in such a way. This new clone may consist entirely or partly of polyploid or aueuploid cells.

Changes in chromosome numbers have been observed by the author (unpublished) in plants propagated by tissue culture. Out of 205 plants propagated from a diploid *Dendrobium* xMay Neal 'Srisobhon', five were tetraploid and near tetraploid. These plants produced larger flowers (Plate 7-1-**H**) with an increased fertility. Their vegetative parts were not very different from the diploid except that the guard cells were significantly larger (Plate 7-2-**A**, **B**). By contrast, five hexaploid variants arising from a triploid (*Dendrobium* xLady Hamilton × *D*. xMay Neal) showed deformities in their leaves. These were very thick, curled upward, and their upper surfaces were rough and dull. The plants were stunted and produced fewer roots. Their flowers were slightly smaller but thicker than the original triploid. Abnormalities such as these are characteristic of orchids, as well as other plants, whenever chromosome numbers are too high for the type of plant concerned (Stebbins, 1950). *Cattleya*, *Cymbidium*, and *Dendrobium* plants having chromosome numbers higher than the pentaploid level do not grow well (Plate 7-2-**E**, **F**) while some hexaploid *Phalaenopsis* and *Vanda* do. Chromosome numbers in each cell can be altered deliberately by colchicine treatment of actively growing points or by drastic changes in such environmental factors as temperature and radiation (see below).

Chimeras

Chimeras have occurred sporadically in orchids, but only a few of them have been described. A plant of *Calanthe* xVeitchii produced two sprays which bore flowers of

Plate 7-1.
Variations in *Cymbidium* (**A-B**) and *Dendrobium* (**C-H**) which arose during clonal propagation by tissue culture. **A**, *Cymbidium* xBurgundian 'Chateau' FCC/RHS; **B**, *Cymbidium*
xBurgundian 'Flambeau', a variant of the former (courtesy of Messrs. Vacherot and Lecoufle,
Boissy St. Leger, France); **C**, *Dendrobium* xPompadour, a flower of the original clone (top),
a variant with wider labellum and petals (left), and a variant with long and twisted labellum
(right); **D**, *Dendrobium* xPompadour, short mentum, a characteristic of a variant (top), and
a normal mentum (bottom); **E-F**, *Dendrobium* xPompadour, variegation of petals (**E**) and
pronounced variegation of petals with a reverse pattern (**F**); **G**, *Dendrobium* xPompadour,
a normal flower (right) and a variant with light-colored keels and petal bases and a different
shape of labellum (left); **H**, *Dendrobium* xMay Neal 'Srisobhon', the diploid clone (left) and
a tetraploid variant; note size and shape differences.

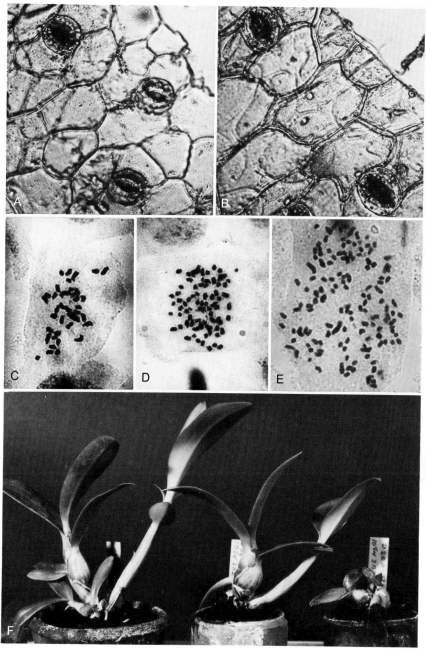

Plate 7-2.
   A-B: Epidermal cells of *Dendrobium* xCaesar showing guard cells; ×36; **A**, diploid; **B**, tetraploid. **C-E:** Chromosome complements of *Dendrobium superbiens*; ×1200; **C**, diploid (2n = 38); **D**, tetraploid (2n = 76); **E**, near octoploid (2n = 154 ± 2). **F**, Plants of *Dendrobium superbiens* having diploid, tetraploid, and octoploid chromosome complements (from left to right); note the stunted growth and abnormal leaves of the octoploid.

different colors; the flowers on one were a rosy pink whereas the others were a pale flesh color (Swan, 1906). Similar chimeras have also been reported in *Cymbidium* (Lenz and Wimber, 1959). Flowers on one spray with markedly different coloration along the side of the throat have also been observed (Lenz and Wimber, 1959).

Leaf variegation is a chimera that usually involves chlorophyll production. The amount of chlorophyll varies from area to area, resulting in mottling or striping. Such variegation has been found in several orchid genera, e.g., *Angraecum, Cattleya, Cymbidium, Dendrobium, Paphiopedilum* and *Phalaenopsis* (Lenz and Wimber, 1959; Vajrabhaya, unpublished). In one case the variegation of *Brassocattleya* xLanguedoc 'Singapore Welcome' was not limited to leaves and stems but extended to the flowers as well, which were striped purple and white. This means that cells in the mutated regions were unable to produce enough chlorophyll or other pigments.

In tissue culture, variegation has been observed in leaves of *Cattleya, Cymbidium, Odontoglossum,* and *Dendrobium* plantlets (Michel Vacherot, personal communication; Vajrabhaya, unpublished). Occasionally an albino also arises (Arditti, personal communication; Vajrabhaya, unpublished), presumably from unstable chimeras (sectorial and mericlinal). Conversely, a normal green plant can arise from a variegated one. Albino orchids grow slowly and develop into individuals which look very much like normal plants except for the color, but they have never reached maturity (Arditti, personal communication; Vajrabhaya, unpublished). However, from a theoretical point of view, these plants should be able to grow indefinitely if supplied with the proper nutrients.

Variegation of flowers is known to occur in mericlones (plants produced through shoot-tip culture). *Cymbidium* xBurgundian 'Flambeau' is a variant of *Cymbidium* xBurgundian 'Chateau' (Plate 7-1-**A**, **B**) which arose in a population of mericlones belonging to Messrs. Vacherot and Lecoufle (Michel Vacherot, personal communication). The firm cites other instances of *Cymbidium* variegation which are less striking. Similar variegations were found in *Dendrobium* xPompadour (Vajrabhaya and Vajrabhaya, 1974). The color differences between affected areas varied from plant to plant. Some had a lighter color at the edge of the petal while others exhibited a darker color. Color brilliance in affected areas also varied (Plate 7-1-**E**, **F**, **G**). At least five different types of variegation were found (Vajrabhaya, unpublished). The variegations of both *Cymbidium* and *Dendrobium* described above were not caused by virus infection (Michel Vacherot, personal communication; Vajrabhaya and Vajrabhaya, 1974).

Viruses are known to cause variegations in orchid flowers. These variegation patterns are of a mosaic type, unlike those described above (Jensen, 1959).

Color Variations

Variations in color other than variegation or mosaic have been observed in orchids. One type of color change was observed on sepal bases in some mericlones of *Dendrobium* xPompadour, the affected areas becoming white (Vajrabhaya and Vajrabhaya, 1974). Color variations in lip markings of *Cymbidium* propagated by division have also been reported and studied (Casamajor, 1950; Lenz, Wimber, and Dodson, 1955; Wimber,

Lenz, and Dodson, 1956). Another kind of variation was a change in color of the keels in *Dendrobium* xPompadour (Vajrabhaya and Vajrabhaya, 1974). Normally these are much darker than the labellum as a whole. However, in some variants, the keel color is similar to that of the labellum (Plate 7-1-**G**). Color spotting in individual plants of *Odontoglossum crispum* and *Odontoglossum pescatorei* have been noted to disappear entirely one year and reappear the next (Crawshay, 1897). This, however, would appear to be a purely environmental phenomenon.

These color variations can be detected easily because of contrast between adjacent areas. Difficulties may arise in detecting color changes of complete floral parts, e.g., sepals, petals, or labella, if the differences between them are not sufficiently great. However, minor changes in petal color can be detected by reflection densitometry (Vajrabhaya and Vajrabhaya, 1974). In seven selected mericlones of *Dendrobium* xPompadour which were visually different, densitometry confirmed the visual observation. The measurements also revealed that the colors of two mericlones which appeared darker had shifted toward the red (density of the red remained the same but the densities of blue and green increased appreciably). One mericlone showed both a reduction in overall color density and an alteration in the proportions of reflected colors which made the flower look very pale. Two variants with color shift in opposite directions can be compared effectively by photographing both flowers on the same plate.

Variations in the Size of Floral Parts

The size of floral parts is affected by environmental factors. Repeated observations and statistical analysis can tell the researcher which variations are due to external condition. Statistical analyses (Vajrabhaya and Vajrabhaya, 1974) of petals and labella of 20 selected mericlones of *Dendrobium* xPompadour showed clearly that the differences in length and width of petals and labella were genuine variations and not merely the results of chance (Plate 7-1-**C**). Exceptional mericlones of *Cymbidium* and *Dendrobium* which show improvement over the original clone (e.g., large and thicker flowers with better coloring) have also been found (Michel Vacherot, personal communication; Vajrabhaya, unpublished). These are likely to result from somatic chromosome doubling from diploid to tetraploid. Cytological studies of these plants should reveal the actual situation.

Variations in Flower Shape

The shape of orchid flowers is determined largely by the length-to-width ratio of their petals. One study of *Dendrobium* xPompadour (Vajrabhaya and Vajrabhaya, 1974) found that length/width ratios range from 0.979:1 to 1.313:1. Such large variations in ratio affect the appearance of the flower. In the labellum, however, considerable variations in length/width ratio (e.g., 0.832:1 to 1.058:1) can escape unnoticed by purely visual observation because the side lobes in this hybrid are turned upward. Even larger variations with respect to the mid-lobe (from 0.653:1 to 1.494:1) were observed, and those most certainly affect the visual appearance of the whole flower (Plate 7-1-**C**). Changes in length of the mentum were also noted. Some variants were found to have a mentum only half the normal length (Plate 7-1-**D**). Variations in flower shape of *Cymbidium* xAlexanderi 'Westonbirt' grown by different growers were recorded, but there is some doubt whether these plants did really belong to the same clone (Casamajor, 1950).

Variations in Petals

In *Dendrobium* xPompadour, keels normally appear only on labella, but in three mericlones keels were found on petals as well. Two others had labellum-like petals with keels and mentums. Petals of tetraploid variants of *Dendrobium* xMay Neal were concave at the tips (Vajrabhaya, unpublished).

Bases of Variation

Characteristics of a whole plant may be modified by either physical or biological factors in the environment. Under a set of given environmental conditions, variations must originate either nongenetically (e.g., from viral infection or cytoplasmic factors) or genetically (Swanson, 1957; Jensen, 1959).

Virus Diseases

A frequently occurring disease called "breaking" has been known in tulips since the sixteenth century. This disease, which brings about striking color aberrations, is now known to be caused by a virus. At present, many other virus-infected plants have been found to show various changes in morphology and color. They are often associated with degeneration of a clone (Tincker, 1945).

There are several reports concerning viruses in orchids, but there is disagreement concerning the number of strains involved. Only three viruses have been definitely identified (Murakishii, 1958a,b). These are *Cymbidium* mosaic virus (CymMV), *Odontoglossum* ringspot virus (ORSV), and *Vanda* mosaic virus (VMV). The symptoms of the three vary in different species of orchid. In *Cattleya*, ORSV produces flower-color break instead of ringspot on the leaves. CymMV produces chlorotic spots or streaks on the leaves of *Cymbidium*, *Phalaenopsis*, and *Vanda*, but brown necrosis in *Cattleya* flowers (Lawson, 1970; Ishii and Martinez, 1973). Affected plants may show severe symptoms one year and few the next. The other two viruses (ORSV and VMV) are of lesser importance but they too cause drastic changes in both the shape and color of flowers. The symptoms of a fourth virus, tobacco mosaic virus (TMV), may be caused by one of these or by TMV itself.

Variations in Tissue Culture

In propagating orchids by tissue culture, explant from either the growing point or other parts of the plant are used. Tissues in inner layers which normally do not develop any further may be heterogeneous after differentiation (D'Amato, 1952; Torrey, 1961; Fox, 1963; Partanen, 1965; Murashige and Nakano, 1966; Shimada and Tabata, 1967; Stern, 1969). Furthermore, the environment *in vitro* is very different from that *in vivo* and probably has a considerable effect on the selection of various cell types. The possibility of mutations in tissue cultures should also not be excluded. Selection of new cell types during culture, whether among existing variants or newly mutated cells, will lead to the production of new genotypes or phenotypes *in vitro*. It is quite safe to assume that it also occurs in orchids.

Clonal propagation of plants through tissue culture generally involves the regeneration of a new plant from a callus or from differentiated tissues. However, not all variants occurring in a culture will survive and develop into complete plants which can be grown under natural conditions. Some may not regenerate organs due to imbalance of their chromosome complements, i.e. extreme aneuploidy or high polyploidy (Torrey, 1967; Murashige and Nakano, 1967). Others may produce certain organs when the medium is suitably adjusted. For example, one of our triploid *Dendrobium* tissues (Vajrabhaya and Vajrabhaya, 1974), in which differentiation normally took place easily, suddenly changed its behavior, remaining in the callus state. Occasionally complete plants have arisen from these cultures. They have abnormally thick leaves and grow slowly. Chromosome counts of these plants revealed that they are hexaploid. Other cultures of explants from diploid *Dendrobium* cultivars have shown similar growth patterns after periods of one or more years. Their chromosome numbers are near the octoploid level.

Despite the rigid limitation on survival imposed by selection, not all surviving plantlets will be exact replicas of the original plants. In many cases, they grow true to type, but in some instances variations of certain characteristics can be expected. Tobacco plants regenerated from tumorous cultures did not resemble normal plants at all (Sacristan and Melchers, 1969). The new plants were all characterized by abnormal morphology and sterility, which seem to result from extreme aneuploidy. The stability of cells in tissue culture is questionable. Recent progress in techniques has revealed that animal or plant cells are likely to change during culture (Westwood and Titmuss, 1957; Lederberg, 1958; Hsu, 1961; Cooper *et al.*, 1964; Muir, 1965; Torrey, 1965; Heinz, Mee, and Nickell, 1969; Sacristan, 1971). Murashige and Nakano (1965) state definitely: "It is commonly agreed that stability is the exception in tissue culture". Orchids propagated asexually through tissue culture have been reported to retain their original characteristics (Blowers, 1967; Lecoufle, 1967). However, marked variations in *Cymbidium* mericlones (Plate 7-1-**A**, **B**) have been reported (Vacherot, personal communication). Our *Dendrobium* xPompadour mericlones exhibit extreme variation in stems, leaves, and flowers, and we have recorded at least twenty distinct variants (Vajrabhaya and Vajrabhaya, 1974).

Chimeras and Bud Sports

A chimera is a plant (an organ or tissue) composed of two or more genetically distinct tissues lying adjacent to each other. It can only originate from cell division following somatic segregation. The area of the plant which has phenotypic variations of this kind may range in size from a few cells to a large portion of the tissues or organs. Many fruit and foliage variations exist in horticultural crops (Shamel and Pomeroy, 1936).

All chimeras are relatively unstable and may revert to the original tissue types. The degree of stability depends on their structure, i.e., (1) location of new cell types in shoot tips, (2) direction of cell division, or (3) the location of lateral buds which may affect the development of chimeras. A lateral shoot which develops from the mutated portion of a stem becomes a bud sport, whereas a shoot from the other side is un-affected. If a shoot develops from a bud composed of two different kinds of tissue, it remains a chimera. Undoubtedly, the occurrence of chimeras and bud sports in orchids should follow patterns similar to those of fruit trees (which have been described by Dermen, 1960) but to a lesser extent because orchids grow at a much slower rate.

Prevention of Variation

As a result of the enormous popularity orchids have gained during the last two decades, a very large number of varieties has come into existence. Many more new varieties are to be expected in the future. Some of them may prove valuable in many respects, whereas other will undoubtedly be inferior to the original plants.

Nothing could be more disastrous for a commercial orchid cut-flower grower than to find (despite perfect cultural conditions) a whole greenhouse of plants from a single clone yielding blooms at the wrong time of the year, or blooms of an undesirable color, or, worse still, both! Amateurs may also obtain unexpected and perhaps spectacular or depressing results due to modification of shape or color when flowering a clonally propagated plant. Such variations may become the subject of heated arguments between orchid growers, amateur and professional alike.

The occurrence of variations cannot be prevented entirely, although an under-standing of their nature will allow for substantial suppression. In addition, the oc-currence of proportion of affected plants can also be controlled.

Variations due to Viral Infection

Virus diseases are a serious problem in orchid culture. They are commonly respon-sible for the degeneration of clones as well as for shortening the life of flowers or chang-ing their color.

Viruses are transmitted from plant to plant mainly by cutting tools either during propagation or when flowers are harvested. The best method of killing viruses is heat. All cutting tools should, therefore, be flamed or baked before using them on a new plant. Chemical inactivation of viruses is also possible. Tools should be dipped in a solution of 2% sodium hydroxide or a commercial bleaching solution such as Clorox for 30 to 60 seconds (Lawson, 1967). The use of cutting tools may be avoided entirely in picking certain types of sprays. Some sprays come off easily when pulled if they are bent slightly at the node. This method is being successfully applied in Thailand for *Dendrobium*, *Oncidium*, *Phalaenopsis*, and *Vanda*.

Generally, plant viruses are transmitted by insects (Tincker, 1945; Jensen, 1959). Insects can carry a virus from one plant to another, even to plants of different fami-lies. Fortunately, the host range of orchid viruses is very limited (Murakishii, 1958a; Jensen, 1959), and some insects which thrive on orchids are not virus carriers. Two species of aphids, *Cerataphis orchidearum* and *Myzus persicae*, which are pests of *Cattleya*, do not transmit *Odontoglossum* ringspot and *Cymbidium* mosaic viruses from plant to plant (Namba and Ishii, 1971). At present, insect populations in greenhouses are low, even though they are a prevalent problem, owing to improved insect control methods. Therefore, the spreading of orchid viruses by insects is only a minor problem in greenhouses.

Some viruses are transmitted through pollination in some fruit trees (George and Davidson, 1963; Gilmer, 1965) but there is no proof that this may occur in orchids. Pollen-borne viruses do not enter the tissues of orchid embryos (Jensen, 1959). However, they may spread through the tissues of the mother plant. Altogether, the experience with fruit trees suggests caution in orchid breeding. Selected plants of each important clone should be left unpollinated in order to keep them virus-free.

Since orchid viruses are systemic, any division from diseased plants is certain to contain virus particles. At the time of writing no satisfactory method is yet known of eliminating a stable virus such as CymMV by inactivation with heat or chemicals in living plants without killing the host (Morel, 1960; Lawson and Hearon, 1973). However, virus-free *Cymbidium* plants can be obtained from infected ones, even those exhibiting severe symptoms (Morel, 1960). The method involves the excision of a very small tissue section (0.1 mm thick) from the meristematic region of the shoot tip. This is then cultured on a nutrient medium. The combination of heat therapy and shoot-tip culture has been reported to be effective in elimination of various viruses in several plant species (Paludan, 1971). This should have some application in orchids. Recent advances in the elimination of orchid viruses through treatment of tissue during culture have been made with promising results (Ishii, 1973; Lawson and Hearon, 1973). Therefore it appears that the hope of rescuing important clones which have been infected with virus may be realized in the not too distant future.

Variations Arising during Tissue Culture

As already mentioned, variation can arise easily during tissue culture, but relatively few such plants will reach maturity. However, even a minute fraction may cause trouble later because many variations cannot be detected until the flowering stage. Various precautions should, therefore, be taken in order to reduce the number of variants.

Consideration must be given to the original tissues. Differentiated tissues should be avoided, whether taken below the meristem proper or from other tissues. Differentiated tissues are often found to consist of cells with different genotypes (Murashige and Nakano, 1967; Shimada and Tabata, 1967). Therefore, small blocks of tissue containing a meristem and one or two leaf primodia should be used. Even smaller explants have been used in the culture of tobacco (Smith and Murashige, 1970) and *Cymbidium* (Morel, 1960). Tissues should not be cultured from plants which show variegation of leaves or flowers since they may be chimeras.

Culture media composition has considerable influence on the selection of genotypes in developing tissues. Hence, the incorporation of undefined complex organic components such as coconut water or yeast extract into culture media is not recommended.

It is true that some of these components have the merit of causing profuse tissue growth, but caution is necessary. For example, pea tissues grown in a synthetic medium supplemented with yeast extract were a mixture of diploid, octoploid, and tetraploid cells, with the latter predominating; in a medium without yeast extract only diploid cells were found (Torrey, 1961, 1965). Other workers found similar results when using growth factors that have cytokinin activity (Venketeswaran and Spiess, 1963). Although auxins are a necessary ingredient for growth promotion of most plant tissues, the use of strong ones such as 2,4-dichlorophenoxyacetic acid (2,4-D) is to be avoided because they tend to stimulate polyploidy (Shamina, 1966). During the early stage of culture the tissues may require both cytokinins and auxins for their growth. For subsequent growth, normal tissues may need extremely low concentrations of these factors, or none at all. It may, therefore, be a good practice to use very low concentrations of growth factors (just enough to support normal growth), and to omit them whenever possible. Such treatment will greatly suppress the growth of the cells with abnormal and subnormal genotypes.

The physical environment usually has a considerable effect on the growth and development of tissues; it may also affect the genotypes that survive. Liquid media favor cell division and growth, and also support the growth of polyploid cells. In contrast, solid media do not favor the division and growth of polyploid cells (Demoise and Partanen, 1969). Light intensities and the alternation of dark and light period also have profound effects on the survival of specific genotypes of tobacco tissue (Guo, 1972) but the effects on other tissues have yet to be determined. Avoiding extreme environment in the orchid culture room is of prime importance for good growth and development and for the stability of genotypes *in vitro*. Tissue culture periods should also be kept to a minimum to avoid excessive variants.

Even when all necessary measures are taken to prevent variations, their occurrence should be anticipated, especially from polyploid parental clones. Variants cannot be prevented, but their numbers can be controlled. It would be disastrous if most (or all) mericlones in commercially produced populations were inferior in quality to the original plant. To this end, as many excisions as possible from a given clone should be used in initial cultures. Precautions must also be taken to prevent the excessive division of inferior plants. The procedure is a simple one. Tissues should be separated into four or more sections at an early stage. These sections should then be divided repeatedly and equally into subsections until the required number is reached. This will prevent the overproduction of unwanted variants, especially when they grow faster than the normal plants.

Deliberate Production of Variations

Sometimes it may be desirable to introduce variants deliberately, in the hope of obtaining a few, perhaps spectacular types. The basic requirement must be to obtain genetic diversity from which specially desired qualities can be selected. At present, most of the genetic diversity in orchids has been the result of plant exploration, collection, introduction, evaluation, and conservation. The natural gene pool has been utilized to good effect in the hybridization and selection of individuals carrying desirable genes. Tremendous advances in orchid breeding have been realized as a result of these efforts, but the search for future improvement must still go on.

Today, techniques are available for increasing the number of variations. These can be used to improve many food crops, but such techniques have rarely been applied to orchids. They include the use of ionizing radiation and of chemical mutagens (Sparrow and Konzak, 1958; Freese, 1971). Since orchids are slow-growing plants which produce relatively few shoots per year, experiments along these lines are very difficult. Recent investigations have contributed much to the induction of mutation *in vitro* (Nickell, 1973), and the results with orchids are promising (Wimber and VanCott, 1967; Chaichareon, 1973; Sanguthai and Sagawa, 1973; Sanguthai, Sanguthai, and Kamemoto, 1973). It has been reported that tissue culture greatly facilitates the application of mutagens to tissues or cells (Nickell, 1973). Theoretically, cells grown *in vitro* can be separated individually before treatment. In such cases, each regenerating tissue would consist entirely of cells which are descendants of the affected ones. The treatment of a single cell greatly reduces the chances of chimera formation as long as the single cell forms an embryoid directly. Even if the separation of a single cell is technically impossible in most laboratories, treatment of a small cluster is still a much better proposition than treating the whole growing point.

Spontaneous mutations apparently occur only infrequently but their rate can be increased considerably by application of chemical mutagens or by radiation. External chemical or physical agents can cause mutations either directly or indirectly after enzymatic activation by interfering with enzymes necessary for chromosome duplication or segregation.

Chimeral Isolation

It was mentioned earlier that the chromosome complements of cells in differentiated tissues may vary to some extent. For instance, isolation of tetraploid cells from diploid tobacco tissue is possible and such cells differentiate into tetraploid plants (Murashige and Nakano, 1966). In addition, several acres of new clones of sugarcane have been produced by isolation of cells from inside the stalk (Nickell, 1973). Each of these clones has a different chromosome number. Chromosome or gene mutation may occur spontaneously *in vitro*. Any of the affected cells may divide and form chimeras, which subsequently become complete plant(s) with new characteristics. Such occurrences have also been found in orchids.

Chemical Mutagens

The number of different chemical compounds known to act as mutagens is large and diverse and continues to grow. (A detailed account of the mechanisms of mutation and mutagens may be found in Drake, 1969.)

Mutagens that act on specific parts of the DNA molecule have long been sought in plant genetic research, but limited success has been achieved. Ethylmethanesulfonate (EMS) is probably one of the most effective chemical mutagens for use on higher plants (Heslot *et al.*, 1959). It gives a high percentage of mutation with little damage to chromosomes. The other well-known chemical mutagen is the alkaloid colchicine, which acts as a suppressor of spindle formation rather than on the chromosome itself (Eigsti, 1938; Inoue, 1952; Eigsti and Dustin, 1957). At present, only colchicine has been used effectively in inducing chromosome doubling in orchids.

Colchicine. Colchicine has long been used for the induction of polyploidy in many plant species (Blakeslee and Avery, 1937; Emsweller and Ruttle, 1941). There are several reports on the application of colchicine to orchids (Moore, 1947; MacLeod, 1947; Rotor, 1958) but they do not furnish any data on chromosome numbers. Occurrence of tetraploids after submerging backbulbs of *Cymbidium* xConingsbyanum 'Brockhurst' in colchicine solution twice within an interval of ten days has been reported (Menninger, 1963). The first treatment was carried out in 0.4% solution for 74 minutes and the second in 1% for one hour. Flowers of the resulting tetraploid were larger, and the floral parts were wider and thicker, than those of the original diploid. Colchicine solution was first used on *Cymbidium* orchids *in vitro* (Wimber and VanCott, 1967). Approximately 40% tetraploids arose both in populations of young seedlings and among plantlets regenerated from colchicine-treated tissue cultures. Similar techniques have been applied successfully to *Dendrobium* (Chaicharoen, 1973; Sanguthai, Sanguthai, and Kamemoto, 1973). In *Vanda,* the results are moderately good (Sanguthai and Sagawa, 1973). The technique consists of introducing a sterile concentrated colchicine solution into a liquid culture medium to produce a final concentration ranging between 0.05% and 0.2%. When only a colchicine solution in glass-distilled water was used for treatments instead of culturing tissues in a liquid medium containing the alkaloid, 63% to 72% of the *Dendrobium* in such treatments were found to have doubled chromosome numbers as against 30% to 50% by other workers (Chaicharoen, 1973; Chaicharoen and Vajrabhaya, in press). One reason for the increased percentage may be that deprivation of nutrients during treatment may intensify the effect of colchicine simply through lack of the energy necessary for chromosome movement during anaphase. Optimum treatment periods ranged from three to ten days, after which the tissues or plantlets were transferred to an ordinary nutrient medium for further growth and differentiation. Extension of these techniques should enable orchid growers to exploit the possibility of obtaining either new and desirable phenotypes directly or stud plants for future breeding.

Other Chemicals. Chemical mutagens, specific for gene mutation, have not yet been used in orchids. However, the prospects are very good since a wide range of chemical mutagens are available today that can produce mutations without deleterious effects.

Physical Mutagens

Physical factors which increase mutation rates are heat, ultraviolet light, and ionizing radiation. Of these, ionizing radiation has been known longest as a mutagen, yet its mechanisms in molecular terms remain poorly understood (Smith, 1971).

Ionizing Radiation. The first demonstration that X rays could induce mutation in *Drosophila* (Muller, 1927) was a very significant contribution to biology, for X rays

V. *Ascocenda* xMeda Arnold
(courtesy of Robert Ernst).

VI. *Elythranthera emarginata*.

VII. *Sophronitis grandiflora* (courtesy of Robert Ernst).

VIII. *Vanda* xMiss Joaquim (courtesy of Robert Ernst).

(or other ionizing radiation) produce a large numbers of mutant genes in many organisms. These enable geneticists to study the relationship between mutations and the nature of genes as well as the nature of the mutation process itself.

Ionizing radiation can interact with cells to produce a genetic effect in the immediate vicinity of its ionization track (Muller, 1954a,b). Different kinds of radiation vary in their tissue-penetrating capacities. Generally speaking, the more penetrating a radiation, the more effective it is in inducing mutations.

Tolerances of tissues to radiation varies greatly depending on organism and stage of growth. Dosages of gamma rays ranging from 2,000 to 4,000 R at a rate of 900 R/hour seem to be optimum for the purpose of inducing mutation in *Cymbidium* protocorms (Harn, 1970). Young protocorms are more sensitive than older ones. Sliced protocorms are even more sensitive. However, whole protocorm treatments are preferable (Harn, 1970). *Dendrobium* mericlones 2 to 2.5 cm high can tolerate gamma radiation up to a strength of 5,000 R without much apparent loss of viability. Plants irradiated with higher dosages do not produce new growth in later years. Some of the irradiated *Dendrobium* xPompadour produced flowers with modifications in shape or color or both (Vajrabhaya, unpublished).

Besides mutation, radiation may also cause phenotypic changes owing to developmental abnormality. White Sim carnation, for example, could produce red flowers after irradiation (Sagawa and Mehlquist, 1957). Histological analysis indicated that the normal White Sim is, in fact, a periclinal chimera. Cells in the internal layers are genetically red, whereas those in the epidermal layers are genetically white. The effect of irradiation in the experiment was to damage the epidermal cells, and the new cells which replaced the damaged ones came from the genetically red internal layers. In this instance the effects of irradiation were equivalent to purely mechanical damage such as is produced by piercing a young bud with a needle, which results in a red spot around the puncture (Richter and Vajrabhaya, unpublished). Such variation, which is not a somatic mutation, can also occur in an orchid clone which is a periclinal chimera.

Anticipated Variants

As has been seen, there are a number of external factors which can modify mutations, but the nature of the plant material itself is the major determining factor of mutation rates and kinds. Knowledge of the nature of each plant is therefore of considerable help in forecasting mutation types and frequencies. For instance, in diploid species where many of the genes are homozygous, the occurrence of a gene mutation can increase heterozygosity. However, only dominant mutations will affect phenotypes immediately. Heterozygotes arising as a result of recessive mutation can not be detected readily, but they will affect subsequent generations. On the other hand, diploid hybrids consisting of heterozygous genes in many loci stand a greater chance of changing their pheonotypes owing to the occurrence of recessive mutations. In addition, the genes in hybrids are less stable than those in species and tend to cause chromosomal aberrations. The F_1 and F_2 hybrids of *Tradescantia paludosa* and *Tradescantia canaliculata* showed a threefold increase in frequency of chromosome breakage (Gile, 1940).

Usually a polyploid orchid is hybrid in origin and therefore has more genes at any locus than a diploid. Hence, gene mutations per nucleus can be expected to be more numerous than in diploid hybrids. In contrast, the frequency of phenotypic variations is likely to be very low because the recessive characters can appear only when all (i.e., more than two) genes at each particular locus become recessive. However, these mutant genes may become homozygous in subsequent generations, either by selfing or out-crossing the affected plants.

When tissues of a diploid are cultured, the occurrence of tetraploids, octoploids and aneuploids may be expected (Cooper et al., 1964; Murashige and Nakano, 1965; Sacristan, 1971). Of these, tetraploids and near-tetraploids grow well, whereas octoploids are subnormal (Chaicharoen, 1973). Tetraploid individuals have been obtained from four different diploid clones of *Dendrobium* (Vajrabhaya, unpublished). These plants produce large flowers with heavy substance, which may be considered an improvement. Aneuploids which deviate from diploids by only a few chromosomes may arise and produce various phenotypes, of which many may be subnormal due to gene imbalance. However, some exceptional ones may arise and can be selected for future use (Smith, 1971). By contrast, when the original tissues are triploid or higher, chromosome doubling will not be beneficial because orchids with chromosome numbers higher than hexaploid are stunted (Chaicharoen, 1973). Still, a good number of aneuploid variants can be expected to occur during tissue culture of polyploids. Orchid with chromosome complements deviating from straight polyploids (aneuploids) can grow well and reach maturity (Vajrabhaya and Randolph, 1960, 1961). Therefore, the number of such variations are expected to be highest. Since many desirable orchids are polyploids (Kamemoto, Tanaka, and Kosaki, 1961), numerous variations due to aneuploidy are expected in the propagation of orchids through tissue culture.

When mutagens are used, the resulting mutations depend largely on the type of mutagen employed. Mutations of all types can be expected from irradiated tissues, but with chromosome rearrangements prevailing. Ethylmethanesulfonate, which acts specifically on DNA, produces gene mutation almost exclusively, whereas col-chicine doubles chromosome numbers by suppressing spindle formation (Eigsti, 1938; Inoue, 1952; Eigsti and Dustin, 1957; Konzak, 1957; Heslot et al., 1959).

Utilization of Variants

Some of the variants produced during clonal propagation are inferior, whereas others give rise to improved plants. The latter will undoubtedly be very useful in the future improvement of orchids as a supplement to the usual breeding methods.

Polyploids

Orchid cytologists generally agree that polyploid orchids have many desirable traits which have some value for exhibition, as cut flowers, or as stud plants (Randolph, 1951; Niimoto and Randolph, 1958; Kamemoto, Tanaka, and Kosaki, 1961). Flower shape is often improved owing to an increase in width relative to length of floral parts; i.e., they tend to be rounder (Wimber and Wimber, 1968; Chaicharoen, 1973). For these reasons it is easy to understand why many award-winning plants are polyploids; and of these, the majority are tetraploids. On the other hand, when orchids are grown for cut-flower purposes, flower numbers are a prime factor. In this connection, diploid and triploid orchids are found to be more productive than higher polyploids. Many diploid hybrids of *Dendrobium* and *Vanda* dominate the field of commercial cut flowers. Among these are *Dendrobium* xJaquelyn Thomas, *D.* xNeo Hawaii, and *Vanda* xMiss Joaquim (Kamemoto, Tanaka, and Kosaki, 1961). However, the tetraploid (or near tetraploid) *Dendrobium* xPompadour and the triploid *Vanda* xT.M.A. are very productive. In *Cattleya* and *Cymbidium*, triploidy appears to be a balanced compromise level of ploidy. Tetraploids possess quality, diploids are floriferous, and triploids have both properties. It should be borne in mind that although many excellent plants are polyploids, not all polyloids are excellent plants. Genes are the ultimate determinants, and an increase in number of poor genes due to chromosome duplication may even worsen the quality of already undesirable plants.

Once desirable variants are found, they can be propagated asexually to maintain their qualities. Variants which show improvements in only certain respects may be valuable for breeding programs. For example, the tetraploid *Dendrobium* xMay Neal 'Mon', which I recently registered as a new clone arose spontaneously from the diploid *Dendrobium* xMay Neal 'Srisobhon'. It has a larger flower, heavier substance, and increased fertility over the original diploid. However, the shape of the spray of the new clone has to be improved. On the other hand, the tetraploid variants of *Dendrobium* xCaesar induced by colchicine treatment (Chaichareon, 1973) appear very promising since they show great improvement in size and color without loss of flower numbers.

The fertility of any plant will always change after alteration of ploidy. Generally, a tetraploid variant arising from a sterile diploid interspecific or intergeneric hybrid is fertile. The most common cause of sterility in hybrids among distantly related species is lack of homology of chromosomes, which results in partial or complete lack of pairing during meiosis. Doubling the chromosome number of these sterile hybrids gives rise to homologs for each individual chromosome, and fertility is restored. Such plants are called allotetraploids or amphidiploids. Several orchid stud plants belong to this group. Two famous examples are *Sophrolaeliocattleya* xAnzac 'Orchidhurst' (Mehlquist, 1974), which has long been used as a parent in producing triploid or tetraploid red *Cattleya*-like orchids, and *Vanda* xJosephine van Brero 'Tan Hoon Siang', which is a very valuable parent for producing uniform and productive triploid progenies. Polyploidy in these plants is believed to originate spontaneously during either sexual or asexual reproduction.

High polyploids with six to eight chromosome sets (hexaploid to octoploid) should not be overlooked. Genetically, they are potential stud plants if crossed with a plant of a lower ploidy level to produce tetraploid or pentaploid progenies. One of the outstanding hybrids of this type is *Phalaenopsis* xPrincess Grace, presumably a pentaploid resulting from crossing the hexaploid *Phalaenopsis* xCast Iron Monarch 'The King' with the tetraploid *Phalaenopsis* xGrace Palm 'Easter Parade'. It will be very interesting to follow the breeding behavior of the hexaploid *Dendrobium* xUniwai

Crystal which was induced artificially (Sanguthai, Sanguthai, and Kamemoto, 1973). The same is true of several other *Dendrobium* hybrids with high chromosome numbers which have arisen either spontaneously or artificially in our experiments (Chaichareon and Vajrabhaya, in press).

At present, the method of polyploid induction *in vitro* has been established successfully and gives positive results (Wimber and VanCott, 1967; Sanguthai and Sagawa, 1973; Sanguthai, Sanguthai, and Kamemoto, 1973; Chaichareon and Vajrabhaya, in press). It is likely that in the future artificially induced polyploids will play an important role in orchid improvement through either asexual or sexual reproduction.

Other Variants

Aneuploid variants with one- or two-chromosome deviation from euploids are of interest. At the polyploid level the loss or gain of a few chromosomes does not cause much physiological disturbance in many orchids (Vajrabhaya and Randolph, 1960, 1961; Kamemoto, Tanaka, and Kosaki, 1961; Kamemoto, Takeshita, and Meeyot, 1972) Addition of a chromosome (a set of genes) may affect certain characteristics (e.g., shape or color of the flower) and produce excellent results. On the other hand, deletion of chromosomes carrying undesirable genes will also result in improvement of certain characteristics, e.g., increase in vigor or size of flower (Gustafsson, 1951; Smith, 1971). Clonal propagation from such aneuploid variants may perpetuate useful plants. However, transmission of desired chracteristics through breeding is uncertain because gametes carrying an abnormal number of chromosomes are unlikely to compete successfully with normal gametes.

Variants arising from the modification of a single gene can also be of great use if this results in the improvement of one particular characteristic, leaving all other desirable features unchanged. These variants will obviously be of great value for breeding purposes. However, such an occurrence is a matter of pure chance and, in any case, can only take place during clonal propagation, since breeding causes an intermingling of many genes and not just of a single pair.

Thus, variants hold a promise for the future. Many can be induced under more or less controlled conditions and may be put to good use in the never-ending search for more perfect orchids.

Literature Cited

Blakeslee, A. F., and A. G. Avery. 1937. Methods of inducing doubling of chromosomes in plants. J. Hered. 24:393–411.

Blowers, J. 1967. Mericlones at Vacherot and Lecoufle, France. Amer. Orchid Soc. Bull. 36:579–581.

Casamajor, R. 1950. Do you own *Cymbidium* Alexanderi Westonbirt variety? Cymbidium Soc. News 5. (Cited by Lenz and Wimber, 1959.)

Chaichareon, K. 1973. Induction of polyploidy in *Dendrobium* by colchicine treatment. M.Sc. Thesis. Chulalongkorn Univ., Bangkok.

Chaichareon, K., and T. Vajrabhaya. In press. Induction of polyploidy in *Dendrobium*. Amer. Orchid Soc. Bull.

Champagnat, M., and G. Morel. 1969. Multiplication végétative des *Cattleya* à partir de bourgeons cultivées *in vitro*. Soc. Bot. Fr., Mémoires 116:111–132.

Champagnat, M., G. Morel, and B. Mounetou. 1970. La multiplication végétative des *Cattleya* à partir de jeunes feuilles cultivées aseptiquement *in vitro*. Ann. Sci. Nat. Bot., Ser. 12, 11:97–114.

Churchill, M.-E., J. Arditti, and E. A. Ball. 1971. Clonal propagation of orchids from leaf tips. Amer. Orchid Soc. Bull. 40:109–113.

Cooper, L. S., D. C. Cooper, A. C. Hildebrandt, and A. J. Riker. 1964. Chromosome numbers in single-cell clones of tobacco tissue. Amer. J. Bot. 51:284–290.

Crawshay, de B. 1897. Are varieties constant? Orchid Rev. 5:183.

D'Amato, F. 1952. Polyploidy in the differentiation and function of tissue and cells in plants. Caryologia 4:311–358.

Demoise, C. F., and C. R. Partanen. 1969. Effects of subculturing and physical condition of medium on the nuclear behavior of a plant tissue cultures. Amer. J. Bot. 56:147–152.

Dermen, H. 1960. Nature of plant sports. Amer. Hort. Mag. 39:123–173.

Drake, J. W. 1969. Mutagenic mechanisms. Ann. Rev. Genet. 3:247–268.

Duncan, R. E. 1945. Production of variable aneuploid numbers of chromosomes within the root tips of Paphiopedilum wardii. Amer. J. Bot. 32:506–509.

Eigsti, O. J. 1938. A cytological study of colchicine effects in the induction of polyploidy in plants. Proc. Nat. Acad. Sci. 24:56–63.

Eigsti, O. J., and P. Dustin, Jr. 1957. Colchicine in agriculture, medicine, biology, and chemistry. Iowa State College Press, Ames.

Emsweller, S. L., and M. L. Ruttle. 1941. Induced polyploidy in floriculture. Amer. Nat. 75:310–327.

Fox, J. E. 1963. Growth factor requirements and chromosome number in tobacco tissue cultures. Physiol. Plant. 16:793–802.

Freese, E. 1971. Molecular mechanisms of mutations, p. 1–56. *In* A. Hollaender (ed.), Chemical mutagens. Vol. 1. Plenum, New York and London.

George, J. A., and T. R. Davidson. 1963. Pollen transmission of necrotic ringspot and sour cherry yellow viruses from tree to tree. Can. J. Plant Sci. 43:267–288.

Gile, N. H., Jr. 1940. Spontaneous chromosome aberrations in *Tradescantia*. Genetics 25:69–87.

Gilmer, R. M. 1965. Additional evidence of tree to tree transmission of sour cherry yellow virus by pollen. Phytopath. 55:482–483.

Guo, Chung-Le. 1972. Effects of chemical and physical factors on the chromosome number in *Nicotiana* anther callus cultures. In Vitro 7:381–386.

Gustafsson, A. 1951. Induction of changes in genes and chromosomes. II. Mutation, environment and evolution. Cold Spring Harbor Sym. Quant. Biol. 16:263–281.

Harn, C. 1970. Radiosensitivity of *Cymbidium* protocorms. Amer. Orchid Soc. Bull. 39:499–505.

Heinz, D. J., G. W. P. Mee, and L. G. Nickell. 1969. Chromosome numbers of Saccharum species hybrids and their cell suspension cultures. Amer. J. Bot. 56:450–456.

Heslot, H., R. Ferrary, R. Levy, and C. Monard. 1959. Recherches sur les substances mutagenes (halogeno-2-ethyl) amines, derives oxygénés du sulfure de bis-(chloro-2-ethyle), esters sulfoniques et sulfuriques. C. R. Acad. Sci. Paris 248:729–732.

Hsu, T. C. 1961. Chromosome evolution in cell populations. Int. Rev. Cytol. 12:69–161.

Inoue, S. 1952. The effect of colchicine on the microscopic and submicroscopic structure of the mitotic spindle. Expt. Cell Res. Suppl. 2:305–311.

Intuwong, O., and Y. Sagawa. 1973. Clonal propagation of Sarcanthine orchids by aseptic culture of inflorescences. Amer. Orchid Soc. Bull. 42:209–215.

Ishii, M. 1973. Partial elimination of virus from doubly infected orchids by meristem explants culture. Proc. 3d Int. Sym. Virus diseases of Ornamental Plants.

Ishii, M., and A. P. Martinez. 1973. Significant orchid diseases in Hawaii. Hawaii Orchid J. 2:6–10.

Jensen, D. D. 1959. Virus disease of orchids, p. 431–458. *In* C. L. Withner (ed.), The orchids: a scientific survey. Ronald Press, New York.

Kamemoto, H., M. Takeshita, and W. Meeyot. 1972. Simultaneous pollination with pollinia from diploid and tetraploid Dendrobium. Amer. Orchid Soc. Bull. 41:781–785.

Kamemoto, H., R. Tanaka, and K. Kosaki. 1961. Chromosome numbers of orchids in Hawaii. Hawaii Agric. Exp. Sta. Bull. 127.

Kim, K. K., J. T. Kunisaki, and Y. Sagawa. 1970. Shoot-tip culture of *Dendrobiums*. Amer. Orchid Soc. Bull. 39:1077–1080.

Konzak, C. F. 1957. Genetic effects of radiation on higher plants. Quart. Rev. Biol. 32:27–45.

Kunisaki, J. T., K. K. Kim, and Y. Sagawa. 1972. Shoot-tip culture of *Vanda*. Amer. Orchid Soc. Bull. 41:435–439.

Lawson, R. H. 1967. Chemical inactivation of Cymbidium mosaic and Odontoglossum ringspot viruses. Amer. Orchid Soc. Bull. 36:998–1001.

———. 1970. Etiology of flower necrosis in *Cattleya* orchid. Phytopath. 60:36–40.

Lawson, R. H., and S. S. Hearon. 1973. Symptomatology of Cattleya mericlones infected with Cymbidium mosaic virus. Amer. Orchid Soc. Bull. 42:1071–1074.

Lecoufle. M. 1967. A mass blooming of mericlones. Amer. Orchid Soc. Bull. 36:405–406.

Lederberg, J. 1958. Summary comment. Symposium on genetic approaches to somatic cell variation. J. Cellular Comp. Physiol. 52 (suppl. I):383–401.

Lenz, L. W., and D. E. Wimber. 1959. Hydridization and inheritance in orchids, p. 261–314. *In* C. L. Withner (ed.), The orchids: a scientific survey. Ronald Press, New York.

Lenz, L. W., D. E. Wimber, and C. Dodson. 1955. Intraclonal lip pattern variation in cymbidiums. Cymbidium Soc. News 10:17–20.

Lindemann, E. G. P., Gunkel, and O. W. Davidson, 1970. Meristem culture of Cattleya. Amer. Orchid Soc. Bull. 39:1002–1004.

MacLeod, R. A. 1947. Some effects of colchicine in orchids. Amer. Orchid Soc. Bull. 16:336–337.

Mehlquist, G. A. L. 1974. Some aspects of polyploidy in orchids, with particular reference to Cymbidium, Paphiopedilum, and Cattleya alliance, p. 393–409. *In* C. L. Withner (ed.), The orchids: scientific studies. Wiley-Interscience, New York.

Menninger, E. D. 1963. Diary of a colchicine-induced tetraploid Cymbidium. Amer. Orchid Soc. Bull. 32:885–887.

Moore, E. T. 1947. The use of colchicine on orchids. Amer. Orchid Soc. Bull. 16:512.

Morel, G. M. 1960. Producing virus-free cymbidiums. Amer. Orchid Soc. Bull. 29:495–497.

———. 1964. Tissue culture—a new means of clonal propagation of orchids. Amer. Orchid Soc. Bull. 33:473–478.

Muir, W. H. 1965. Influence of variation in chromosome number on differentiation in plant tissue cultures, p. 485–492. *In* P. R. White and A. R. Grove (eds.), Proc. Int. Conf. Plant Tissue Culture. McCutchan, Calif.

Muller, H. J. 1927. Artificial transmutation of the gene. Science 66:84–87. Reprinted in S. Fogel (ed.), 1955. Great experiments in biology. Prentice-Hall, Englewood Cliffs, N.J.

———. 1954a. The nature of the genetic effects produced by radiation, p. 351–473. *In* A. Hollaender (ed.), Radiation biology. Vol. 2. McGraw-Hill, New York.

———. 1954b. The manner of production of mutation by radiation, pp. 475–626. *In* A. Hollaender (ed.), Radiation biology. Vol. 2. McGraw-Hill, New York.

Murakishii, H. H. 1958a. Host range, symptomatology, physical properties and cross-protection studied of orchid virus isolates. Phytopath. 48:132–137.

———. 1958b. Serological and morphological relationships among orchid viruses. Phytopath. 48:137–140.

Murashige, T., and R. Nakano. 1965. Morphogenetic behavior of tobacco tissue cultures and implication of plant senescence. Amer. J. Bot. 52:819–827.

———. 1966. Tissue culture as a potential tool in obtaining polyploid plants. J. Hered. 57:115–118.

———. 1967. Chromosome complement as a determinant of the morphogenic potential of tobacco cells. Amer. J. Bot. 54:963–970.

Namba, R., and M. Ishii. 1971. Failure of aphids to transmit the *Odontoglossum* ringspot and *Cymbidium* mosaic viruses to orchid plantlets derived from meristem cultures. Phytopath. 61:582–583.

Nickell, L. G. 1973. Test-tube approaches to bypass sex. Hawaiian Planters' Record 58:293–314.

Niimoto, D. H., and L. F. Randolph. 1958. Chromosome inheritance in Cattleya. Amer. Orchid Soc. Bull. 27:157–162.

Paludan, N. 1971. Etablering af virusfrie meristemkulturer af havebrugsplanter. Tidsskrift for Planteavl. 75:387–410.

Partanen, C. R. 1965. On the chromosomal basis for cellular differentiation. Amer. J. Bot. 52:204–209.

Randolph, L. F. 1951. Chromosomes and orchid breeding. Amer. Orchid Soc. Bull. 20:395–398; 464–468.

Reinert, R. A., and H. C. Mohr. 1967. Propagation of *Cattleya* by tissue culture of lateral bud meristems. Proc. Amer. Soc. Hort. Sci. 91:664–671.

Reychler, L. 1928. Mutation with orchids. Goemere, Brussels.

Rotor, G. B., Jr. 1958. Colchicine as a tool in orchid hybridization. Proc. 2d World Orchid Conf., Honolulu (1957), p. 159–170.

Sacristan, M. D. 1971. Karyotypic changes in callus culture from haploid and diploid plants of *Crepis capillaris*. Chromosoma (Berl.) 33:273–283.

Sacristan, M. D., and G. Melchers. 1969. The caryological analysis of plants regenerated from tumorous and other callus cultures of tobacco. Molec. Gen. Genetics 105:317–333.

Sagawa, Y., and G. A. L. Mehlquist. 1957. The mechanism responsible for some X-ray induced changes in flower color of the carnation, Dianthus caryophyllus. Amer. J. Bot. 44:397–403.

Sagawa, Y., and T. Shoji. 1967. Clonal propagation of dendrobiums through shoot meristem culture. Amer. Orchid Soc. Bull. 36:856–859.

Sagawa, Y., T. Shoji, and T. Shoji. 1966. Clonal propagation of cymbidiums through shoot meristem culture. Amer. Orchid Soc. Bull. 35:118–122.

Sanguthai, O., S. Sanguthai, and H. Kamemoto. 1973. Chromosome doubling of a Dendrobium hybrid with colchicine in meristem culture. Hawaii Orchid J. 2(2):12–16.

Sanguthai, S., and Y. Sagawa. 1973. Induction of polyploidy in Vanda by colchicine treatment. Hawaii Orchid J. 2(2):17–19.

Scully, R. M., Jr. 1967. Aspects of meristem culture in the Cattleya alliance. Amer. Orchid Soc. Bull. 36:103–108.

Shamel, A. D., and C. S. Pomeroy. 1936. Bud mutations in horticultural crops. J. Hered. 27:487–494.

Shamina, Z. B. 1966. Cytogenetic study of tissue culture of *Haplopappus gracilis*, p. 377–380. *In* Z. Landa (ed.), Proc. Sym. on the mutational process mechanism of mutation and inducing factors. Prague Academia.

Shimada, T., and M. Tabata. 1967. Chromosome numbers in cultured pith tissue of tobacco. Japan. J. Genet. 42:195–201.

Smith, H. H. 1971. Broadening the bases of genetic variability in plants. J. Hered. 62:265–276.

Smith, R. H., and T. Murashige. 1970. In vitro development of the isolated shoot apical meristem of angiosperm. Amer. J. Bot. 57:562–568.

Sparrow, A. H., and C. F. Konzak. 1958. The use of ionizing radiation in plant breeding: accomplishments and prospects, p. 425–452. *In* E. C. Tourje (ed.), Camellia culture. Macmillan, New York.

Stearn, W. T. 1949. The use of the term "clone." J. Roy. Hort. Soc. 74:41–47.

Stebbins, G. L. 1950. Variation and evolution in plants. Columbia Univ. Press, New York.

Stern, C. 1969. Somatic recombination within the white locus of *Drosophila melanogaster*. Genetics 62:573–581.

Stout, A. B. 1940. The nomenclature of cultivated plants. Amer. J. Bot. 27:339–347.

Swan, E. 1906. *Calanthe* Veitchii sport. Gard. Chron., 3d ser., 39:14. (Cited by Lenz and Wimber, 1959.)

Swanson, C. P. 1957. Cytology and cytogenetics. Prentice-Hall, New York.

Tanaka, R., and H. Kamemoto. 1963. Tabulation of chromosome numbers of orchids. Japan Orchid Society, Kobe.

——. 1974. List of chromosome numbers in species of the Orchidaceae, p. 411–483. *In* C. L. Withner (ed.), The orchids: scientific studies. Wiley-Interscience, New York.

Teo, C. K. H., J. T. Kunisaki, and Y. Sagawa. 1973. Clonal propagation of strap-leafed Vanda by shoot-tip culture. Amer. Orchid Soc. Bull. 42:402–405.

Tincker, M. A. H. 1945. Propagation degeneration, and vigour of growth, J. Roy. Hort. Soc. 70:333–337.

Torrey, J. G. 1961. Kinetin as trigger for mitosis in mature endomitotic plant cells. Expt. Cell. Res. 23:281–299.

——. 1965. Cytological evidence of cell selection by plant tissue culture media, p. 473–484. *In* P. R. White and A. R. Grove (eds.), Proc. Int. Conf. Plant Tissue Culture. McCutchan, Calif.

——. 1967. Morphogenesis in relation to chromosomal constitution in long term plant tissue cultures. Physiol. Plant. 20:265–275.

Vajrabhaya, M., and T. Vajrabhaya. 1970. Tissue culture of Rhynchostylis gigantea, a monopodial orchid. Amer. Orchid Soc. Bull. 39:907–910.

——. 1974. Variations of Dendrobium arising in meristem. Proc. 7th World Orchid Conf., Medellin, Colombia (1972), p. 231–243.

Vajrabhaya, T., and L. F. Randolph. 1960. Chromosome studies in Dendrobium. Amer. Orchid Soc. Bull. 29:507–517.

——. 1961. Chromosome inheritance in pentaploid and aneuploid Cattleya. Amer. Orchid Soc. Bull. 30:209–213.

Venketeswaran, S., and E. B. Spiess. 1963. Tissue culture studies of *Vicia faba*. III. Effect of growth factors on chromosome morphology. Cytologia 28:201–212.

Webber, H. J. 1903. New horticultural and agricultural terms. Science, N.S. 18:501–503.

Westwood, J. C. N., and D. H. J. Titmuss. 1957. Transformation in tissue culture cell lines: the possible genetic mechanism. Brit. J. Expt. Pathol. 38:587–600.

White, P. R. 1954. The cultivation of animal and plant cells. Ronald Press, New York.

Wimber, D. E. 1963. Clonal multiplication of Cymbidiums through tissue culture of the shoot meristem. Amer. Orchid Soc. Bull. 32:105–107.

Wimber, D. E., L. W. Lenz, and C. Dodson. 1956. Further studies in intraclonal lip pattern variation in cymbidiums. Amer. Orchid Soc. Bull. 25:153–158.

Wimber, D. E., and A. VanCott. 1967. Artificially induced polyploidy in cymbidiums. Proc. 5th World Orchid Conf., Long Beach, p. 27–32.

Wimber, D. E., and D. R. Wimber. 1968. Floral characteristics of diploid and neo-tetraploid Cymbidium. Amer. Orchid Soc. Bull. 37:572–576.

Bibliography

The following publications are presented for further reading.

Belling, J. 1924. Detachment (elimination) of chromosome in *Cypripedium acaule*. Bot. Gaz. 78:458–460.

Berger, C. A., and E. R. Witkus. 1946. Polyploid mitosis as a normally occurring factor in the development of Allium cepa L. Amer. J. Bot. 33:785–787.

Bertsch, W. 1967. A new frontier: orchid propagation by meristem tissue culture. Amer. Orchid Soc. Bull. 36:32–37,

Blakeslee, A. F., and J. Belling. 1924. Chromosomal mutations in the Jimson weed, *Datura stramonium*. J. Hered. 15:195–206.

D'Amato, F. 1965. Endopolyploidy as a factor in plant tissue development, p. 449–462. *In* P. R. White and A. R. Grove (eds.), Proc. Int. Conf. Plant Tissue Culture. McCutchan, Calif.

Darrow, G. M., R. A. Gibson, W. E. Toenjes, and H. Dermen. 1948. The nature of giant apple sports. J. Hered. 39:45–51.

Dermen, H. 1945. The mechanism of colchicine-induced cytohistological changes in cranberry. Amer. J. Bot. 32:387–394.

——. 1947. Periclinal cytochimeras and histogenesis in cranberry. Amer. J. Bot. 34:32–43.

——. 1953. Periclinal cytochimeras and origin of tissues in stem and leaf of peach. Amer. J. Bot. 40:154–168.

DeTorok, D., and T. H. Roderick. 1961. Associations between growth rate, mitotic frequency and chromosome number in plant tissue culture. Cancer Res. 22:174–181.

Duncan, R. E., and R. A. MacLeod. 1950. Chromosome of Eremantha tesselata. Amer. Orchid Soc. Bull. 19:137–142.

Gustafsson, A. 1954. Mutations, viability and population structure. Acta Agr. Scand. 4:601–632.

Harn, C. 1968. Propagation of orchids and mutation breeding. Amer. Orchid Soc. Bull. 37:1066–1068.

Harris, M. 1964. Cell culture and somatic variation. Holt, Rinehart and Winston, New York.

Heinz, D. J., and G. W. P. Mee. 1969. Plant differentiation from callus tissue of *Saccharum* species. Crop Sci. 9:346–348.

——. 1970. Colchicine-induced polyploids from cell suspension cultures of sugarcane. Crop Sci. 10:696–699.

Hughes, D. T. 1968. Cytogenetical polymorphism and evolution in mammalian somatic cell populations *in vivo* and *in vitro*. Nature 217:518–523.

Huskins, C. L. 1948. Segregation and reduction in somatic tissues. I. Initial observations on *Allium cepa*. J. Hered. 39:311–325.

Kao, K. N., R. A. Miller, O. L. Gamborg, and B. L. Harvey. 1970. Variations in chromosome number and structure in plant cells grown in suspension cultures. Can. J. Genet. Cytol. 12:297–301.

Kihlman, B. A. 1966. Actions of chemicals on dividing cells. Prentice-Hall, Englewood Cliffs, N.J.

Lawson, R. 1970. Virus-induced color-breaking in Cattleya orchid flowers. Amer. Orchid Soc. Bull. 39:395–400.

Levan, A., and T. Lotfy. 1950. Spontaneous chromosome fragmentation in seedlings of *Vicia faba*. Hereditas 36:470–482.

MacKey, J. 1956. Mutation breeding in Europe. Genetics in plant breeding. Brookhaven Sym. Biol. No. 9:141–156.

Miller, E. V. 1954. The natural origins of some popular varieties of fruit. Econ. Bot. 8:337–348.

Mitra, J., M. O. Mapes, and F. C. Steward. 1960. Growth and organized development of cultured cells. IV. The behavior of the nucleus. Amer. J. Bot. 47:357–368.

Nickell, L. G., and A. Maretski. 1972. Developmental and biochemical studies with cultural sugarcane cell suspensions. Proc. IV IFS: Ferment. Technol. Today 681–688.

Nielsen, E. L., and J. Nath. 1961. Somatic instability in derivatives from Agroelymus turneri resembling Agropyron repens. Amer. J. Bot. 48:345–349.

Nyland, G. A. 1962. Possible virus-induced genetic abnormalities in tree fruits. Science 137:598–599.

Olmo, H. P. 1936. Bud mutation in the vinifera grape. II. *Sultamina gigas*. Proc. Amer. Soc. Hort. Sci. 33:437–439.

Partanen, C. R. 1959. Quantitative chromosomal changes and differentiation in plants, p. 21–35. *In* D. Rudnick (ed.), Developmental cytology. Ronald Press, New York.

Randolph, L. F. 1932. Some effects of high temperature on polyploidy and other variations in maize. Proc. Nat. Acad. Sci. 18:222–229.

Riker, A. J., and A. C. Hildebrandt. 1962. The problem of single cell manipulation as applied to plant sciences. J. Cell. Comp. Physiol. 60 (suppl. 1):173–182.

Sach, L. 1952. Chromosome mosaics in experimental amphidiploids in *Triticinae*. Heredity 6:157–170.

Satina, S., and A. F. Blakeslee. 1941. Periclinal chimeras in Datura stramonium in relation to development of leaf and flower. Amer. J. Bot. 28:862–871.

Sax, K., and J. W. Gowen. 1923. Permanence of tree performance in a clonal variety and a critique of the theory of bud mutation. Genetics 8:179–211.

Sievert, R. C., and A. C. Hildebrandt. 1965. Variation within single cell clones of tobacco tissue cultures. Amer. J. Bot. 52:742–750.

Stebbins, G. L. 1956. Artificial polyploid as a tool in plant breeding. Genetics in plant breeding. Brookhaven Sym. Biol. No. 9:37–52.

Stern, C. 1936. Somatic crossing over and segregation in *Drosophila melanogaster*. Genetics 21:625–730.

Straus, J. 1954. Maize endosperm tissue grown in vitro. II. Morphology and cytology. Amer. J. Bot. 41:833–839.

U.S. Department of Agriculture. 1951. Virus diseases and other disorders with virus-like symptoms of stone fruits in North America. USDA Agric. Handbook No. 10. G.P.O., Washington, D.C.

Vig, B. K. 1969. Relationship between mitotic events and leaf spotting in *Glycine max*. Can. J. Genet. Cytol. 11:147–152.

Wright, J. C., and R. Casamajor. 1953. Two confused cymbidiums. Cymbidium Soc. News 8:8–9.

APPENDIX

Clonal Propagation of Orchids by Means of Tissue Culture—A Manual*

JOSEPH ARDITTI[†]

---

* The literature survey for this appendix was completed in December, 1974, but several additions were made in 1975 and a few as late as November, 1976.

† Dedicated to Professor Ernest A. Ball, on his retirement, because of his pioneering work in this field.

Introduction

Methods which at present are generally associated with the broad concept of tissue culture have been of considerable importance for orchid propagation during nearly three quarters of a century. It is entirely possible that orchids may have been the first horticultural plant to be propagated by tissue culture, or at least through aseptic methods.

Orchidologists have had to cope with propagation problems since the early days of orchid culture. For many years, methods for seed germination were simply not available. Then, seeds were germinated by scattering them at the base of their mother plant. Germination was generally poor and limited, but this technique seems to have been used from 1852 until about 1909 (for a review, see Arditti, 1967a).

Following the discovery that fungal infection was required for orchid seed germination (Bernard, 1899), a method was developed in which tubes were inoculated with both orchids and fungi. This was an elaborate procedure, but not very reliable or productive (Arditti, 1967a; Bernard, 1908). Still, it was better than scattering the seeds and it was used for nearly fifteen years.

Propagation and hybridization of orchids were revolutionized in 1921–1922 by the discovery that seeds can be germinated on a relatively simple sugar-containing medium (Knudson, 1921, 1922). Following rather stormy debates (Arditti, 1972a,b; Shechter and Arditti, 1972), the validity of asymbiotic orchid-seed germination as a practical and experimental method became firmly established. The original medium was improved twenty-five years after it was first published (Knudson, 1946). This made large-scale hybridization and seedling production possible, but did not provide a means of fast clonal propagation. If anything, it increased the need for such a method since many outstanding hybrids came into existence annually.

For a long time, the major means for clonally propagating orchids was the division of plants. Yet the basic discovery which was to make fast, large-scale clonal propagation of orchids possible was made during the year Professor Knudson introduced his medium C (Knudson, 1946). At that time, plant meristems were first cultured *in vitro* (Ball, 1946). The methods were developed with *Tropaeolum* and *Lupinus*, but fifteen years later they were applied to orchids (Morel, 1960, 1963, 1964a,b, 1965a,b). After that, tissue-culture methods for the clonal propagation of orchids were introduced by several workers using various plant parts and a number of media (Bergman, 1972a,b).

Worldwide interest in the use of tissue culture for clonal propagation was enormous and descriptions were soon published in many languages (for example, Arditti, Ball, and Churchill, 1971, 1972; Ball, Arditti, and Churchill, 1971; Champagnat and Morel, 1969; Churchill, Arditti, and Ball, 1972; Churchill *et al.*, 1971, 1973; Hahn, 1970; Kukulczanka, 1969, 1970; Leffring, 1968; Morel, 1965b; Murashige, 1974; van Raalte, 1967; Ueda and Torikata, 1968, 1969a,b).

In addition to a means for large-scale clonal propagation (Bertsch, 1967; Ilsley, 1965, 1966; Marston and Voraurai, 1967), tissue culture of orchids has also proven to be a valuable tool for basic plant research (Champagnat *et al.*, 1966; Champagnat, Morel, and Gambade, 1968; Fonnesbech, 1972a,b; Marston, 1969; Matsui, Kawai, and Samata, 1970; Morel, 1971b; Morel and Champagnat, 1969; Penningsfeld, 1973; Ruldolph, Ball, and Arditti, 1972; Steward and Mapes, 1971; Ueda and Torikata, 1968, 1969a,b, 1972; Werckmeister, 1970, 1971).

As with any new procedure, there were doubts. Here they were expressed in the question: "Will the 'mericlones' be true reproductions of their parent plants?" The theoretical answer was, of course: "Yes, for the most part." Practical (Blowers, 1967) and scientific (Vajrabhaya, in press, and a chapter in this book) observations have borne out the theoretical predictions.

As might be expected, some of the publications dealing with orchid "meristeming" were first-person reflections (Rutkowski, 1967a, 1971), more heat than light (Rutkowski, 1967b), not very informative (Jasper, 1966a,b), general considerations (Jessel, 1966), or of the news-item type (Anonymous, 1967). Some tried to capitalize quickly on the discovery. One publication (Jasper, 1966b) promised to disclose all secrets and make an expert out of the "hobbyest" (sic). Fortunately, this not-very-well-written *magnum opus* soon achieved the oblivion it so richly deserved.

Perhaps the most unique occurrence connected with orchid "meristeming" was an attempt to control it by means of a patent. It was not a matter of a plant patent, which is an accepted practice (Kock, 1967). Rather, someone claimed to have developed and used the process as early as 1950 (still, four years after Dr. Ball first cultured *Tropaeolum* and *Lupinus* meristems; Ball, 1946), keeping it secret, and obtained patent No. 3,514,900 to cover the process (Bergman, 1972a,b). This was followed by an attempt to collect royalties from users and to sell the patent itself. In addition, efforts were made to hinder further research. After publishing our papers on the culture of leaf tips (Churchill, Arditti, and Ball, 1971; Churchill, Ball, and Arditti, 1970; Ball, Arditti, and Churchill, 1971), we received a letter informing us that this research constituted an infringement on the patent. We referred the entire matter to the University of California attorney, who did whatever was necessary.

At least three arguments can be advanced against the patent claims. First, the development of shoot-tip and meristem culture methods was not a simple matter. It required considerable knowledge of plant morphology, anatomy, physiology, and development. Therefore, it seems highly unlikely (possible, but not very probable) that a person not generally known to be active in scientific circles could have discovered or stumbled upon it. Second, when applied properly "mericloning" can bring considerable financial rewards to its users. This has indeed happened. It is surprising, therefore, that the process was not advertised and used commercially as early as 1950 if, indeed, it was developed at that time. The method, after it was developed by Dr. Georges Morel, found almost immediate commercial use and received wide publicity (Blowers, 1967). Third, it is surprising that no effort to patent and use or sell the process were reported or publicized immediately after it was reportedly discovered around 1950. Instead, word of the patent spread approximately ten years later, after the procedures were described in great detail by others (Morel, 1960, 1963, 1964a,b, 1965a,b; Wimber, 1963). In any case, as of this writing, the furor seems to have died down, or at least gone dormant.

A major problem with tissue-culture techniques for orchids is that they have never been collected in one place with enough detail to allow interested growers and scientists to employ them in their work. This appendix is intended to remedy the situation. It includes techniques which have been published or come to my attention by December 1974. The purpose is to provide working information only, not a critical review of the literature. Such a review will appear in the future.

To insure uniformity, the entire appendix was written by me, but it is based on the original papers, which are always credited. In some instances, I have exercised writers' and editors' prerogatives to express opinions or select methods. For convenience, the appendix is arranged alphabetically and the same format is used throughout. When several methods are available for a species, a representative of each is described.

We cannot undertake to provide reprints of any of the papers mentioned in this section, or give additional information in private correspondence. A certain basic background is required for the use of tissue culture and it can be obtained from the original articles or elementary textbooks. As an aid to those not familiar with tissue-culture procedures, details are given on media preparation, culture conditions, vessels, manipulations, and explant excision. The appendices in *Experimental Plant Physiology* (Arditti and Dunn, 1969) contain detailed discussions of pH and the use of laboratory glassware, as well as instructions and recipes for the preparation of solutions and construction of a sterile box.

Anacamptis pyramidalis

This seems to be the first European terrestrial orchid which has been propagated by meristem culture (Morel, 1970).

Plant Material. Few details are given, but it appears that meristems are excised like those of *Cymbidium* (p. 233) or *Cattleya* (p. 222). They are then put in culture (Morel, 1974).

Surface Sterilization. Since no details are given, the assumption is, again, that it is accomplished as with *Cymbidium* (p. 233) or *Cattleya* (p. 222; Morel, 1974).

Culture Vessels. Use 16-mm-diameter test tubes and 50- or 125-ml Erlenmeyer flasks, containing 3–5 ml, 15 ml, and 25 ml medium, respectively.

Culture Conditions. No details are given regarding photoperiods, light intensity, or temperature. Therefore, it seems that the same conditions as for *Cymbidium* (p. 233) or *Cattleya* (p. 222) should be employed (Morel, 1974). Or use 12-hr photoperiods and 100–200 ft-candles provided by Sylvania Gro Lux lamps at 22° C.

Culture Medium. "The meristem of *Anacamptis pyramidalis* which was cultured on . . . Murashige-Skoog medium . . . " (Murashige-Skoog, 1962) is the statement given

Table A-1. Modified Murashige-Skoog (1962) medium for the culture of *Anacamptis pyramidalis* meristem (Morel, 1970)

Item number	Component	Amount per liter of culture medium (final concentration in culture medium)	Stock solution (a concentrate prepared for repeated and convenient use)	Volume of stock solution per liter of culture medium	Remarks
	Macroelements[a]				
1	Ammonium nitrate, NH_4NO_3[a]	1.65 g	82.5 g/liter	20 ml	or weigh
2	Potassium nitrate, KNO_3[a]	1.9 g	85 g/liter	20 ml	or weigh
3	Calcium chloride, $CaCl_2 \cdot 2H_2O$	440 mg	44 g/liter	10 ml	
4	Magnesium sulfate, $MgSO_4 \cdot 7H_2O$	370 mg	37 g/liter	10 ml	
5	Potassium phosphate, KH_2PO_4	170 mg	17 g/liter	10 ml	
6	*Iron chelate*[b,c]				
a	Na_2EDTA	37.3 mg	3.73 g/liter	10 ml	one solution[b,c]
b	Ferrous sulfate, $FeSO_4 \cdot 7H_2O$	27.8 mg	2.78 g/liter		
7	*Microelements*[c]				
c	Boric acid, H_3BO_3	0.2 mg	620 mg/liter		
d	Manganese sulfate, $MnSO_4 \cdot 4H_2O$	22.3 mg	2.23 g/liter		
e	Zinc chloride, $ZnCl_2$	3.93 mg	393 mg/liter		
f	Potassium iodide, KI	0.83 mg	83 mg/liter	10 ml	one solution[c]
g	Sodium molybdate, $Na_2MoO_4 \cdot 2H_2O$	0.25 mg	25 mg/liter		
h	Copper sulfate, $CuSO_4 \cdot 5H_2O$	0.025 mg	2.5 mg/liter		
i	Cobalt chloride, $CoCl_2 \cdot 5H_2O$	0.025 mg	2.5 mg/liter		
8	*Auxin*[d,e] IAA or NAA	1 mg	100 mg/50 ml acidified 95% ethanol[e]	0.5 ml	
9	*Cytokinin*[f,g] Kinetin	2.60 mg	100 mg/50 ml basic 95% ethanol[g]	1.3 ml	
10	*Amino acid*[h] Glycine	20 mg	2 g/100 ml 70% ethanol	1 ml	
11	*Vitamin*[i] Thiamine (Vitamin B_1)	0.1 mg	100 mg/100 ml 95% ethanol	0.1 ml	
12	*Complex additive*[j,k] Coconut water from immature (green) nuts	100–250 ml	no stock	no stock	if available
13	*Sugar*[j,k] Sucrose	30 g	no stock	no stock	
14	Water, distilled[j,k]	to 1000 ml			
15	*Solidifier*[k] Agar	10–15 g	no stock	no stock	

[a] Solutions containing ammonium and nitrate may become contaminated. Therefore, stock solutions should not be prepared. If made, they must be kept frozen between uses.

[b] Items a and b are added to the same one liter. Add 10 ml per liter of culture medium.

[c] Add all microelements to the same one liter and keep at 60° C (a waterbath might be suitable) for 24 hr in the dark. It is possible to combine solutions 6 and 7: add a–i to the same one liter and keep at 60° C for 24 hr. In such cases, the amount of Na_2EDTA should be doubled. Use 10 ml per liter culture solution in either case.

[d] 2,4-D may also be used at the rate of 1 mg/liter of culture medium (0.5 ml of a 50 mg/25 ml 95% ethanol stock). Keep refrigerated.

Table A-1. Footnotes

ᵉ If the auxin does not dissolve, add a drop or two of HCl. Keep refrigerated.

ᶠ BA may also be used at the rate of 1 mg/liter of culture medium (0.5 ml of a 50 mg/25 ml 95% ethanol stock). Keep refrigerated.

ᵍ If the cytokinin does not dissolve, add a pellet of KOH. Keep refrigerated.

ʰ Keep frozen between uses to prevent contamination.

ⁱ Keep refrigerated between uses.

ʲ If the solution is to remain liquid, items 1–12 are mixed with 500 ml of distilled water (item 14); the pH is then adjusted to 5.2–5.5; sugar (item 13) is added and the volume brought to 1000 ml with more distilled water (item 14). The medium is sterilized through 0.45 μ or 0.22 μ millipore filters (Millipore Filter Corporation, Bedford, Mass. 01730), or a Morton UF fritted glass filter (Corning Glass Co., Corning, N.Y. 14830). An alternative method is to mix items 1–7 with 500 ml of distilled water (item 14); adjust the pH to 5.2–5.5; add sugar (item 13); bring the volume to 750 ml and autoclave (Solution A). Items 8–11 are then added to 200 ml of green coconut water (item 12); the pH is adjusted to 5.2–5.5; the volume brought to 250 ml with more coconut water (item 12) and the solution is filter-sterilized (Solution B). Solutions A and B are mixed in a sterile box after each has been sterilized. If no coconut water (item 12) is to be used, items 1–7 can be mixed with 500 ml of distilled water (item 14); the pH is adjusted to 5.2–5.5; sugar (item 13) is then added; the volume brought to 1000 ml (or 997.1 ml for those who are extra fussy) with distilled water (item 14) and the solution is autoclaved. Items 8–11 are added to this solution under sterile conditions (with sterilized pipettes or syringes) when it has cooled to about 60° C. The sterile medium is then dispersed into sterilized (i.e., autoclaved) culture vessels (test tubes, bottles, Erlenmeyer flasks, etc.).

ᵏ Agar (item 15) should be added only if a solid medium is desired. Sterilization can be accomplished in several ways. One is to mix items 1–12 (or 1–11 if no coconut water is used) with 100 ml of distilled water; adjust the pH to 5.2–5.5; add sugar (item 13); bring the volume to 250 ml and filter-sterilize. The agar is added to 750 ml of distilled water, dissolved by bringing the solution to a gentle boil, and autoclaved. The two solutions are mixed while the agar is still liquid and dispersed into sterilized containers. A second method is to mix items 1–7 with 500 ml of distilled water; adjust the pH to 5.2–5.5; add sugar (item 13); bring the volume to 750 ml with more distilled water; dissolve the agar as above and autoclave. Items 8–11 are then added to 200 ml of coconut water; the pH is adjusted to 5.2–5.5; the volume brought to 250 ml with more coconut water and the solution sterilized by filtration. The two solutions are mixed and dispersed as above. Third, if no coconut water is used, items 1–7 can be mixed with 500 ml distilled water and the pH adjusted to 5.2–5.5. Then sugar (item 13) is added, the volume adjusted to 1000 ml (or 997.1 ml for the extra fussy), the agar dissolved as above, and the solution autoclaved. Items 8–11 are added under sterile conditions following autoclaving and the solution is dispersed as above.

(Morel, 1970). However, only the minerals of this medium are listed along with the suggestions that auxin [indoleacetic acid (IAA), naphthaleneacetic acid (NAA), or indolebutyric acid (IBA)], 0.5–1 mg/liter, and coconut water must be included in the solution. The medium listed for use with *A. pyramidalis* is based on these suggestions (Table A-1). However, it is possible that the versions of the Murashige-Skoog medium used for *Epidendrum* leaf tips (Table A-23) and Knop's solution employed for *Dendrobium* nodes (Table A-21) could also be used.

Procedure. Place explants in culture and treat like *Cymbidium* (p. 233) or *Cattleya* (p. 222).

Developmental Sequence. "Das Meristem von *Anacamptis pyramidalis*, das auf einem Nährboden von Murashige und Skoog gezüchtet wird, bildet ebenfalls protokormartige Gewebe, die man unendlich vermehren kann; ihr Wachstumprozess ist allerdings sehr langsam" (Meristems of *A. pyramidalis* cultured on Murashige-Skoog medium form protocorm-like bodies which can be used for unlimited propagation; however, their growth is very slow; Morel, 1970).

General Comments. According to a recent report (F. R. Gomm, Nature Conservancy Council, Merlewood Research Station, Grange-over-Sands, Lancashire, England, personal communication, 1974), only 2–3 plants of native *Cypripedium calceolus* are left in England. An effort was being made to save the species by seed and, if possible, tissue-culture propagation (for which no method is yet available). Hence, propagation using tissue culture may well be applied in conservation efforts. The development of such a method for *A. pyramidalis* points to the fact that this is possible and should serve as encouragement for others to devise procedures for other species.

Aranda

Aranda is a hybrid genus (*Arachnis hookeriana* × *Vanda lamellata*) of some importance, especially in Singapore. It is not surprising, therefore, that a tissue-culture method for it was developed at the University of Singapore (Goh, 1973).

Plant Material. Meristematic tissues from shoot apices and axillary buds of *Aranda* Deborah are used. Leaves are removed to expose the axillary buds. Following a wash, sterilization, and rinse, a wedge-shaped tissue section containing the bud is removed with a sterile scalpel. With apical meristems, the larger leaves are removed first and the tissue is washed, sterilized, and rinsed. Then the remaining younger leaves and leaf primordia are removed and the apical portion (about 4 mm long) is cultured.

Surface Sterilization. Following removal of leaves to expose the axillary buds, stems are washed thoroughly with tap water. This is followed by a distilled-water wash. Then the tissue is cut in sections, 2–3 nodes in length. These sections are sterilized in 10% Clorox (see notes; 10 ml Clorox made up to 100 ml with distilled water) for 10 min, washed three times with sterile distilled water, and placed in sterilized petri dishes.

Following removal of all leaves, apical buds are sterilized with 10% Clorox for 5 min only, washed as above, and placed into culture.

Culture Vessels. Use 100-ml Erlenmeyer flasks containing 25 ml medium.

Culture Conditions. Liquid cultures are placed on a rotary shaker adjusted to 100 rpm under 12-hr photoperiods (no details are given on light intensity and quality) at 27° C.

Culture Medium. White's medium (White, 1943) enriched with 10% coconut water and 2 g/liter peptone and adjusted to pH 5.2 is used (Table A-29). A solid medium containing 0.8% agar is employed for differentiating plantlets.

Procedure. After removal, washing, sterilization, and the final rinse, both apical and axillary buds are placed in liquid medium and cultured. If plantlets are formed, they should be transferred to solid medium. When protocorm-like bodies are formed, portions of the callus can be subcultured to obtain further proliferation.

Developmental Sequence. Apical shoots enlarge and appear quiescent for nearly two months. After that, some of them start to develop and form plantlets. Protocorm-like bodies and calli are not produced.

Axillary buds remain green for about four weeks without any apparent growth. After that, growth starts and some buds produce plantlets. Others produce protocorm-like bodies; and within 4–6 months, a mass of protocorms is formed. After 8–9 months, roots and plantlets begin to form.

General Comments. Using this method, meristematic tissues of *Aranda* Deborah produce a "multitude of protocorms" (Goh, personal communication) and plants.

Arundina bambusifolia

An investigation of seed germination, seedling development, and morphogenesis of *Arundina bambusifolia* led to the development of tissue-culture methods which can be used for clonal propagation (Mitra, 1971).

Plant Material. Shoot tips 1–2 mm long from seedlings (Table A-2), 6–8 mm high (2–3 internodes, one only visible) and stem disks (1–2 mm in diameter and thickness), are used. Removal of the tissues appears to involve merely cutting under sterile conditions. The explants are then placed on culture media.

Surface Sterilization. This is not required since explants are obtained from seedlings grown under aseptic conditions.

Culture Vessels. Wide-mouth, 150-ml Erlenmeyer flasks and 25 × 180 mm culture tubes containing 50 ml and 25 ml medium, respectively, were used in the original work. Other vessels could, no doubt, also be used.

Culture Conditions. Maintain cultures at 26° ± 1° C under a light intensity of 3000 lux and 12-hr photoperiods. Philips "Natural" fluorescent tubes were originally used, but equivalent ones (Sylvania Gro Lux, for example) will probably prove to be equally suitable.

Culture Media. Enriched RT (Raghavan and Torrey, 1964) medium (itself a modification of a medium first used by Spoerl, 1948) is employed for 6–8-mm shoot tips and stem disks (Tables A-2, A-3). A modified version of the same medium is used for 1–2 mm shoot tips (Tables A-2, A-4).

Procedure. Place explants on media under the appropriate culture conditions.

Developmental Sequence. Leaf development on shoot tips was invariably associated with root production. When leaves did not develop, roots were not formed.

Table A-2. Effects of media used for the culture of shoot tip and stem sections of *Arundina bambusifolia* (Mitra, 1971)

Raghavan and Torrey (1964) medium	Seedling shoot tips, 8 mm long, containing 2 nodes, "one only" visible	Seedling shoot tips, 1–2 mm long	Seedling stem disks, 1–2 mm in diameter and thickness
Plus: Urea, 25–50 mg/liter (Table A-3)	Development of leaf primordia Root formation at basal end Protocorm formation at basal end Development of shoot buds		Plantlet formation on 25 mg/liter
Peptone, 1 g/liter (Table A-3)	Protocorm formation at basal end Development of shoot buds Slight development of leaf primordia		Plantlet formation
Vitamin-free casein hydrolysate, 400 mg/liter (Table A-3)	Development of leaf primordia Root formation at basal end		
Yeast extract, 200 mg/liter (Table A-3)			Plantlot formation
Ribonucleic acid, 25–50 mg/liter (Table A-3)	Slight development of leaf primordia Root formation at basal end Development of shoot buds		
Coconut water, 100 ml/liter (Table A-3)	Development of leaf primordia Root formation at basal end		
Coconut water, 200 ml/liter	Development of shoot buds Development of leaf primordia Root formation at basal end Development of individual shoot tips into "full-fledged plantlets"		
Control, no additives (Table A-3)	Development of leaf primordia Root formation at basal end Development of shoot buds		
Modified (Table A-4)		Complete plant formation	

General Comments. Since seedlings are the tissue source, this method does not allow for the propagation of proven plants. However, it is entirely possible that one of the media employed (Tables A-3, A-4) could be used to culture shoot tips or stem disks from mature plants. The method should prove useful in cases when only a few seedlings of a valuable cross can be obtained from a capsule.

Ascofinetia

In monopodial orchids, removal of buds may cause the loss of the mother plant. Hence, methods have been developed which use other tissues (Intuwong and Sagawa, 1973).

Table A-3. Raghavan and Torrey (1964) medium as used for the culture of *Arundina bambusifolia*, 6–8 mm long shoot tips and stem disks (Mitra, 1971)

Item number	Component	Amount per liter of culture medium (final concentration in culture medium)	Stock solution (a concentrate prepared for repeated and convenient use)	Volume of stock solution per liter of culture medium	Remarks
	Macroelements[a]				
1	Potassium phosphate, KH_2PO_4	270 mg	27 g/liter	10 ml	
2	Magnesium sulfate, $MgSO_4 \cdot 7H_2O$	240 mg	24 g/liter	10 ml	
3	Calcium sulfate, $CaSO_4 \cdot 2H_2O$	80 mg	8 g/liter	10 ml	
4	Calcium phosphate, $CaH_4(PO_4)_2$	100 mg	10 g/liter	10 ml	
5	Ammonium nitrate, NH_4NO_3[a]	80 mg	8 g/liter[a]	10 ml[a]	or weigh[a]
6	*Microelements*[b]				
a	Boric acid, H_3BO_3	0.60 mg	600 mg/liter	⎤	⎤
b	Manganese chloride, $MnCl_2 \cdot 4H_2O$	0.40 mg	400 mg/liter		
c	Zinc sulfate, $ZnSO_4 \cdot H_2O$	0.05 mg	50 mg/liter		
d	Copper sulfate, $CuSO_4 \cdot H_2O$	0.05 mg	50 mg/liter	1 ml	one solution[b]
e	Sodium molybdate, $Na_2MoO_4 \cdot 2H_2O$	0.05 mg	50 mg/liter		
f	Potassium iodide, KI	0.03 mg	30 mg/liter		
g	Cobaltous nitrate, $Co(NO_3)_2$	0.05 mg	50 mg/liter	⎦	⎦
	Iron[c]				
7	Ferric tartrate, $Fe_2(C_4H_4O_6)_3$[c]	3 mg	300 mg[c]	10 ml[c]	
	Organic additives[a]				
8	Urea	25 mg or 50 mg	2.5 g/liter[a] 5 g/liter[a]	10 ml[a] 10 ml[a]	use as needed (see Table A-2)
9	Ribonuclei acid[a]	25 mg or 50 mg	2.5 g/liter[a] 5 g/liter[a]	10 ml[a] 10 ml[a]	
	Complex additives[a,d]				
10	Peptone	1 g	no stock[a]	no stock[a]	weigh
11	Vitamin-free casein hydrolysate	400 mg or 1 g	no stock[a] no stock[a]	no stock[a] no stock[a]	weigh weigh
12	Yeast extract	200 mg	no stock[a]	no stock[a]	weigh
13	Coconut water[d]	100 ml or 200 ml			
	Sugar[d]				
14	Sucrose	20 g	no stock	no stock	weigh
15	Water, distilled[d]	to 1000 ml			
	Solidifier[d]				
16	Agar	9 g	no stock	no stock	weigh

[a] Solutions of nitrogenous salts or organic substances may become contaminated. Therefore, stock solutions should not be prepared. If made, they must be kept frozen between uses.

[b] Add all microelements to the same one liter, stir and/or heat until dissolved. Add 1 ml to culture medium.

[c] Ferric tartrate is relatively insoluble. Grinding it with a mortar and pestle before dissolving helps. The addition of a pellet or two of KOH to the solution will increase solubility, but a precipitate may form nevertheless. To insure equal distribution, shake stock solution well before dispensing.

[d] Dissolve items 1–13 as needed (see Table A-1) in 500 ml distilled water (item 15); adjust the pH to 5.2–5.5; add the sugar (item 14) and the coconut water (item 13), if used; bring volume up to 1000 ml with distilled water. Add agar (item 16) slowly, while stirring, to the gently boiling solution. When fully dissolved, dispense into culture vessels and autoclave.

Table A-4. Raghavan and Torrey (1964) medium modified for the culture of *Arundina bambusifolia*, 1–2 mm long stem tips (Mitra, 1971)

Item number	Component	Amount per liter of culture medium (final concentration in culture medium)	Stock solution (a concentrate prepared for repeated and convenient use)	Volume of stock solution per liter of culture medium	Remarks
	Macroelements[a]				
1	Ammonium nitrate, NH_4NO_3[a]	50 mg	5 g/liter[a]	10 ml[a]	or weigh[a]
2	Potassium phosphate, KH_2PO_4	100 mg	10 g/liter	10 ml	
3	Magnesium sulfate, $MgSO_4 \cdot 7H_2O$	240 mg	24 g/liter	10 ml	
4	Calcium nitrate, $Ca(NO_3)_2 \cdot 4H_2O$[a]	100 mg	10 g/liter[a]	10 ml[a]	or weigh[a]
5	Potassium nitrate, KNO_3[a]	85 mg	8.5 g/liter[a]	10 ml[a]	or weigh[a]
6	Potassium chloride, KCl	65 mg	6.5 g/liter	10 ml	
7	Calcium phosphate, $CaH_4(PO_4)_2$	100 mg	10 g/liter	10 ml	
8	*Microelements*[b]				
a	Boric acid, H_3BO_3	0.60 mg	600 mg/liter		
b	Manganese chloride, $MnCl_2 \cdot 4H_2O$	0.40 mg	400 mg/liter		
c	Zinc sulfate, $ZnSO_4 \cdot H_2O$	0.05 mg	50 mg/liter		
d	Copper sulfate, $CuSO_4 \cdot H_2O$	0.05 mg	50 mg/liter	1 ml	one solution[b]
e	Sodium molybdate, $Na_2MoO_4 \cdot 2H_2O$	0.05 mg	50 mg/liter		
f	Potassium iodide, KI	0.03 mg	30 mg/liter		
g	Cobaltous nitrate, $Co(NO_3)_2$	0.05 mg	50 mg/liter		
9	*Chelated iron*[c]				
a	Ferrous sulfate, $FeSO_4 \cdot 7H_2O$	2.78 mg	278 mg/liter	10 ml	one solution
b	Na_2EDTA	3.73 mg	373 mg/liter		
	Sugar[d]				
10	Sucrose	20 g	no stock	no stock	weigh
11	Water, distilled[d]	to 1000 ml			
	Solidifier[d]				
12	Agar	9 g	no stock	no stock	weigh

[a] Solutions containing ammonium and nitrate may become contaminated. Therefore, stock solutions should not be prepared. If made, they must be kept frozen between uses.

[b] Add all microelements to the same one liter, stir and/or heat until dissolved. Add 1 ml per liter of culture medium.

[c] Add items a and b to the same one liter, dissolve. Add 10 ml per liter of culture medium.

[d] Dissolve items 1–9 in 900 ml distilled water (item 11), adjust pH to 5.2–5.5; add sugar (item 10), and bring volume up to 1000 ml with distilled water. Add agar (item 12) slowly, while stirring, to the gently boiling solution. When fully dissolved, dispense into vessels and autoclave.

Plant Material. Inflorescences, 1.5 cm long or less, with flower primordia are used. Those of 3 cm or longer elongated and produced flowers which either aborted and turned brown or developed normally and opened (Table A-5).

Surface sterilization. Inflorescences are removed and sterilized for 10 min with 100 ml of 10% Clorox plus one drop of Tween 20. The bracts are then removed and the inflorescences sterilized again, this time with 100 ml of 5% Clorox plus one drop of Tween 20. This is followed by a 3-min rinse in sterile distilled water.

Table A-5. Effects of four culture media on inflorescence explants and tissues of *Ascofinetia*, *Neostylis*, and *Vascostylis* (Intuwong and Sagawa, 1973)

Culture medium[a]	Inflorescence, 1.5 cm long or less	Inflorescence, 3 cm long or less	Protocorm-like bodies	Plantlets
VW + Su + CW	Proliferation	Flowering *in vitro*, or aborted flowers	Yellow color	
VW − Su + CW			Multiplication	
VW − Su + CW + PE + GB			Differentiation into plantlets	
VW − Su + CW + PE + RM				Maintenance of growth

[a] CW, coconut water; GB, 100 g of green banana homogenate; PE, liquid obtained after boiling 100 g of freshly diced potatoes in 200 ml distilled water for 5 min; RB, 100 g of ripe banana homogenate; Su, sucrose; VW, Vacin and Went (1949) medium.

Culture Vessels. Use 125- or 250-ml Erlenmeyer flasks containing 25 ml or 50 ml medium, respectively.

Culture Conditions. Maintain cultures at $26° \pm 3°C$ with continuous illumination of about 200 ft-candles provided by General Electric Power Groove white fluorescent lamps. Liquid cultures should be agitated at approximately 160 rpm (a New Brunswick Scientific Co. Model V shaker was used in the original research).

Culture Media. Vacin and Went (1949) liquid medium containing 20 g sucrose (Su) and 15% coconut water (CW; VW + Su + CW; Table A-6) is used for the initial culture. The medium becomes turbid to brown within 10–14 days and inhibits growth of the protocorm-like bodies (PLB). Therefore, it must be changed every 10–14 days. If left in this medium, the PLB will turn yellow. Because of that, the PLB must be subcultured for proliferation on sugar-free liquid medium (VW − Su + CW). They proliferate on this medium. For differentiation into plants, the PLB are transferred onto potato extract (PE) and green banana containing solid medium (GB; VW − Su + CW + PE + GB; Tables A-5, A-6). Growth is maintained on a solid medium containing CW, PE, and ripe banana (RB; VW − Su + CW + PE + RB; Tables A-5, A-6).

Procedure. Remove inflorescences 1.5 cm long or less, sterilize, and place in liquid VW + Su + CW. Change medium every 10–14 days or when it becomes turbid-brown. When PLB are produced, transfer them to liquid VW − Su + CW. To obtain differentiation, subculture PLB onto solid VW − Su + CW + PE + GB. Once plantlets are formed, their growth is maintained on solid VW − Su + CW + PE + RB.

Developmental Sequence. The explants proliferate in liquid VW + Su + CW within 20–51 days. Proliferation is acropetal. Further multiplication occurs on liquid VW − Su + CW. Differentiation takes place on solid VW − Su + CW + PE + GB and growth is maintained on VW − Su + CW + PE + RB.

Table A-6. Vacin and Went (1949) medium with modifications for use in the culture of *Ascofinetia* inflorescences (Intuwong and Sagawa, 1973)

Item number	Component	Amount per liter of culture medium (final concentration in culture medium)	Stock solution (a concentrate prepared for repeated and convenient use)	Volume of stock solution per liter of culture medium	Remarks
	Macroelements[a,b,c]				
1	Tricalcium phosphate, $Ca_3(PO_4)_2$ [a]	200 mg	20 g/liter[a]	10 ml[a]	or weigh[a]
2	Potassium nitrate, KNO_3 [b]	525 mg	52.5 g/liter[b]	10 ml[b]	or weigh
3	Potassium phosphate, KH_2PO_4	250 mg	25 g/liter	10 ml	
4	Ammonium sulfate, $(NH_4)_2SO_4$ [b]	500 mg	50 g/liter[b]	10 ml[b]	or weigh[b]
5	Ferric tartrate, $Fe_2(C_4H_4O_6)_3$ [c]	28 mg	2.8 g/liter[c]	10 ml[c]	
6	Manganese sulfate, $MnSO_4 \cdot 4H_2O$	7.5 mg	750 mg/liter	10 ml	
7	Magnesium sulfate, $MgSO_4 \cdot 7H_2O$	250 mg	25 g/liter	10 ml	
	Complex additives[d,e]				
8	Coconut water (CW)	150 ml	no stock	no stock	fresh
9	Potato extract (PE)[d]	200 ml	no stock	no stock	
10	Ripe banana (RB)[e]	100 g	no stock	no stock	weigh
	or				
	Green banana (GB)[e]	100 g	no stock	no stock	weigh
	Sugar[f]				
11	Sucrose	20 g	no stock	no stock	weigh
12	Water, distilled[f]	to 1000 ml			
	Solidifier[f]				
13	Agar	9 g	no stock	no stock	weigh

[a] If the salt does not dissolve completely, shake the stock solution well before dispensing to insure an even suspension; or better yet, weigh out each time.

[b] Solutions containing ammonium and nitrate may become contaminated. Therefore, stock solutions should not be prepared. If made, they must be kept frozen between use.

[c] Ferric tartrate is relatively insoluble. Grinding it with a mortar and pestle before dissolving helps. The addition of a pellet or two of KOH to the solution will increase solubility, but a precipitate may form nevertheless. To insure equal distribution, shake stock solution well before dispensing.

[d] Liquid PE obtained by boiling 100 g of freshly diced potato (1-cm cubes) in 200 ml distilled water for 5 min.

[e] Homogenize 100 g banana with 200 ml water in a blender for 30–60 sec at high speed (RB or GB).

[f] To prepare the basic medium (VW + Su), mix components 1–7 with 750 ml distilled water (item 12); adjust pH to 5.5; add sugar (item 11) and adjust volume to 1000 ml with more distilled water (item 12). If a liquid medium is desired, dispense the solution and autoclave. When solid medium is needed, dissolve the agar (item 13) by adding it slowly, while stirring, to the gently boiling solution. Then dispense and autoclave. When sugar is not desired (VW − Su), simply omit item 11 and prepare as before. To prepare media containing RB, GB, CW, or PE, simply use the homogenate or liquid instead of an equal volume of water. Media prepared are: VW + Su + CW; VW − Su + CW; VW − Su + CW + PE + GB; VW − Su + CW + PE + RB.

General Comments. This is a very effective method for clonal propagation which does not require sacrificing or even setting back a plant.

Brassocattleya

Because of the large interest in species and hybrids of the *Cattleya* alliance, there are reports of experiments with several members of the group. One procedure was developed using *Brassocattleya* xPrincess Patricia as the source of explants (Kako, 1973).

Plant Material. Best results are obtained with the third bud from 15-cm-long, newly growing shoots. However, the other buds also grow. When using back bulbs, it is best to remove buds which are just starting to grow.

Surface Sterilization. Use the same procedure as for *Cattleya* (p. 226; Scully, 1967).

Culture Vessels. This information was not given. However, it seems that 50-ml Erlenmeyer flasks containing 5 ml of medium should be appropriate (Scully, 1967).

Culture Conditions. Explants are placed in liquid medium which is not shaken or rotated ["liquid standing medium" (Kako, 1973)] and maintained at 25°C under continuous illumination.

Culture Medium. As a starting medium, use liquid Murashige-Skoog medium (Table A-1) containing 0.1 mg/liter auxin [i.e., 0.1 ppm napthaleneacetic acid (NAA) or 2,4-D instead of indoleacetic acid (IAA; Table A-1, item 8)]. To induce callus from cultured explants, the medium should be solidified with agar (Table A-1, item 15) and enriched with 10 mg 2,4-dichlorophenoxyacetic acid (2,4-D)/liter and 10 mg kinetin/liter instead of 2.5 mg (Table A-1, item 9). Replace the coconut water (Table A-1, item 12) with an equal volume of distilled water (Table A-1, item 14).

Procedure. Buds are excised like those of *Cattleya* (Scully, 1967) and placed into the culture medium, which is allowed to stand (not shaken). Within a month they grow and must be subcultured by cutting them in half and transferring the sections to liquid medium for a month and subculturing again. After 3 months, halves are transferred to a solid medium. Addition of 2,4-D and kinetin enhance callus formation. When transferred to Knudson C (Tables A-9, A-16), these will form plantlets.

Developmental Sequence. Explants swell after a few days in culture. Larger cells are formed at the cut sides 2–4 weeks later, and vascular bundles develop. Active cell division can be noted among epidermal cells.

General Comments. An interesting aspect of this procedure is that the cultures need not be shaken. This reduces costs without eliminating quick proliferation. When whole protocorm-like bodies, instead of halves, are transferred to solid medium, survival rates are better. However, since halving doubles the number of sections, even with higher losses more calli are obtained.

Calanthe

Not much information has been presented about clonal propagation through tissue culture of this genus. What is available amounts to: ". . . had little difficulty in producing tissue cultures from excised *Cymbidium* meristems"; "the cultures apparently could be divided indefinitely"; "within one year . . . had extended the technique to

. . . *Calanthe*" (Bertsch, 1967). From the content of the article, it appears that the techniques were similar to those used for *Cattleya* (p. 222) and/or *Cymbidium* (p. 233) by Michel Vacherot (Vacherot, 1966) and/or Dr. Georges Morel (Morel, 1974).

Cattleya

In the minds of the general public, *Cattleya* is synonymous with orchids. For cut-flower growers, *Cattleya* is a very important crop. Clones of disease-free, photoperiodically controllable varieties, well-suited as cut flowers, are very desirable and can be profitable. Many hobby growers would like to have in their possession plants of awarded varieties or those that appeal to them in particular. Hence, it is not surprising that several techniques have been developed for the clonal propagation of *Cattleya* through tissue culture (Arditti, 1974; Arditti *et al.*, 1971, 1972; Ball *et al.*, 1971; Bergman, 1972a,b; Champagnat and Morel, 1969; Champagnat, Morel, and Mounetou, 1970; Churchill, Arditti, and Ball, 1971, 1972; Churchill, Ball, and Arditti, 1973; Churchill *et al.*, 1971; Ichihashi and Kako, 1973; Kukulczanka, 1969, 1970; Lindemann, 1967a,b; Lindemann, Gunckel, and Davidson, 1970; Lis, 1970; Marston and Voraurai, no date; Morel, 1964a, 1965a,b, 1971a,b; Reinert and Mohr, 1967; Scully, 1967). Since a number of techniques have been developed and each has its adherents and advantages, seven methods will be presented.

Clonal Propagation of *Cattleya* through Shoot-Meristem Culture

The procedure is the same as that for *Brassocattleya* (p. 216; Kako, 1973).

Meristem Culture of *Cattleya*

Solutions for orchid tissue culture contain four component groups: (1) minerals (macro and micro), (2) an energy source; always a sugar, usually sucrose, (3) substances like vitamins and hormones, and (4) undefined complex additives (coconut water, potato extract, banana homogenate, peptone, casein hydrolysate, etc.). The most appropriate combination can be expected to produce the best results. Hence, the media used for this procedure include the most suitable components of a number of previously published solutions (Lindemann *et al.*, 1970).

Plant Material. Use enlarging, nondormant axillary shoots.

Surface Sterilization. Remove dead scales and swab the surface with 95% ethyl alcohol, rinse with distilled water, soak (i.e., sterilize) for 20–30 min in 0.4–0.5% calcium hypochlorite, and rinse in a large volume of sterile distilled water.

Culture Vessels. Use screw-cap vials containing a few ml of solution or Erlenmeyer flasks.

Culture Conditions. Details are not given. However, the conditions used in any of the other procedures for *Cattleya* would, no doubt, be appropriate. Liquid cultures are placed on a shaker (New Brunswick Scientific Co. Roller Tube Apparatus was used in the original research).

Culture Media. Three media are used: (1) starting (Table A-7), (2) maintenance (Table A-8), and (3) rooting (Table A-9).

Procedure. Remove the bud, sterilize it, and make four longitudinal-tangential cuts with a sterile scalpel to expose the base of the leaf primordia. Next, make horizontal cuts "above and below the meristem region to provide a 5-mm cube of tissue." This

Table A-7. Starting medium for the culture of *Cattleya* explants (Lindemann *et al.*, 1970)

Item number	Component	Amount per liter of culture medium (final concentration in starting medium)	Stock solution (a concentrate prepared for repeated and convenient use)	Volume of stock solution per liter of culture medium	Remarks
	Macroelements[a,b]				
1	Ammonium sulfate, $(NH_4)_2SO_4$[a]	1000 mg	100 g/liter[a]	10 ml[a]	or weigh[a]
2	Calcium nitrate, $Ca(NO_3)_2 \cdot 4H_2O$[a]	500 mg	50 g/liter[a]	10 ml[a]	or weigh[a]
3	Potassium chloride, KCl	1050 mg	105 g/liter	10 ml	
4	Magnesium sulfate, $MgSO_4 \cdot 7H_2O$	120 mg	12 g/liter	10 ml	
5	Potassium phosphate, KH_2PO_4	135 mg	13.5 g/liter	10 ml	
6	Iron citrate, $FeC_6H_5O_7 \cdot 3H_2O$[b]	5.4 mg	540 mg/liter[b]	10 ml[b]	
7	*Microelements*[c]				
a	Zinc sulfate, $ZnSO_4 \cdot 7H_2O$	0.565 mg	565 mg/liter		
b	Boric acid, H_3BO_3	1.014 mg	1014 mg/liter		
c	Manganese sulfate, $MnSO_4 \cdot 4H_2O$	0.068 mg	68 mg/liter		
d	Cupric sulfate, $CuSO_4 \cdot 5H_2O$	0.019 mg	19 mg/liter	1 ml	one solution[c]
e	Aluminium chloride, $AlCl_3$	0.031 mg	31 mg/liter		
f	Nickel chloride, $NiCl_2$	0.017 mg	17 mg/liter		
g	Potassium iodide, KI	0.099 mg	99 mg/liter		
	Auxin				
8	Naphthaleneacetic acid, NAA[d]	0.1 mg	10 mg/100 ml 95% ethanol[d]	1 ml	
	Cytokinin				
9	Kinetin[e]	0.2 mg	20 mg/100 ml 95% ethanol[e]	1 ml	
	Complex additive				
10	Coconut water	150 ml	no stock	no stock	
	Sugar[f]				
11	Sucrose[g]	0.500 g	no stock	no stock	weigh
12	Water, distilled[f]	to 1000 ml			

[a] Solutions containing ammonium and nitrate may become contaminated with standing. Therefore, stock solutions should not be prepared. If made, they should be kept frozen between uses.

[b] If the substance does not dissolve, add a pellet of KOH. Shake well before dispensing.

[c] Add all microelements to the same one liter; stir or heat until they are dissolved and add 1 ml per liter of culture medium.

[d] If the auxin does not dissolve, add a drop or two of HCl. Keep solution refrigerated.

[e] If the kinetin does not dissolve, add a pellet of KOH. Keep refrigerated.

[f] Add all components to 600 ml of distilled water (item 12); adjust pH to 5.2–5.5; add the sugar (item 11) and bring the volume to 1000 ml with more distilled water (item 12). Then dispense into culture vessels and autoclave.

[g] The range is 0.5–20 g/l.

Table A-8. Standard maintenance medium for proliferating callus cultures of *Cattleya* (Lindemann *et al.*, 1970)

Item number	Component	Amount per liter of culture medium (final concentration in culture medium)	Stock solution (a concentrate prepared for repeated and convenient use)	Volume of stock solution per liter of culture medium	Remarks
	Macroelements[a,b]				
1	Ammonium sulfate, $(NH_4)_2SO_4$ [a]	1000 mg	100 g/liter [a]	10 ml [a]	or weigh [a]
2	Calcium nitrate, $Ca(NO_3)_2 \cdot 4H_2O$ [a]	500 mg	50 g/liter [a]	10 ml [a]	or weigh [a]
3	Potassium chloride, KCl	1050 mg	105 g/liter	10 ml	
4	Magnesium sulfate, $MgSO_4 \cdot 7H_2O$	120 mg	12 g/liter	10 ml	
5	Potassium phosphate, KH_2PO_4	135 mg	13.5 g/liter	10 ml	
6	Iron citrate, $FeC_6H_5O_7 \cdot 3H_2O$ [b]	5.4 mg	540 mg/liter	10 ml	
7	*Microelements*[c]				
a	Zinc sulfate, $ZnSO_4 \cdot 7H_2O$	0.565 mg	565 mg/liter		
b	Boric acid, H_3BO_3	1.014 mg	1014 mg/liter		
c	Manganese sulfate, $MnSO_4 \cdot 4H_2O$	0.068 mg	68 mg/liter		
d	Cupric sulfate, $CuSO_4 \cdot 5H_2O$	0.019 mg	19 mg/liter	1 ml	one solution[c]
e	Aluminium chloride, $AlCl_3$	0.031 mg	31 mg/liter		
f	Nickel chloride, $NiCl_2$	0.017 mg	17 mg/liter		
g	Potassium iodide, KI	0.099 mg	99 mg/liter		
8	*Vitamins*[d]				
a	Calcium-d-pantothenate	0.48 mg	48 mg/liter		
b	Pyridoxine, HCl (vitamin B_6)	0.21 mg	21 mg/liter		
c	Inositol (myo or iso)	18.0 mg	1.8 g/liter		
d	Folic acid	4.4 mg	440 mg/liter	10 ml	one solution[d]
e	Thiamine HCl (vitamin B_1)	0.34 mg	34 mg/liter		
f	Niacin (nicotinic acid)	1.22 mg	122 mg/liter		
g	Biotin	0.024 mg	24 mg/liter		
9	*Amino acids*[e]				
a	Glutamic acid	15.0 mg	1.5 g/liter	10 ml	one solution
b	Asparagine	13.0 mg	1.3 g/liter		
10	*Nucleotides*[f]				
a	Guanylic acid	182.0 mg	18.2 g/liter	10 ml	one solution
b	Cytidylic acid	162.0 mg	16.2 g/liter		
	Hormones[g]				
11	Naphthaleneacetic acid (NAA)	0.18 mg	20 mg/100 ml 95% ethanol	0.9 ml	
12	Gibberellic acid (GA_3) [h]	0.35 mg	35 mg/100 ml 95% ethanol	1 ml	
13	Kinetin[i]	0.22 mg	22 mg/100 ml 95% ethanol	1 ml	
	Complex additive[j]				
14a	Coconut water[j] or	50–150 ml			
14b	Casein hydrolysate	100 mg			
	Sugar[k]				
15	Sucrose	20 g	no stock	no stock	weigh
16	Water, distilled[k]	to 1000 ml			

[a] Solutions containing ammonium and nitrate may become contaminated with standing. Therefore, stock solutions should not be prepared. If made, they should be kept frozen between uses.

[b] If the substance does not dissolve, add a pellet of KOH. Shake well before dispensing.

[c] Add all microelements to the same one liter; stir or heat until they are dissolved and add 1 ml per liter of culture medium.

[d] Dissolve in the same one liter to save time in preparation. However, separate solutions to meet solubility requirements can also be made. Aqueous solutions must be kept frozen between uses.

[e] Add both to the same one liter. Use 10 ml per liter of medium. Separate solutions can also be made. If solubility problems arise, add a few drops of HCl. Keep frozen between uses.

[f] Add both to the same one liter. Use 10 ml per liter of medium. Although stock solutions can be made, it would be much better to weigh these substances before use. If stocks are made, they must be kept frozen.

[g] If the auxin (NAA) fails to dissolve, add a few drops of HCl. Keep solution refrigerated.

[h] If the GA_3 fails to dissolve, add a few drops of HCl. Keep solution refrigerated.

[i] If the kinetin does not dissolve, add a pellet of KOH. Keep solution refrigerated.

[j] Add either coconut water or casein hydrolysate, not both. This improves proliferation.

[k] Mix items 1–13 with 750 ml of distilled water (item 16); adjust the pH to 5.2; add the sugar (item 15); bring the volume up to 1000 ml with more distilled water (item 16); distribute into culture vessels and autoclave.

Table A-9. Modified Knudson C (1946) medium for rooting and plantlet formation

Item number	Component	Amount per liter of culture medium (final concentration in culture medium)	Stock solution (a concentrate prepared for repeated and convenient use)	Volume of stock solution per liter of culture medium	Remarks
	Macroelements[a,b]				
1	Calcium nitrate, $Ca(NO_3)_2 \cdot 4H_2O$[a]	1 g	100 g/liter[a]	10 ml[a]	or weigh[a]
2	Monopotassium phosphate, KH_2PO_4[b]	250 mg	25 g/liter[b]	10 ml[b]	
3	Magnesium sulfate, $MgSO_4 \cdot 7H_2O$	250 mg	25 g/liter	10 ml	
4	Ammonium sulfate, $(NH_4)_2SO_4$[a]	500 mg	50 g/liter[a]	10 ml[a]	or weigh[a]
5	Ferrous sulfate, $FeSO_4 \cdot 7H_2O$	25 mg	2.5 g/liter	10 ml	
6	Manganese sulfate, $MnSO_4 \cdot 4H_2O$	7.5 mg	750 mg/liter	10 ml	
7	*Microelements*[c]				
a	Boric acid, H_3BO_3	0.056 mg	56 mg/liter	⎤	⎤
b	Molybdic acid, MoO_3	0.016 mg	16 mg/liter		
c	Cupric sulfate, anhydrous, $CuSO_4$	0.040 mg	40 mg/liter	1 ml	one solution
d	Zinc sulfate, $ZnSO_4 \cdot 7H_2O$	0.331 mg	331 mg/liter	⎦	⎦
	Sugar[d]				
8	Sucrose	20 g	no stock	no stock	weigh
9	Water, distilled[d]	to 1000 ml			
	Solidifier[d]				
10	Agar	12–15 g	no stock	no stock	weigh

[a] Solutions containing ammonium and nitrate may become contaminated with standing. Therefore, stock solutions should not be prepared. If made, they should be kept frozen between uses.

[b] Or a phosphate buffer which will keep the pH steady may be substituted here. Prepare buffer by mixing 975 ml of 0.1 M KH_2PO_4 (monopotassium phosphate) solution (13.6 g/liter) with 25 ml of a 0.1 M K_2HPO_4 (dipotassium phosphate) solution (17.4 g/liter); measure the pH to be certain it is correct (pH 5.1–5.4) and use 18ml/liter of culture medium.

[c] Add all microelements to the same one liter of distilled water; stir and/or heat until they are dissolved, and add 1 ml per liter of culture medium.

[d] Add items 1–7 to 800 ml of distilled water (item 9) and dissolve; adjust the pH to 5.3; add sugar (item 8) and bring volume up to 1000 ml with more distilled water. The agar (item 10) is added, while stirring, to the gently boiling solution. When dissolved, distribute into culture vessels and autoclave.

cube will probably contain some nonmeristematic tissue as well. The explant is then transferred to a petri dish containing sterile distilled water where all further operations are performed. Remove all remaining leaf primordia with sterile microscalpels using a dissecting microscope. Great care must be taken to maintain complete sterility of the working space.

Cut the tissue just below the youngest leaf primordium, discard the base, and place the explant into autoclaved starting medium (Table A-7). After about 2 months, or when the explant reaches 2 mm in diameter, it can be quartered and transferred to the second medium (Table A-8). Addition of 5–10% (v/v) coconut water or 100 mg/liter casein hydrolysate speeds up proliferation. Subdivisions of the tissue can be made at monthly intervals. Finally, the protocorm-like bodies are transferred to the solid rooting medium (Table A-9) for root development and plantlet formation. After that, the plantlets are treated like seedlings.

Developmental Sequence. Explant enlargement is apparent within 3 days while cultures are maintained on a roller-tube apparatus. After 2 months, the explants reach 2 mm in diameter and are ready for subdivision. Proliferation occurs on the second medium and callus masses are formed. Roots appear after about 10 days on the rooting (Knudson C) medium (Table A-9).

General Comments. Although a bit complicated due to the use of three media, this technique can produce unlimited numbers of plants of a desired clone. Excision of the tissue may require a certain amount of practice.

Propagation of *Cattleya* by *in vitro* Culture of Bud Meristems

Development of tissue-culture methods for *Cattleya* was not as easy as doing the same for *Cymbidium*. More complex media and different culture conditions were required. Even with these media, the mortality rate of explants is high (Morel, 1970).

Plant Material. "Nur die Knospen, die an dem Ansatz junger Triebe sitzen . . ." (only the buds from the base of the younger shoots) can be used (Morel, 1970).

Surface Sterilization. This was not given. Use the same procedures as in the preceding section (Lindemann *et al.*, 1970).

Culture Vessels. Test tubes (no other details are given) or Erlenmeyer flasks can be used.

Culture Conditions. The test tubes containing liquid medium and explants are placed on a klinostat which rotates at 2 rpm. Best results are obtained in the dark at 25–30°C.

Culture Medium. Several media are suggested, but few details are given about them. One medium which can be used is that of Murashige-Skoog. Only the minerals for it are listed, however. In addition to them, the medium must contain auxin, indoleacetic acid (IAA) or naphthaleneacetic acid (NAA), 0.5–1 mg/liter, and coconut water (no concentration given). Growth is improved when glutamic acid (or glutamine), asparagine, peptone, or casein hydrolysate are added (no concentrations given). Cytokinins are not of much benefit. In addition to the MS medium, the minerals of another medium are also listed. Altogether, it seems that the following combinations can be used:

1. MS medium (Table A-1) plus coconut water and auxin as in the starting medium (Table A-7, items 8 and 10) and the amino acids of the maintenance medium (Table A-8, items 8a and 8b).

2. The same as above, but using casein hydrolysate (Table A-8, item 14b) instead of coconut water.

3. Starting medium (Table A-7) followed by maintenance medium (Table A-8).

4. Use the minerals of modified Knudson C (Table A-10) medium (Morel, 1965a,b) plus coconut water and auxin as in the starting medium (Table A-7, items 8 and 10) and the amino acids of the maintenance medium (Table A-8, items 8a and 8b).

Table A-10. Knudson C (1946) medium modified for the culture of *Cattleya* meristems (Morel, 1965a,b, 1970)[a]

Item number	Component	Amount per liter of culture medium (final concentration in culture medium)	Stock solution (a concentrate prepared for repeated and convenient use)	Volume of stock solution per liter of culture medium	Remarks
	Macroelements[b,c]				
1	Ammonium sulfate, $(NH_4)_2SO_4$[b,c]	1 g[b]	100 g/liter[c]	10 ml[c]	or weigh[c]
2	Ferrous sulfate, $FeSO_4 \cdot 7H_2O$	25 mg	2.5 g/liter	10 ml	
3	Magnesium sulfate, $MgSO_4 \cdot 7H_2O$	250 mg	25 g/liter	10 ml	
4	Manganese sulfate, $MnSO_4 \cdot 4H_2O$	7.5 mg	750 mg/liter	10 ml	
5	Ammonium nitrate, NH_4NO_3[b,c]	500 mg[b]	50 g/liter[c]	10 ml[c]	or weigh[c]
6	Calcium nitrate, $Ca(NO_3)_2 \cdot 4H_2O$[c]	500 mg	50 g/liter[c]	10 ml[c]	or weigh[c]
7	Potassium phosphate, KH_2PO_4	250 mg	25 g/liter	10 ml	
8	Potassium chloride, KCl	250 mg	25 g/liter	10 ml	
	Sugar[d]				
9	Sucrose	20 g	no stock	no stock	
10	Water, distilled[d]	to 1000 ml			
	Solidifier[d]				
11	Agar	17.5 g	no stock	no stock	weigh

[a] Only the inorganic salts are listed (Morel, 1965a,b, 1970; also see Morel, 1974).

[b] Either use 1 g of ammonium sulfate and omit the ammonium nitrate, or use 0.5 g of each.

[c] Solutions containing ammonium and nitrate may become contaminated with standing. Therefore, stock solutions should not be prepared. If made, they should be kept frozen between uses.

[d] Add items 1–8 to 700 ml of distilled water (item 10) and dissolve; adjust the pH to 5.2–5.5; add the sugar (item 9) and dissolve; bring the volume up to 1000 ml with more distilled water. Distribute into culture vessels and autoclave. For solid culture medium, the agar (item 11) is added slowly, while stirring, to the gently boiling solution. When fully dissolved, dispense into culture vessels and autoclave.

Whatever medium is used, it should be liquid. Once protocorm-like bodies are formed, they should be transferred to Knudson C medium (Table A-9).

Procedure. Remove buds from the base of young shoots before the shoots reach 5–15 cm. Sterilize and excise the portion to be cultured. Take explants at least 5 mm in size since the mortality rate of smaller ones is very high. In fact, the entire bud is taken for culture, "of which the two outer scales are removed; the piece still contains 3–6 scales besides the apical meristem" (translated from Morel, 1970). Place explants in the liquid medium because, "it should be mentioned that the growth is accelerated." When the tissue proliferates it will form protocorm-like bodies which should be sub-cultured onto Knudson C medium (Table A-9) for differentiation and growth.

Developmental Sequence. As a first reaction, callus formation is observed on the severed leaf rudiment (or connective tissue of the leaf) where large cells occur, which form layers of palisade cells. Later, it is possible to note between these giant hyper-trophic cells formation of small meristematic groups which may lie next to the necrotic tissue or near the shoot tip. At the same time, the outermost scales become green, their connective tissues increase in volume and become wavy. After 2 months, meri-stematic areas appear and eventually form protocorm-like bodies. These develop into plants.

General Comments. This is a reliable method for the clonal propagation of *Cattleya* even if mortality of explants may be high at times.

Propagation of *Cattleya* by *in vitro* Culture of Lateral Bud Meristems

The difficulties encountered with the culture of *Cattleya* explants have spurred research by several groups. One method involves the culture of meristematic tissue from lateral buds (Reinert and Mohr, 1967).

Plant Material. Swollen lateral buds are obtained from rhizomes below new vegetative shoots of *Cattleya*.

Surface Sterilization. Rhizomes are placed in 5% (v/v) Clorox for 10 min, followed by 5 min in 70% ethanol, concluding with 80 g/liter calcium hypochlorite for 20 min. They are then allowed to dry in a sterilized (i.e., autoclaved) glass container.

Culture Vessels. Use 125-ml Erlenmeyer flasks containing 20 ml medium.

Culture Conditions. Explant-containing flasks are placed on a wheel which revolves at 1 rpm. Photoperiods are 16 hr long at an intensity of 200 ft-candles provided by four 6-foot cool white fluorescent tubes. The temperature should range between 24°C and 28°C.

Culture Media. A defined liquid medium (Table A-11) is used for the first three weeks. After that, the tissues are transferred onto solid medium of the same composition with the addition of 1 mg/liter kinetin and 100 mg/liter inositol (Table A-11, items 15 and 16).

Procedure. To excise meristems from swollen buds, make longitudinal cuts until the upper surface of the meristem is visible. This is evidenced by a change in color from creamy-white to an almost transluscent white. Block out the meristem by deep vertical cuts, removing an explant 1–3 mm³ in size. These sections contain the meristem and small areas of leaf sheath tissue. Place the explants into culture medium and position the flasks on the revolving wheel. After 3 weeks, transfer the tissues to the solid medium.

Developmental Sequence. The meristems grow well in the liquid medium with a survival rate of at least 75%. Chlorophyll formation becomes evident fairly soon and the tissues reach diameters of approximately 3 mm and 6 mm within 3 and 6 weeks, respectively. Following transfer onto solid medium, some browning may be noted, and growth is slow for the first 2 weeks. Proliferation is evident after 3 weeks. Most explants produce 1–3 protocorm-like bodies which grow into plantlets. When the growing explants are cut in half, growth may be slow. Occasionally callus masses may develop; but in many cases, each half develops into a new protocorm-like body which eventually forms a plantlet.

Item number	Component	Amount per liter of culture medium (final concentration in culture medium)	Stock solution (a concentrate prepared for repeated and convenient use)	Volume of stock solution per liter of culture medium	Remarks
	Macroelements[a]				
1	Ammonium sulfate, $(NH_4)_2SO_4$[a]	400 mg	40 g/liter[a]	10 ml[a]	or weigh[a]
2	Calcium nitrate, $Ca(NO_3)_2 \cdot 4H_2O$[a]	1000 mg	100 g/liter[a]	10 ml[a]	or weigh[a]
3	Potassium chloride, KCl	500 mg	50 g/liter	10 ml	
4	Potassium phosphate, KH_2PO_4	250 mg	25 g/liter	10 ml	
5	Magnesium sulfate, $MgSO_4 \cdot 7H_2O$	400 mg	40 g/liter	10 ml	
6	*Microelements*[a]				
a	Manganese sulfate, $MnSO_4 \cdot 4H_2O$	7.5 mg	7.5 g/liter	⎤	⎤
b	Boric acid, H_3BO_3	0.03 mg	30 mg/liter		
c	Zinc sulfate, $ZnSO_4 \cdot 7H_2O$	0.03 mg	30 mg/liter	1 ml	one solution[b]
d	Copper sulfate, $CuSO_4 \cdot 5H_2O$	0.001 mg	1 mg/liter	⎦	⎦
	Organic acid				
7	Citric acid	150 mg	no stock		weigh
8	*Iron*				
a	Ferric sulfate, $Fe_2(SO_4)_3$	10.70 mg	1.07 g/liter	⎤	⎤ one
b	Na_2EDTA	22.40 mg	2.24 g/liter	10 ml	solution ⎦
	Vitamins[c]				
9	Thiamine HCl (vitamin B_1)[c]	0.1 mg	10 mg/100 ml 95% ethanol	1 ml	⎤ these
10	Niacin (nicotinic acid)[c]	0.5 mg	50 mg/100 ml 95% ethanol	1 ml	may be com-
11	Pyridoxine HCl (vitamin B_6)	0.5 mg	50 mg/100 ml 95% ethanol	1 ml	bined[c] ⎦
	Amino acid				
12	Glycine	2 mg	200 mg/100 ml 95% ethanol[d]	1 ml	
	Auxins[e]				
13	Indole-3-butyric acid (IBA)[e]	1.75 mg	175 mg/100 ml 95% ethanol[e]	1 ml	⎤ these may be com-
14	Napthaleneacetic acid (NAA)[e]	1.75 mg	175 mg/100 ml 95% ethanol[e]	1 ml	bined[e] ⎦
	Cytokinins				
15	Kinetin, 6-furfuryl amino purine[f]	1 mg	100 mg/100 ml 95% ethanol[f]	1 ml	
	Polyol				
16	myo Inositol[g]	100 mg	10 g/liter[g]	1 ml	or weigh
	Sugar[h,i]				
17	Sucrose[h]	15–30 g[h]	no stock	no stock	weigh
18	Water, distilled[i]	to 1000 ml			
	Solidifier[i]				
19	Agar	6 g	no stock	no stock	weigh

[a] Solutions containing ammonium and nitrate may become contaminated with standing. Therefore, stock solutions should not be prepared. If made, they should be kept frozen between uses.

[b] Add all microelements to the same one liter of distilled water; stir and/or heat until they are dissolved; add 1 ml per liter of culture medium.

[c] If desired, all three vitamins can be dissolved in the same 100 ml and 1 ml of this solution used per liter of culture medium. Keep frozen between uses.

[d] Keep refrigerated or frozen between uses.

[e] If the auxins do not dissolve easily, add a few drops of HCl. If desired, the two auxins can be combined in the same 100 ml of 95% ethanol. If so, 1 ml of the combined solution is used per liter of culture medium. Keep refrigerated.

[f] If the cytokinin fails to dissolve, add a pellet of KOH. Keep refrigerated.

[g] The stock solution must be kept frozen between uses.

[h] Sugar does not appear in the recipe (Table 1 in Reinert and Mohr, 1967). Since this seems to be a typographical error, an amount in the usual range is suggested (item 17).

[i] For the initial solution, mix items 1–14 with 750 ml of distilled water (item 18); adjust the pH to 5.0; add the sugar (item 17); bring up the volume to 1000 ml with more distilled water (item 18); dispense into culture vessels and autoclave. To prepare the second medium, mix items 1–16 with 750 ml of distilled water (item 18); adjust the pH to 5.0; add sugar (item 17) and bring the volume to 1000 ml with more distilled water (item 18). The agar (item 19) is dissolved by adding it slowly, while stirring, to the gently boiling solution. When it is fully dissolved, dispense into the culture flasks and autoclave.

General Comments. This method can produce multiplication of up to 3000-fold with relative ease and should, therefore, prove useful.

Propagation of *Cattleya* by the Culture of Explants from Vegetative Shoots

When mortality of explants is high, a tissue-culture method which does not carry with it the danger of losing an entire plant is very desirable. The utilization of explants from vegetative shoots is one such method. Failure may result in the loss of a shoot, but at least the plant is safe. Once the requirements of each genus are understood, at least partially suitable media can be developed. This, indeed, is the case with explants from vegetative shoots of *Cattleya* (Scully, 1967).

Plant Material. Use lateral meristems removed from vegetative shoots 1–8 cm long.

Surface Sterilization. Shoots are surface-sterilized for 5 min in 20% (v/v) Clorox. After exposure of the lateral buds, the shoots are again sterilized with the same solution, this time for 10 min.

Culture Vessels. Use 50-ml flasks containing 5 ml liquid solution or 20 ml solid medium.

Culture Conditions. Liquid cultures are placed on a rotary action shaker (a New Brunswick Model V was used in the original research) operating at 160 rpm under continuous illumination of 100–180 ft-candles from fluorescent light (Sylvania Gro Lux or a mixture of cool or warm white plus incandescent bulbs) and a temperature of $26° \pm 4°C$.

Culture Medium. Liquid modified Vacin and Went (1949) medium is used for the initial explants. Tissue masses are subcultured on solidified medium (Table A-12).

Procedure. Remove a vegetative shoot 1–8 cm long and sterilize it for 5 min. Expose the lateral meristems by removing 1–2 young leaves and sterilize for 5 min using the same Clorox solution as before. Make incisions just below the nodal origin and along the two sides of the bud. Separate the explant by making a cut behind the bud itself. Remove all but one of the remaining leaves and make four vertical incisions and a horizontal one to remove the apical meristem as a 1-mm cube. The volume of explants should range between 1 and 2 mm^3. Collect the explants on sterile moist filter paper in sterilized petri dishes.

Transfer the explants to the liquid medium (Table A-12) and place on the shaker for 2–5 weeks. Depending on development, section the tissue mass after that and subculture. Once formation of protocorm-like bodies (PLB) has begun, the proliferating masses can be divided and cultured on solid medium (Table A-12). If left undisturbed, the PLB will form fully rooted plants within 6–8 weeks.

Development Sequence. The explant develops into a callus. PLB are formed which give rise to plantlets.

Table A-12. Modified Vacin and Went (1949) medium for the culture of explants from vegetative shoots of *Cattleya* (Scully, 1967)

Item number	Component	Amount per liter of culture medium (final concentration in culture medium)	Stock solution (a concentrate prepared for repeated and convenient use)	Volume of stock solution per liter of culture medium	Remarks
	Macroelements[a,b.]				
1	Tricalcium phosphate, $Ca_3(PO_4)_2$[a]	200 mg	20 g/liter[a]	10 ml[a]	or weigh[a]
2	Potassium nitrate, KNO_3	525 mg	52 g/liter[b]	10 ml[b]	or weigh[b]
3	Potassium phosphate, KH_2PO_4	250 mg	25 g/liter	10 ml	
4	Ammonium sulfate, $(NH_4)_2SO_4$	500 mg	50 g/liter[b]	10 ml[b]	or weigh[b]
5	Ferric tartrate, $Fe_2(C_4H_4O_6)_3$[c]	28 mg	2.8 g/liter[c]	10 ml[c]	
6	Manganese sulfate, $MnSO_4 \cdot 4H_2O$	7.5 mg	750 mg/liter	10 ml	
7	Magnesium sulfate, $MgSO_4 \cdot 4H_2O$	250 mg	25 g/liter	10 ml	or weigh
	Sugar[d]				
8	Sucrose	20 g	no stock	no stock	weigh
	Complex additive				
9	Coconut water	250 ml	no stock	no stock	fresh
10	Water, distilled[d]	to 1000 ml			
	Solidifier[d]				
11	Agar	9 g	no stock	no stock	weigh

[a] If all of the material does not dissolve, shake stock solution well before dispensing to insure an even suspension; or better yet, weigh out each time.

[b] Solutions containing nitrate and ammonium may become contaminated with time. Therefore, it is preferable not to make stock solutions. If stock solutions are prepared, they should be kept frozen between uses.

[c] If the substance fails to dissolve, add a pellet or two of KOH and shake well. Also shake well before dispensing.

[d] Mix items 1–7 with 600 ml of distilled water (item 10); adjust pH to 5.0–5.2; add the sugar (item 8) and bring the volume up to 1000 ml with more distilled water (item 10). If a liquid medium is desired, distribute into culture vessels and autoclave for 10–12 min at 15 lb pressure. When solid medium is needed, bring the solution to a gentle boil and add the agar (item 11) slowly while stirring; distribute into culture vessels and autoclave.

General Comments. This is a successful method, but the author suggests that every worker may have to make a few modifications (Scully, 1967). An important point to keep in mind is that the initial culture medium must be liquid and requires shaking.

Vegetative Multiplication of *Cattleya* by the Culture of Leaf Bases

The ideal method for clonal propagation would utilize an organ or small mass of tissue which can be removed without damaging or endangering the plant. Leaves are one obvious source for such tissues. Meristems at the base of *Cattleya* leaves can be used to produce protocorm-like bodies (Champagnat, Morel, and Mounetou, 1970).

Plant Material. Leaves are removed from seedlings maintained in sterile culture.

Surface Sterilization. This is not necessary.

Culture Vessels. Use 5-cm-diameter petri dishes containing medium to a height of 5 mm; or test tubes and Erlenmeyer flasks filled with medium to $\frac{1}{5}$ of their volume.

Culture Conditions. As for germinating seeds of *Cattleya* or its meristems (p. 222; Morel, 1971a).

Culture Medium. The usual salts (including the microelements of Heller), plus 1 mg kinetin/liter solidified with 9 g agar/liter (Table A-13).

Procedure. Under aseptic conditions, remove leaves 6–10 mm long from seedlings growing in flasks. Excise and discard axillary meristem from the base, but culture the rest. When protocorm-like bodies are formed, subculture.

Table A-13. Culture medium for *Cattleya* leaf bases (Champagnat, Morel, and Mounetou, 1970)

Item number	Component	Amount per liter of culture medium (final concentration in culture medium)	Stock solution (a concentrate prepared for repeated and convenient use)	Volume of stock solution per liter of culture medium	Remarks
	Macroelements[a]				
1	Ammonium sulfate, $(NH_4)_2SO_4$[a]	1 g	100 g/liter[a]	10 ml[a]	or weigh[a]
2	Potassium chloride, KCl	1 g	100 g/liter	10 ml	
3	Magnesium sulfate, $MgSO_4 \cdot 7H_2O$	125 mg	12.5 g/liter	10 ml	
4	Calcium nitrate, $Ca(NO_3)_2 \cdot 4H_2O$[a]	500 mg	50 g/liter[a]	10 ml[a]	or weigh[a]
5	Potassium phosphate, KH_2PO_4	125 mg	12.5 g/liter	10 ml	
6	*Microelements of Heller* Solution A[b,c]				
a	Zinc sulfate, $ZnSO_4 \cdot 7H_2O$	1 mg	1 g/liter		
b	Manganese sulfate, $MnSO_4 \cdot 4H_2O$[b]	0.010 mg	10 mg/liter		
c	Copper sulfate, $CuSO_4 \cdot 5H_2O$	0.030 mg	30 mg/liter	1 ml	one solution
d	Aluminium chloride, $AlCl_3$	0.030 mg	30 mg/liter		
e	Nickel chloride, $NiCl_2 \cdot 6H_2O$	0.030 mg	30 mg/liter		
f	Potassium iodide, KI Solution B	0.010 mg	10 mg/liter		
7	Ferric chloride, $FeCl_3 \cdot 6H_2O$	1 mg	1 g/liter	1 ml	
8	*Cytokinin*[d] Kinetin	1 mg	100 mg/100 ml 95% ethanol	1 ml	
9	*Sugar*[e] Sucrose	20 g	no stock	no stock	weigh
10	Water, distilled[e]	to 1000 ml			
11	*Solidifier*[e] Agar	8 g	no stock	no stock	

[a] Solutions containing ammonium and nitrate tend to become contaminated. Therefore, stock solutions are not advisable. If prepared, they must be kept frozen.

[b] As given in the paper (Champagnat *et al.*, 1970), this solution contains magnesium, but no manganese. Since the medium already contains magnesium (item 3), a correction was made (item 6b) in the usual range.

[c] All salts are added to the same one liter. Stir or heat until dissolved and use 1 ml per liter of medium.

[d] If the cytokinin fails to dissolve, add a pellet of KOH. Keep refrigerated.

[e] Mix items 1–8 with 700 ml of distilled water (item 10); adjust the pH to 5.3; add sugar (item 9) and bring up volume to 1000 ml with more distilled water (item 10). To dissolve the agar (item 11), bring solution to a gentle boil. Add the agar (item 11) slowly while stirring. Then dispense the solution into the culture vessels and autoclave.

Developmental Sequence. When the axillary meristem at the base of a leaf is left in place, it starts to grow and inhibits the formation of adventitious buds. If it is removed, numerous protocorm-like bodies are formed at the cut end and on the leaf blade.

General Comments. This is a simple, easy, and effective method. However, since the tissues to be cultured are obtained from seedlings, the procedure cannot be used for the propagation of established clones. Nevertheless, it should prove useful in cases where only very few seedlings can be obtained from a cross. It can also be used in cases where only a limited number of plantlets can be obtained from a meristem.

Cattleya Leaf Tips

In 1967, Professor Ernest A. Ball, who first cultured meristems (Ball, 1946) gave a lecture at the University of California, Irvine, about the culture of leaf-parenchyma cells. He had succeeded in producing whole plants (but not orchids) from them. This suggested to me that perhaps orchid leaf cells could be cultured. When he joined our department in 1968, we decided to try. The work was done by an undergraduate named Mary-Ellen Farrar. By the time her project was completed, she was Mrs. Churchill. We tried to culture all parts of a leaf but succeeded only with tips, and even those did not always grow. But this method barely damages the plant and therefore approaches an ideal procedure (Churchill, Arditti, and Ball, 1971, 1972; Churchill, Ball, and Arditti, 1973; Churchill, Flick, *et al.*, 1971; Ball *et al.*, 1971; Arditti *et al.*, 1971, 1972).

Plant Material. Leaf tips are obtained from young leaves on old plants before the appearance of the characteristic notch.

Surface Sterilization. Tips are sterilized for 10 min in saturated calcium hypochlorite solution. To prepare the solution, mix 10 g calcium hypochlorite with 140 ml water. Stir well, allow to stand for a few minutes, and stir again. Repeat this three times and filter or decant the supernatant, which is the sterilizing solution. Use within 6 hr.

Culture Vessels. We use 125-ml Erlenmeyer flasks containing 25 ml medium for both liquid and solid media.

Culture Conditions. Liquid cultures are placed on a reciprocating shaker (60 oscillations per minute) at 22–25°C under 18-hr photoperiods. The light intensity produced by a combination of two 40-watt Sylvania Gro Lux tubes and two 50–100-watt incandescent bulbs per fixture placed 50 cm above the cultures should be 150 ft-candles. Solid cultures may be maintained on a table top or shelf under the same conditions. After transfer to Knudson C, the cultures are maintained under 22–25° C, 12-hr photoperiods, 36 cm from the same light sources.

Culture Media. Tips are cultured and callus formation occurs in liquid Heller's medium (Table A-14). These calli consist of protocorm-like bodies (PLB). Proliferation continues very well, without much differentiation on solid Murashige-Skoog

Table A-14. Modified Heller's medium for the culture of tips from young leaves of mature *Cattleya* plants (Churchill, Arditti, and Ball, 1971)

Item number	Component	Amount per liter of culture medium (final concentration in culture medium)	Stock solution (a concentrate prepared for repeated and convenient use)	Volume of stock solution per liter of culture medium	Remarks
	Macroelements[a]				
1	Potassium chloride, KCl	750 mg	75 g/liter	10 ml	
2	Sodium nitrate, NaNO$_3$,[a]	600 mg	60 g/liter[a]	10 ml[a]	weigh[a]
3	Magnesium sulfate, MgSO$_4$·7H$_2$O	250 mg	25 g/liter	10 ml	
4	Monosodium phosphate, NaH$_2$PO$_4$·H$_2$O	125 mg	12.5 g/liter	10 ml	
5	Calcium chloride, CaCl$_2$·2H$_2$O	75 mg	7.5 g/liter	1 ml	
	Iron				
6	Ferric chloride, FeCl$_3$·6H$_2$O	1 mg	1.0 g/liter	1 ml	
7	*Microelements*[b]				
a	Boric acid, H$_3$BO$_3$	1 mg	1 g/liter		
b	Zinc sulfate, ZnSO$_4$·7H$_2$O	1 mg	1 g/liter		
c	Manganese sulfate, MnSO$_4$·4H$_2$O	0.01 mg	10 mg/liter		
d	Cupric sulfate, CuSO$_4$·5H$_2$O	0.03 mg	30 mg/liter	1 ml	one solution[b]
e	Aluminium chloride, AlCl$_3$	0.03 mg	30 mg/liter		
f	Nickel chloride, NiCl$_2$·6H$_2$O	0.03 mg	30 mg/liter		
g	Potassium iodide, KI	0.01 mg	10 mg/liter		
	Auxin[c]				
8	2,4-D	1 mg	30 mg/30 ml 95% ethanol	1 ml	
	Cytokinin[d]				
9	6-Benzyl amino purine (benzyl adenine)	500 µg	30 mg/30 ml 95% ethanol[d]	0.5 ml	
	Vitamins[e]				
10	Thiamine (vitamin B$_1$)	1 mg	100 mg/100 ml 95% ethanol[e]	1 ml	
	Sugar[f]				
11	Sucrose	30 g	no stock	no stock	weigh
12	Water, distilled[f]	to 1000 ml			
	Solidifier[f]				
13	Agar	10 g	no stock	no stock	weigh

[a] Solutions containing nitrate and ammonium tend to become contaminated. Therefore, it is better to weigh the salt each time. If prepared, stock solutions must be kept frozen.

[b] Add all microelements to the same one liter of distilled water. Stir or gently heat the solution until all salts are dissolved.

[c] If the auxin does not dissolve, add a few drops of HCl. Keep refrigerated.

[d] If the cytokinin does not dissolve, add a few drops of KOH. Keep refrigerated.

[e] Keep refrigerated.

[f] Mix items 1–10 with 800 ml of distilled water (item 12); adjust the pH to 5.3; add sugar (item 11) and bring up the volume to 1000 ml with more distilled water (item 12). If a liquid medium is required, distribute into culture vessels and autoclave. When a solid medium is needed, the solution is brought to a gentle boil and the agar (item 13) is added slowly while stirring. After the agar has dissolved, distribute the medium into culture flasks and autoclave.

Table A-15. Linsmaier-Skoog (1965) medium for the maintenance of callus cultures derived from *Cattleya* leaf tips

Item number	Component	Amount per liter of culture medium (final concentration in culture medium)	Stock solution (a concentrate prepared for repeated and convenient use)	Volume of solution per liter of culture medium	Remarks
	Macroelements[a]				
1	Ammonium nitrate, NH_4NO_3[a]	1.65 g	82.5 g/liter[a]	20 ml[a]	or weigh[a]
2	Potassium nitrate, KNO_3[a]	1.9 g	95 g/liter[a]	20 ml[a]	or weigh[a]
3	Calcium chloride, $CaCl_2 \cdot 2H_2O$	440 mg	44 g/liter	10 ml	
4	Magnesium sulfate, $MgSO_4 \cdot 7H_2O$	370 mg	18.5 g/liter	20 ml	
5	Potassium phosphate, KH_2PO_4	170 mg	8.5 g/liter	20 ml	
6	*Chelated iron*				
a	Na_2EDTA	37.3 mg	3.70 g/liter	⎤ 10 ml ⎦	⎤ one solution ⎦
b	Ferrous sulfate, $FeSO_4 \cdot 7H_2O$	27.8 mg	2.80 g/liter		
7	*Microelements*[b]				
a	Boric acid, H_3BO_3	6.2 mg	620 mg/liter	⎤	⎤
b	Manganese sulfate, $MnSO_4 \cdot 4H_2O$	22.3 mg	2.23 g/liter		
c	Zinc sulfate, $ZnSO_4 \cdot 7H_2O$	9 mg	9 g/liter		
d	Potassium iodide, KI	0.83 mg	83 mg/liter	10 ml	one solution[b]
e	Sodium molybdate, $Na_2MoO_4 \cdot 2H_2O$	0.25 mg	25 mg/liter		
f	Copper sulfate, $CuSO_4 \cdot 5H_2O$	0.025 mg	2.5 mg/liter		
g	Cobalt chloride, $CoCl_2 \cdot 6H_2O$	0.025 mg	2.5 mg/liter	⎦	⎦
	Polyol				
8	myo Inositol	100 mg	no stock	no stock	weigh
	Cytokinin				
9	Kinetin[c]	0.1 mg	20 mg/100 ml 95% ethanol[c]	0.5 ml	
	Auxin[d]				
10	Indoleacetic acid, IAA	2 mg	200 mg/100 ml 95% ethanol[d]	1.0 ml	
	Vitamin[e]				
11	Thiamine HCl (vitamin B_1)	0.4 mg	80 mg/100 ml 95% ethanol[e]	0.5 ml	
	Sugar[f]				
12	Sucrose	30 g	no stock	no stock	weigh
13	Water, distilled[f]	to 1000 ml			
	Solidifier[f]				
14	Agar	10 g	no stock	no stock	weigh

[a] Solutions containing nitrate and ammonium tend to become contaminated. Therefore, it is preferable not to make stock solutions. If prepared, they must be kept frozen.

[b] Add all microelements to the same one liter, stir and/or heat until dissolved. Add 10 ml per liter of culture medium.

[c] If there are difficulties in dissolving the kinetin, add a pellet of KOH. Keep refrigerated.

[d] If there are difficulties in dissolving the IAA, add a few drops of HCl. Keep the stock solution refrigerated.

[e] Keep the stock solution refrigerated.

[f] Mix items 1–11 with 700 ml of distilled water (item 13); adjust pH to 5.5; add sugar (item 13). Bring the solution to a gentle boil and add the agar (item 14) slowly while stirring. When the agar is completely dissolved, distribute the medium into culture flasks and autoclave. However, it is preferable to mix items 1–8 with 700 ml of distilled water (item 13); adjust the pH to 5.5; add the sugar (item 12) and bring the volume to 1000 ml. Then add the agar and autoclave. While the solution is still hot, add a mixture of items 9–11 to it under sterile conditions Swirl to mix and distribute into preautoclaved culture vessels.

(Table A-1) or Linsmaier-Skoog (Table A-15) media. PLB or the callus must be transferred to solid Knudson C medium (Tables A-9, A-10, A-16) in order to obtain plantlets. Addition of banana homogenate (Arditti, 1967a) speeds up growth. Use of a flasking tool designed for seeds (Arditti, 1968b) may facilitate transfers but is not required.

Procedure. Tips 15–25 mm long are removed from young leaves with a sharp scalpel or razor blade and placed on wet filter paper (or paper towels) in a closed container. Following surface sterilization and rinsing in sterile distilled water, the bottom part is removed, leaving a tip 4–5 mm in length. This tip is then placed in culture.

Table A-16. Modified Knudson C (1946) medium for use in the differentiation of plantlets from leaf-tip callus cultures

Item number	Component	Amount per liter of culture medium (final concentration in culture medium)	Stock solution (a concentrate prepared for repeated and convenient use)	Volume of stock solution per liter of culture medium	Remarks
	Macroelements[a,b,c]				
1	Calcium nitrate, $Ca(NO_3)_2 \cdot 4H_2O$[a]	1 g	100 g/liter[a]	10 ml[a]	or weigh[a]
2	Magnesium sulfate, $MgSO_4 \cdot 7H_2O$	250 mg	25 g/liter	10 ml	
3	Ammonium sulfate, $(NH_4)_2SO_4$[a]	500 mg	50 g/liter[a]	10 ml[a]	or weigh[a]
4	Ferrous sulfate, $FeSO_4 \cdot 7H_2O$[b]	25 mg	2.5 g/liter[b]	10 ml[b]	
5	Potassium phosphate, KH_2PO_4[c]	250 mg	25 g/liter	10 ml[c]	
6	Microelements[d]				
a	Boric acid, H_3BO_3	0.056 mg	56 mg/liter		
b	Molybdic acid, MoO_3	0.016 mg	16 mg/liter	1 ml	one
c	Cupric sulfate, $CuSO_4$	0.040 mg	40 mg/liter		solution[d]
d	Zinc sulfate, $ZnSO_4 \cdot 7H_2O$	0.331 mg	331 mg/liter		
	Sugar				
7	Sucrose	20 g	no stock	no stock	weigh
	Organic additive[e]				
8	Banana, ripe	150 g	no stock	no stock	weigh
9	Water, distilled[e]	to 1000 ml			
	Solidifier[e]				
10	Agar	12–15 g	no stock	no stock	weigh

[a] Solutions containing ammonium and nitrate tend to become contaminated upon standing. Therefore, it is better to weigh items 1 and 3 each time. If stock solutions are prepared, they should be kept frozen.

[b] This solution tends to form a rust-colored precipitate on standing. Therefore, it must be shaken before using.

[c] Or a phosphate buffer which will keep the pH steady may be substituted here. Prepare buffer by mixing 975 ml of 0.1 M KH_2PO_4 (monopotassium phosphate) solution (13.6 g/liter) with 25 ml of a 0.1 M K_2HPO_4 (dipotassium phosphate) solution (17.4 g/liter); measure the pH to be certain it is correct (pH 5.1–5.4) and use 18 ml/liter of culture medium.

[d] Add all microelements to the same one liter of distilled water; stir and/or heat until dissolved and add 1 ml per liter of culture medium.

[e] Add items 1–8 to 700 ml of distilled water (item 9); homogenize until the banana (item 8) is completely broken down (about 2–3 min); adjust the pH to 5.3 and bring the volume to 1000 ml with more distilled water. To dissolve the agar (item 10), add it slowly, while stirring, to the gently boiling solution. When dissolved, distribute the medium into culture vessels and autoclave.

Developmental Sequence. Approximately 45 days after being placed in culture, the tip begins to proliferate. Soon thereafter, the original tissue dies and turns brown. Within 10–15 weeks, masses consisting of PLB are formed. When these start to produce vegetative apices and leaves, they should be transferred to solid MS or LS to increase proliferation. Plantlet formation occurs on Knudson C medium (Table A-16). Once placed on Knudson C medium, the PLB and the resulting plantlets should be treated like seedlings.

General Comments. Tips of young leaves from mature plants can be cultured, but the rate of success is not always high. Formation of callus apparently depends on the presence of meristematic or undifferentiated tissue in the leaf tip. If such tissue is no longer present, there is no callus development. Appearance of the characteristic notch in *Cattleya* leaves indicates their tips will no longer form calli. Unfortunately, the potential to form a callus is lost even before the notch becomes evident, but the time at which this happens is not easily apparent. The low rate of success is due to this fact. Hence, it is important to obtain tips from very young leaves. Also, instructions must be followed exactly.

This method was developed to eliminate the need to sacrifice entire plants or shoots and to provide a simple procedure for clonal propagation of *Cattleya*. In this, we have succeeded since less skill is required than for shoot-tip ("meristem") cultures, and damage to the plant is minimal. It is worth noting that at least one orchid, *Malaxis paludosa*, produces foliar embryos (Taylor, 1967).

Cymbidium

This was the first orchid genus to be propagated by shoot-tip ("meristem") culture (Morel, 1960). Since the original publication on the subject, a number of workers have devised additional techniques or used the process for basic research and practical growers have produced countless "mericlones" (Bivins and Hackett, 1969; Champagnat *et al.*, 1966, 1968; Fonnesbech, 1972a,b; Freson and Vanseveren, 1968; Gripp, 1966; Leffring, 1968; Matsui *et al.*, 1970; Morel, 1960, 1963, 1964a,b, 1965a,b, 1971a; Penningsfeld and Fast, 1968; Rutkowski, 1971; Sagawa, Shoji, and Shoji, 1966; Steward and Mapes, 1971; Thompson, 1971; Ueda and Torikata, 1968, 1969a,b, 1972; Vacherot, 1966; Werckmeister, 1970, 1971; Wilfret, 1966; Wimber, 1963). Because each of the methods has its adherents, four procedures will be presented.

In vitro Culture of *Cymbidium* Shoot Meristems

Following the development of tissue culture methods for the meristems of other plants (Ball, 1946), Dr. Georges Morel tried to culture *Cymbidium* shoot tips (Morel, 1960, 1963, 1964a,b, 1970). The rest is history.

Plant Material. Shoot tips from buds on pseudobulbs are used.

Surface Sterilization. Buds are surface-sterilized by being dipped for a few seconds in 75% ethyl alcohol (ethanol), placed in saturated calcium hypochlorite (10 g/140 ml;

stir, allow to stand, stir again, and let precipitate settle before decanting and using; solution should be freshly prepared) for 20 min, and rinsed with sterile distilled water.

Culture Vessels. Use Khan test tubes or Erlenmeyer flasks.

Culture Conditions. The cultures are kept under 12-hr photoperiods provided by flourescent tubes (Sylvania Gro Lux) at 22° C.

Culture Medium. Knudson C medium is appropriate (Tables A-9, A-10, A-16).

Procedure. Remove all adult leaves from the pseudobulbs. Cut down to half-size other leaves around the growing buds. Then sterilize and dissect the buds under aseptic conditions. The exposed apex appears as a brilliant hemisphere, usually surrounded by one or two leaf primordia. Excise it by making four cuts at right angles, delimiting a small cube, which is placed on the culture medium.

Developmental Sequence. Within 2 months, the explant develops into a protocorm-like body, 1–2 mm in size. This body is colorless at first, but soon turns green and produces rhizoids and a leaf primordium. At this point, it may be sectioned into quarters and subcultured. Within a month, each section will produce a new protocorm-like body which can be divided again.

General Comments. This process provides a means of propagation which can reach 4,000,000 plants/year from a single bud.

Clonal Propagation of *Cymbidium* through Shoot-Tip Meristem Culture

The keen interest in procedures for tissue culture of *Cymbidium* meristems has led to the development of a technique in the laboratory of Professor Yoneo Sagawa (Sagawa, Shoji, and Shoji, 1966).

Plant Material. Explants are obtained from shoots 5–7.5 cm long growing on pseudobulbs.

Surface Sterilization. Sterilization is with 1%, 5%, and 10% (v/v) Clorox (see Procedure).

Culture Vessels. Use 50-ml Erlenmeyer flasks containing 15 ml medium.

Culture Conditions. Explants are maintained under 120 ft-candles of continuous illumination (General Electric Power Groove White) at 22–25° C on a shaker for 4 weeks, after which they are kept under the same conditions on solid medium.

Culture Medium. Knudson C (Tables A-9, A-10, A-16) or Vacin and Went (Table A-17) media can be used.

Table A-17. Vacin and Went (1949) medium for the culture of *Cymbidium* shoot-tip meristems (Sagawa, Shoji, and Shoji, 1966)

Item number	Component	Amount per liter of culture medium (final concentration in culture medium)	Stock solution (a concentrate prepared for repeated and convenient use)	Volume of stock solution per liter of culture medium	Remarks
	Macroelements[a,b,c]				
1	Tricalcium phosphate, $Ca_3(PO_4)_2$[a]	200.0 mg	20.0 g/liter[a]	10 ml[a]	or weigh[a]
2	Potassium nitrate, KNO_3[2]	525.0 mg	52.5 g/liter[b]	10 ml[b]	or weigh[b]
3	Potassium phosphate, KH_2PO_4	250.0 mg	25.0 g/liter	10 ml	
4	Magnesium sulfate, $MgSO_4 \cdot 7H_2O$	250.0 mg	25.0 g/liter	10 ml	
5	Ammonium sulfate, $(NH_4)_2SO_4$[b]	500.0 mg	50.0 g/liter[b]	10 ml[b]	or weigh[b]
6	Ferric tartrate, $Fe_2(C_4H_4O_6)_3$[c]	28.0 mg	2.8 g/liter[c]	10 ml[c]	
	Microelement				
7	Manganese sulfate, $MnSO_4 \cdot 4H_2O$	7.5 mg	750.0 mg/liter	10 ml	
	Sugar[d]				
8	Sucrose	20.0 g	no stock	no stock	weigh
9	Water, distilled[d]	to 1000 ml			
	Solidifier[d]				
10	Agar	16.0 g	no stock	no stock	weigh

[a] If the material does not completely dissolve, shake stock solution well before dispensing to insure an even suspension; or better yet, weigh out each time.

[b] Solutions containing nitrate and ammonium may become contaminated with time. Therefore, it is preferable not to make stock solutions. If stock solutions are prepared, they should be kept frozen between uses.

[c] If the substance fails to dissolve, add a pellet or two of KOH and shake well. Also, shake well before dispensing.

[d] Mix items 1–7 with 800 ml of distilled water (item 9); adjust the pH to 5.0–5.5; add the sugar (item 8) and adjust the volume to 1000 ml with more distilled water. To add the agar (item 10), bring the solution to a slow boil and add slowly while stirring. When fully dissolved, dispense into culture vessels and autoclave. For liquid medium, omit the agar (item 10).

Procedure. Remove new growths or leads 5–7.5 cm long from a pseudobulb and cut away 3–4 leaves until an axillary bud is exposed. Sterilize in 5% (v/v) Clorox for 5–8 min. Now remove the remaining leaves (except perhaps one leaf). If axillary buds are used, remove a 2–3-mm cube and sterilize in 1% (v/v) Clorox for 3 min. Place this cube in liquid culture. Tools should be dipped in 10% (v/v) Clorox often and washed in sterile distilled water to insure sterility.

Developmental Sequence. Protocorm-like bodies are formed after 6 weeks (4 on liquid and 2 on solid medium) of culture. These bodies, measuring 2–3 mm in diameter, are quartered and subcultured. The process can be repeated every 10 days. If left undisturbed, the protocorm-like bodies grow into plantlets.

General Comments. This is a well-conceived procedure which can produce many plantlets quickly.

Clonal Multiplication of *Cymbidium* through *in vitro* Culture of Shoot Tips

Following the introduction of *Cymbidium* shoot-tip culture (Morel, 1960), there was a search for a faster method, and the answer turned out to be a liquid medium (Wimber, 1963).

Plant Material. Shoots approximately 3 cm long are used.

Surface Sterilization. Use a 2% solution of calcium hypochlorite (w/v), which must be freshly prepared.

Culture Vessels. Use 125-ml Erlenmeyer flasks containing 25 ml medium.

Culture Conditions. Constant light of 100 ft-candles or less (the light source is not listed, but Sylvania Gro Lux tubes would, no doubt, prove satisfactory) at 22° C on a rotary shaker.

Culture Medium. A modified Tsuchiya medium is used (Table A-18).

Table A-18. Culture medium for *Cymbidium* shoot meristems (Wimber, 1963)

Item number	Component	Amount per liter of culture medium (final concentration in culture medium)	Stock solution (a concentrate prepared for repeated and convenient use)	Volume of stock solution per liter of culture medium	Remarks
	Macroelements[a,b]				
1	Potassium nitrate, KNO_3[a]	525 mg	52.5 g/liter[a]	10 ml[a]	or weigh[a]
2	Dicalcium phosphate, $CaHPO_4$[b]	200 mg	20.0 g/liter[b]	10 ml[b]	or weigh[b]
3	Potassium phosphate, KH_2PO_4	250 mg	25.0 g/liter	10 ml	
4	Ammonium sulfate, $(NH_4)_2SO_4$[a]	500 mg	50.0 g/liter[a]	10 ml[a]	or weigh[a]
5	Magnesium sulfate, $MgSO_4 \cdot 7H_2O$	250 mg	25.0 g/liter	10 ml	
	Iron[c]				
6	Ferric tartrate, $Fe_2(C_4H_4O_6)_3$	300 mg	3.0 g/liter[c]	10 ml[c]	
	Complex additive				
7	Tryptone	2 g	no stock	no stock	weigh
	Sugar[d]				
8	Sucrose	20 g	no stock	no stock	weigh
9	Water, distilled[d]	to 1000 ml			

[a] Solutions containing ammonium and nitrate may become contaminated with standing. Therefore, it is preferable to weigh the salts every time. If prepared, stock solutions must be kept frozen between uses.

[b] If all of the compound fails to dissolve, shake stock solution well before dispensing to insure an even suspension; or better yet, weigh out each time.

[c] If this fails to dissolve, add a pellet of KOH and shake vigorously. Shake well before dispensing.

[d] Mix items 1–7 with 700 ml of distilled water (item 9); adjust the pH to 5.2–5.5; add sugar (item 8); bring volume to 1000 ml with more distilled water (item 9); distribute into culture vessels and autoclave.

Procedure. Remove the outermost leaves and sterilize for 10 min in calcium hypo-chlorite. Under sterile conditions, using sterilized tools, remove the rest of the leaves, exposing the apical meristem, which should be "immediately cut off" and placed into culture.

Developmental Sequence. The explants turn green and show noticeable growth within a week. In a month, protocorm-like bodies are formed. Shoots appear and differentia-tion follows when the protocorm-like bodies reach a size of approximately 4 mm. If the flasks are agitated, proliferation occurs instead of shoot formation. Masses of tissue are formed and can be subcultured after two months. On a rotary shaker, the sub-divisions reach a diameter of 1 cm within 30 days. When tissue fragments are placed on a solid medium, they form plantlets within $2\frac{1}{2}$ months.

General Comments. This is a simple and fast technique requiring inexpensive tools, a shaker, and skills which can be acquired easily.

Propagation of *Cymbidium in vitro*

To determine the precise tissue culture requirements of a species, it is necessary to perform careful comparative experiments in which one factor at a time is added, re-moved, or varied in concentration. The volumes of data which accumulate from these experiments must be analyzed statistically before their full meaning can be appreciated. Such experiments are tedious, often complicated, and always time-consuming. As a result, investigators tend to shy away from them, which is a pity. Occasionally, how-ever, researchers carry out experiments of this type and use them as a basis for articles which are full of information and a pleasure to read (Fonnesbech, 1972a,b). Propaga-tion methods based on such experiments tend to produce a higher degree of success and better plants.

Plant Material. The same material as for shoot meristem culture (p. 234; Sagawa, Shoji, and Shoji, 1966) should be used.

Surface Sterilization. Use the same procedure as for shoot meristem culture (p. 234; Sagawa, Shoji, and Shoji, 1966).

Culture Vessels. Use 150-ml Erlenmeyer flasks containing 30 ml liquid medium, or 25×100 mm test tubes with 10 ml medium. For solid cultures, use 100-ml flasks containing 40 ml medium.

Culture Conditions. Tissues are maintained 90 cm under a light source consisting of three 40-watt Atlas Super-Gro and three Osram L-Fluora 77 fluorescent tubes pro-ducing radiation of 3.3 W/m^2. Illumination may be continuous (Sagawa, Shoji, and Shoji, 1966). When liquid medium in 150-ml flasks is used, the tissues are placed on a reciprocal shaker at 80 rpm. Test tubes are rotated on a vertical wheel at $\frac{2}{3}$ rpm. The temperature should be 22–25° C.

Table A-19. Medium for the *in vitro* propagation of *Cymbidium* (Fonnesbech, 1972a,b)

Item number	Component	Amount per liter of culture medium (final concentration in culture medium)	Stock solution (a concentrate prepared for repeated and convenient use)	Volume of stock solution per liter of culture medium	Remarks
	Macroelements[a]				
1	Calcium nitrate, $Ca(NO_3)_2 \cdot 4H_2O$[a]	400 mg	40 g/liter[a]	10 ml[a]	or weigh[a]
2	Ammonium sulfate, $(NH_4)_2SO_4$[a]	300 mg	30 g/liter[a]	10 ml[a]	or weigh[a]
3	Potassium phosphate, KH_2PO_4	250 mg	25 g/liter	10 ml	
4	Potassium phosphate, K_2HPO_4	212 mg	21.2 g/liter	10 ml	
5	Magnesium sulfate, $MgSO_4 \cdot 7H_2O$	250 mg	25 g/liter	10 ml	
6	*Chelated iron*				
a	Na_2EDTA	37.8 mg	7.5 g/liter	⎤ 5 ml ⎦	⎤ one solution ⎦
b	Ferrous sulfate, $FeSO_4 \cdot 7H_2O$	27.9 mg	5.57 g/liter		
7	*Microelements*[b]				
a	Manganous sulfate, $MnSO_4 \cdot 4H_2O$	25 mg	25 g/liter	⎤	⎤
b	Zinc sulfate, $ZnSO_4 \cdot 7H_2O$	10 mg	10 g/liter		
c	Boric acid, H_3BO_3	10 mg	10 g/liter	1 ml	one solution[b]
d	Sodium molybdate, $Na_2MoO_4 \cdot 2H_2O$	0.25 mg	250 mg/liter		
e	Copper sulfate, $CuSO_4 \cdot 5H_2O$	0.025 mg	25 mg/liter	⎦	⎦
	Amino acid[c]				
8	Glycine	2 mg	2 g/liter 95% ethanol	1 ml	
	Vitamins[d]				
9	Niacin (nicotinic acid)[d]	1 mg	100 mg/100 ml 95% ethanol	1 ml[d]	⎤
10	Pyridoxine (vitamin B_6)[d]	0.5 mg	50 mg/100 ml 95% ethanol	1 ml[d]	or combine[d]
11	Thiamine (vitamin B_1)[d]	0.5 mg	50 mg/100 ml 95% ethanol	1 ml[d]	⎦
	Auxin[e]				
12	NAA	1.86 mg	186 mg/100 ml 95% ethanol[e]	1 ml[e]	
	Polyol				
13	myo Inositol	100 mg	no stock	no stock	weigh
	Cytokinin[f]				
14	Kinetin	0.215 mg	21.5 mg/100 ml 95% ethanol[f]	1 ml[f]	

Table A-19 continued

Item number	Component	Amount per liter of culture medium (final concentration in culture medium)	Stock solution (a concentrate prepared for repeated and convenient use)	Volume of stock solution per liter of culture medium	Remarks
	Complex additives[g,h]				
15	Casamino acids[g]	2–3 g	no stock[g]	no stock[g]	weigh[g]
	or				
	Tryptone[g]	3–4 g	no stock[g]	no stock[g]	weigh[g]
16	Coconut water[h]	100–150 ml	no stock	no stock	
	Sugar[i]				
17	Sucrose	30–40 g	no stock	no stock	weigh
18	Water, distilled[i]	to 1000 ml			
	Solidifier[i]				
19	Agar	8 g			

[a] Solutions containing ammonium and nitrate may become contaminated. Therefore, stock solutions should not be prepared. If made, they must be kept frozen between uses.

[b] Add all microelements to the same one liter, stir and/or heat until dissolved. Add 1 ml to culture medium.

[c] By using 95% ethanol, the stock solution is made sterile. Add 1 ml to the autoclaved medium before it has solidified. Keep stock solution refrigerated.

[d] The vitamins may be combined into one stock solution. Add 100 mg of niacin and 50 mg of pyridoxine and thiamine to the same 100 ml of 95% ethanol and use 1 ml of this per liter of medium. Refrigerate between uses.

[e] If the auxin fails to dissolve, add drops of HCl. Keep the stock solution refrigerated.

[f] If the cytokinin does not dissolve, add a pellet of KOH. Keep the stock solution refrigerated.

[g] Add either 2–3 g of casamino acid or 3–4 g of tryptone; not both.

[h] Coconut water increases growth 10–15%, but its addition is not essential.

[i] Dissolve items 1–7 and 9–16 in 750 ml of distilled water (item 18); adjust the pH to 5.5–5.8; add sucrose (item 17); and bring the volume up to 1000 ml with more distilled water. Agar (item 19) is added to the gently boiling solution while stirring. After it is fully dissolved, autoclave. Before the sterile solution is solidified, add glycine (item 8) with a sterile pipette under sterile conditions; swirl to mix well and distribute the culture medium into preautoclaved culture vessels. For liquid media, omit the agar.

Culture Media. Explants may be started in the medium used for shoot tips (p. 234; Sagawa, Shoji, and Shoji, 1966). To limit root and shoot growth (i.e., to induce proliferation), tissues are transferred to a newly devised medium (Table A-19), which can also be used as a starting solution. To produce plantlets, tissue segments are transferred onto solid medium (Table A-19).

Procedure. Follow the same procedure as for shoot tips (p. 234; Sagawa, Shoji, and Shoji, 1966) using the new medium (Table A-19).

Developmental Sequence. Tissues and plantlets develop like those from shoot tips (p. 234; Sagawa, Shoji, and Shoji, 1966), but there are some differences caused by the differentiation.

General Comments. The medium used for this method is one of the few based on careful comparisons.

Cyrtopodium

A technique is mentioned in an article on the tissue culture of *Phalaenopsis* (Intuwong and Sagawa, 1974).

Dactylorchis

Dormant shoots (early autumn in England) were excised from *D. fuchsii* and disinfected by "immersing briefly in ethanol followed by fifteen minutes in a hypochlorite solution" (concentration not given, but 10 g calcium hypochlorite/140 ml water would probably be appropriate). After rinsing the tissue with sterile distilled water, terminal portions of shoot tips consisting of floral primordia were excised and cultured on "Knudson C and a variant of Reinert and Mohrs' [*sic*] medium." Details regarding the media are not given. Therefore, one can only assume that the original formulation or a slight modification of Knudson C (Tables A-9, A-10, A-16, A-25) would be appropriate. The Reinert and Mohr medium (Table A-11) contained "autoclaved extracts from the parent plants" such as homogenized leaves "filtered to form a leaf extract" and "tubers [similarly treated] to form a salep extract" in concentrations which were not listed. Growth and survival rates on the modified Reinert and Mohr medium were better than on Knudson C.

Cultures were maintained under 16-hr photoperiods provided by warm white fluorescent lamps (no details are given on their number, distance from the plants, or light intensity) and 20° C. Bracts turned green 12 days after inoculation and developed into protocorms within 9 weeks. At that time, the apices can be divided and subcultured. "If left to enlarge without further division, these protocorms gave rise to plantlets, two to three inches in height, each with a single large tuberous root" (the time required for the plants to reach this stage is not given). "On transfer to greenhouse conditions, these plants have so far failed to survive; incorporation of soil from the vicinity of the parent stock could well be needed in order to supply the necessary mycorrhizal fungi" (Stokes, 1974). Or, one could isolate the fungus and infect the plantlets *in vitro*.

Dendrobium

The highly heterozygous nature of *Dendrobium* hybrids and the importance of selected clones to the cut-flower industry as well as to hobby growers has led to the development of several tissue-culture techniques (Arditti, Mosich, and Ball, 1973; Kim, Kunisaki, and Sagawa, 1970; Marston, 1969; Mosich, Ball, and Arditti, 1973, 1974; Mosich *et al.*, 1974; Sagawa and Shoji, 1967; Singh and Sagawa, 1972). A method for the doubling of chromosome numbers in meristem cultures has also been reported (Sanguthai, Sanguthai, and Kamemoto, 1973).

Shoot-Tip Culture of *Dendrobium*

The very first procedure for clonal propagation of *Dendrobium* by tissue culture was developed by Professor Yoneo Sagawa and his collaborators at the University of

Hawaii (Sagawa and Shoji, 1967). Later, they modified and improved their procedure (Kim, Kunisaki, and Sagawa, 1970). No wonder, then, that the techniques are similar to those employed by them for *Cymbidium* (Sagawa, Shoji, and Shoji, 1966).

Plant Material. Explants are obtained from new growths, and the highest percentage of success has been with axillary buds weighing 2 g (range 1.1–3.0) and 4.9 cm (range 3.7–11.5) long (Table A-20).

Surface Sterilization. Use the same procedure as for *Cymbidium* (p. 234), omitting the 1% Clorox step (Sagawa, Shoji, and Shoji, 1966).

Culture Vessels. These are the same as for *Cymbidium* (p. 234).

Culture Conditions. Maintain cultures under 200 ft-candles of continuous illumination provided by General Electric white fluorescent tubes (Power Groove) at $26° \pm 3°$ C. Liquid cultures are placed on a shaker operating at 160 rpm (a New Brunswick Model V shaker was used in the original research).

Culture Medium. Vacin and Went medium (Table A-17) is used, substituting 150 ml coconut water for an equal volume of distilled water. The agar (8 g/liter) is omitted when a liquid medium is desired.

Procedure. This is the same as for *Cymbidium* (p. 234).

Developmental Sequence. Explants form a green mass within 45 days and protocorm-like bodies (PLB) after 3 months. Sectioning the tissue masses within $2\frac{1}{2}$ months and subculturing the divisions result in further proliferation in an equal period of time. The highest yield of new PLB results from subdividing those which do not have obvious leaves. Sections obtained by transverse cuts produce a larger number of PLB than those derived from longitudinal cuts.

General Comments. Dr. Sagawa has told me of complaints by some people that they have not been able to use this method successfully. I have visited his laboratory and

Table A-20. Characteristics and success of cultured *Dendrobium* buds (Kim, Kunisaki, and Sagawa, 1970)

Bud characteristics	Size/Success					Total
Length (cm), average	3.0	4.9	8.2	10.4	15.5	
range	2.5–3.5	3.7–11.5	5.5–14.0	6.5–15.5	9.5–20.0	
Weight (g), average	<1.0	2.0	4.0	6.0	>7.0	
range	1.0	1.1–3.0	3.1–5.0	5.1–7.0	7.1	
Location						
Apical, percent	12.5	46.6	36.4	33.3	17.5	31.5
sc/nc[a]	1/8	7/15	4/11	4/12	1/8	17/54
Axillary, percent	14.3	50.9	38.8	33.3	40.6	38.6
sc/nc[a]	3/21	28/55	19/49	15/45	13/32	78/202

[a] Number of successful cultures/total number of cultures.

seen cultures. The technique obviously works. Therefore, I would suggest that all potential users study the original papers (Sagawa and Shoji, 1967; Kim, Kunisaki, and Sagawa, 1970) very carefully and follow directions meticulously.

Clonal Propagation of *Dendrobium* by Means of Node Cultures

Chances for successful cultures are improved when handling of tissues is reduced. Also, the more complete a structure, the better its survival potential. These considerations have led us to culture entire nodes (Arditti, Mosich, and Ball, 1973; Mosich, Ball, and Arditti, 1973, 1974; Mosich *et al.*, 1974).

Plant Material. Stems ("canes") at least 10–15 cm long are used as the source of nodes.

Surface Sterilization. Leaves, dry sheaths, and other external tissues are removed and the stems are washed by gentle scrubbing with a soft brush and mild household detergent. Then they are rinsed with distilled water and surface-sterilized with Clorox (which contains 6% chlorine from sodium hypochlorite) diluted with water 1:1 (v/v). Following sterilization, the sections are dipped in sterile distilled water for 1–2 min.

Culture Vessels. Use 25×180 mm test tubes containing 20 ml medium.

Culture Conditions. Nodes in culture are maintained under 150 ft-candles and 16-hr photoperiods provided by banks of 40-watt Sylvania Gro Lux tubes and incandescent bulbs. The temperature should be 22–25° C.

Culture Media. Modified Knop's (Gautheret, 1959) medium (Table A-21) is used for initial culture. Depending on which buds are being cultured, the medium must contain 1.5 mg, 14.8 mg, or 148 mg *trans*-cinnamic acid (Table A-21, item 7). The shoots which form are transferred to a modified Murashige-Skoog (1962) medium (Table A-22) for root initiation.

Procedure. After being washed, the stems are divided into three sections: upper, containing 25–33% of the nodes; middle, 30–50%; and basal, 25–33%. Buds from the upper section are sterilized for 5–7 min (longer periods are lethal), those from the middle portion for 10–15 min, and the basal ones for 20–25 min. Discolored tissues near the cut edges are removed following decontamination and the nodes are separated by transverse cuts. Those from the upper section are 5–7.5 cm in length; from the middle, 1.5–7.5 cm; and from the base, 1.5–2 cm (buds should be 0.75 cm from either end when possible). Sections from near the apex sometimes contain two buds which are difficult to separate owing to their proximity to each other.

All sections are placed on the agar basal-end down ("right-side up") and pushed half way into the initial medium (Table A-21) for stability. When shoots reach 1.5–2 cm in length, they are transferred to the rooting medium (Table A-22), where roots form within 14 days.

Table A-21. Modified Knop's medium as used for the culture of *Dendrobium* node sections (Mosich, Ball, and Arditti, 1974)

Item number	Component	Amount per liter of culture medium (final concentration in culture medium)	Stock solution (a concentrate prepared for repeated and convenient use)	Volume of stock solution per liter of culture medium	Remarks
	Macroelements[a]				
1	Calcium nitrate, $Ca(NO_3)_2 \cdot 4H_2O$[a]	500 mg	50 g/liter[a]	10 ml[a]	or weigh[a]
2	Potassium nitrate, KNO_3[a]	125 mg	12.5 g/liter[a]	10 ml[a]	or weigh[a]
3	Magnesium sulfate, $MgSO_4 \cdot 7H_2O$	125 mg	12.5 g/liter	10 ml	
4	Potassium phosphate, KH_2PO_4	125 mg	12.5 g/liter	10 ml	
	Iron[b]				
5	Ferric citrate, $FeC_6H_5O_7 \cdot 3H_2O$	10 mg	1 g/liter[b]	10 ml[b]	
6	*Microelements*[c]				
a	Boric acid, H_3BO_3	0.056 mg	56 mg/liter		
b	Manganese chloride, $MnCl_2 \cdot 4H_2O$	0.036 mg	36 mg/liter		
c	Zinc chloride, $ZnCl_2$	0.152 mg	152 mg/liter		
d	Cobaltous chloride, $CoCl_2$	0.02 mg	20 mg/liter	1 ml	one solution[c]
e	Copper chloride, $CuCl_2 \cdot 2H_2O$	0.054 mg	54 mg/liter		
f	Sodium molybdate, $Na_2MoO_4 \cdot 2H_2O$	0.025 mg	25 mg/liter		
g	Ferric chloride, $Fe_2Cl_3 \cdot 6H_2O$	0.5 mg	500 mg/liter		
h	Na_2EDTA	0.8 mg	800 mg/liter		
	Anti-auxin[d,e,f,g]				
7	*trans*-Cinnamic acid[d]	150,[e] 15,[f] or 1.5[g] mg	15 g/100 ml 95% ethanol	1,[e] 0.1,[f] or 0.01 ml	
	Vitamin[h]				
8	Thiamine (vitamin B_1)	0.4 mg	100 mg/100 ml 95% ethanol	0.4 ml	
	Cytokinin[h]				
9	6-Benzyl amino purine (benzyl adenine)	2.0 mg	100 mg/100 ml 95% ethanol	2.0 ml	
	Sugar[i]				
10	Sucrose	20 g	no stock	no stock	weigh
11	Water, distilled[i]	to 1000 ml			
	Solidifier[i]				
12	Agar	13 g	no stock	no stock	weigh

[a] Solutions containing nitrate and ammonium tend to become contaminated on standing. Therefore, it is better to weigh this component each time. If a stock solution is prepared, it must be kept frozen.

[b] If the substance does not dissolve, add a pellet or two of KOH. Shake well before dispensing.

[c] Add all microelements to the same one liter, stir and/or heat until dissolved. Add 1 ml to the culture medium.

[d] If *trans*-cinnamic acid does not dissolve, add a drop or two of HCl. Keep in the freezer.

[e] For nodes from the basal portion of the stem.

[f] For nodes from the midsection of the stem.

[g] For nodes from near the stem apex.

[h] Keep stock solution refrigerated.

[i] Autoclave agar (item 12) in 750 ml of distilled water (item 11); add items 1–10 for one liter to 250 ml distilled water; adjust pH to 5.5; sterilize by filtration and dispense under sterile conditions into preautoclaved culture flasks. An alternative is to dissolve items 1–6, 10, and 12 in 1000 ml of distilled water (item 11); autoclave; while still hot, add items 7–9 under sterile conditions; swirl to mix well and distribute into preautoclaved culture vessels.

Table A-22. Modified Murashige-Skoog (1962) medium as used for induction of roots on *Dendrobium* shoots obtained from node sections (Mosich, Ball, and Arditti, 1974)

Item number	Component	Amount per liter of culture medium (final concentration in culture medium)	Stock solution (a concentrate prepared for repeated and convenient use)	Volume of stock solution per liter of culture medium	Remarks
	Macroelements[a]				
1	Potassium phosphate, KH_2PO_4	170 mg	17 g/liter	10 ml	
2	Magnesium sulfate, $MgSO_4 \cdot 7H_2O$	370 mg	37 g/liter	10 ml	
3	Calcium chloride, $CaCl_2 \cdot 2H_2O$	440 mg	44 g/liter	10 ml	
4	Potassium nitrate, KNO_3[a]	1.9 g	95 g/liter[a]	20 ml[a]	or weigh[a]
5	Ammonium nitrate, NH_4NO_3[a]	1.65 g	82.5 g/liter[a]	20 ml[a]	or weigh[a]
6	*Chelated iron*[b]				
a	Na_2-EDTA	74.5 mg	7.45 g/liter		
b	Ferrous sulfate, $FeSO_4 \cdot 7H_2O$	27.8 mg	2.78 g/liter		
	Microelements[b]				
o	Boric acid, H_3BO_3	6.2 mg	620 mg/liter		
d	Manganese sulfate, $MnSO_4 \cdot 4H_2O$	22.3 mg	2.23 g/liter		one
e	Zinc chloride, $ZnCl_2$	3.93 mg	393 mg/liter	10 ml	solution[b]
f	Potassium iodide, KI	0.83 mg	83 mg/liter		
g	Sodium molybdate, $Na_2MoO_4 \cdot 2H_2O$	0.25 mg	25 mg/liter		
h	Copper sulfate, $CuSO_4 \cdot 5H_2O$	0.025 mg	2.5 mg/liter		
i	Cobaltous chloride, $CoCl_2 \cdot 6H_2O$	0.025 mg	2.5 mg/liter		
	Growth factor				
7	myo-Inositol	100 mg	no stock	no stock	weigh
	Auxin[c]				
8	Indoleacetic acid	0.1 mg	50 mg/50 ml 95% ethanol[c]	0.1 ml	
	Vitamin[c]				
9	Thiamine (vitamin B_1)	0.4 mg	100 mg/100 ml 95% ethanol	0.4 ml	
	Sugar[d]				
10	Sucrose	30 g	no stock	no stock	weigh
11	Water, distilled[d]	to 1000 ml			
	Solidifier[d]				
12	Agar	13 g	no stock	no stock	weigh

[a] Solutions containing ammonium and nitrate may become contaminated. Therefore, stock solutions should not be prepared. If made, they must be kept frozen between uses.

[b] Add the chelated iron (items a–b) and all microelements (c–i) to the same one liter of distilled water; stir and/or heat until dissolved. Add 10 ml per liter of culture medium.

[c] Keep refrigerated.

[d] Mix items 1–9 with 800 ml of distilled water (item 11); adjust the pH to 5.8; add the sugar (item 10); and bring the volume to 1000 ml with more distilled water (item 11). Distribute into culture vessels and autoclave.

Developmental Sequence. Buds start to grow after 4 weeks on Knop's medium and plantlets develop within 45 days. Most of them do not have roots and must be transferred to the rooting medium 2–3 weeks later (12–13 weeks after placing the nodes in culture). There they form roots within 2 weeks.

General Comments. This is a simple method which does not require sophisticated equipment or advanced skills. Its major disadvantage—the need to remove (and, therefore, endanger) an entire stem—is balanced by the very high rate of success (75–100%). Furthermore, it is possible to use old and/or damaged canes as long as a few buds are intact. Recent evidence suggests that it should be possible to excise basal buds only (leaving the stem otherwise intact) and culture them. We have had limited success with this procedure to date, and hope to refine it. Only one plantlet is formed from each bud, although on rare occasions we have noted considerable proliferation. With further modifications, the procedure could perhaps induce proliferation.

Vegetative Propagation of *Dendrobium* by Flower-Stalk Cuttings

Following removal or wilting of unpollinated blossoms, the flower stalks of *Dendrobium* die. Hence, use of their buds amounts to the proper utilization of material which would otherwise be wasted. Therefore, according to every consideration, a procedure for clonal propagation using flower-stalk cuttings (Singh and Sagawa, 1972) is not only very clever but also economical and safe.

Plant Material. Flower stalks of *Dendrobium* having well-developed buds are used.

Surface Sterilization. Wipe stems several times with a cheesecloth soaked in 95% ethyl alcohol (ethanol), cut into sections, and soak for 15 min in 10% Clorox (v/v). Then remove bracts, transfer into 10% Clorox (v/v) for 10 min, and dip into sterile distilled water for 3 min (Intuwong, Kunisaki, and Sagawa, 1972).

Culture Vessels. Use 25×100 mm vials containing 12 ml medium.

Culture Conditions. Maintain cultures under continuous illumination of approximately 200 ft-candles (provided by General Electric Power Groove white fluorescent lamps) at 23–29° C.

Culture Medium. Modified Vacin and Went (Intuwong, Kunisaki, and Sagawa, 1972) medium (Table A-27) is most suitable.

Procedure. Cut stems into sections, leaving 1–1.5 cm on either side of each bud. Surface-sterilize the flower-stalk sections and remove discolored tissues from near the cut edges. Insert sections into the culture medium to just below the bud.

Developmental Sequence. Plantlets with well-developed shoots and roots can be obtained within a few months.

General Comments. Not all *Dendrobium* plants have a sufficient number of well-developed buds on flower stems. When such buds are available, however, this can be a very useful procedure, even if only one plantlet is obtained per bud.

Epidendrum

Interest in *Epidendrum* is not as wide as that in *Cattleya*, *Cymbidium*, or *Dendrobium*. Therefore, fewer methods have been developed for clonal propagation through tissue culture (Arditti *et al.*, 1971, 1972; Churchill, Arditti, and Ball, 1972; Churchill, Ball, and Arditti, 1970, 1973; Churchill *et al.*, 1971; Scully, 1967). One method has also been used for basic physiological research (Rudolph, Ball, and Arditti, 1972). In addition, root tips can be cultured, but they fail to form calli or to develop into plants (Churchill, Ball, and Arditti, 1972).

Propagation of *Epidendrum* by the Culture of Explants from Vegetative Shoots

The method was developed as part of the work with the *Cattleya* alliance (Scully, 1967). In cases described as "excepted instances," single protocorm-like bodies arose from *Epidendrum conopseum* explants. Subculture of the bodies was unsuccessful. This simply means that additional work is needed to perfect the method.

Production of *Epidendrum* Plants from Leaf Tips

Use of leaf tips as a source of explants has the advantage of not endangering or even seriously damaging a plant. Rather, the donor plant is only disfigured very slightly (Arditti *et al.*, 1971, 1972; Churchill, Arditti, and Ball, 1972; Churchill, Ball, and Arditti, 1970, 1973).

Plant Material. Leaf tips from one-year-old (but possibly older) seedlings growing in flasks under normal conditions are used (Arditti, 1967; Harrison, 1968; Harrison and Arditti, 1970).

Surface Sterilization. This is not necessary since the seedlings are already axenic.

Culture Vessels. Use 125-ml Erlenmeyer flasks containing 50 ml medium.

Culture Conditions. Liquid cultures are placed on a reciprocating shaker moving at the rate of 60 oscillations/min, 50 cm below banks of Sylvania Gro Lux tubes and incadescent bulbs producing 150 ft-candles during 18-hr photoperiods. The temperature is maintained at 22–25° C. Solid cultures are kept under the same conditions on a stationary surface.

Culture Media. A modified liquid Murashige-Skoog (1962) medium (Table A-23) is used for the initial culture. Callus cultures are maintained on solidified Murashige-Skoog or Linsmaier-Skoog (1965) media (Table A-15). Differentiation into normal plantlets is obtained on Knudson C (1946) medium (Table A-16).

Procedure. Seedlings are removed from flasks and placed on sterile petri dishes, microscope slides, or aluminium foil. Tips no larger than 4–5 mm (but the best size is 2 mm, about the size of a pinhead) are removed with sterile scalpels or razor blades and suspended in culture medium. The flasks are then placed on the shaker. When tissue masses form, they should be divided and placed on solid Murashige-Skoog (Table A-23) or Linsmaier-Skoog (Table A-15) media. After a new tissue mass is formed, it should also be subdivided. For plantlet development, portions of the mass (which are in fact pseudobulb-like bodies) are transferred to Knudson C medium (Table A-16).

Developmental Sequence. Leaf tips remain green without any apparent changes or growth for nearly 60 days. After that, approximately 7% form calli. When divided and transferred to solid Murashige-Skoog or Linsmaier-Skoog media, these form large callus masses. After a while, abnormal plantlets are formed on these media. Following 3 weeks on Knudson C medium, callus sections form normal plantlets.

General Comments. Since the explants are obtained from unflowered seedlings, the procedure cannot be used for the propagation of desirable clones. Perhaps with further research a way can be found for the culture of leaf tips from adult plants. In the meanwhile, this method can be useful for the production of *Epidendrum* callus cultures for research purposes. These cultures can apparently be subdivided indefinitely (some of our cultures are still growing well after three years).

Culture of *Epidendrum* Root Tips

It seems reasonable to assume that since orchid root tips contain meristematic zones, they can be made to grow *in vitro*. If so, another logical assumption is that they can be made to form callus cultures and, eventually, plantlets. As of this writing, the first assumption has been proven correct. Proof for the second, at least insofar as orchids are concerned, is still lacking. *Epidendrum* root tips, then, can be cultured, but all they produce is roots, albeit longer roots (Churchill, Ball, and Arditti, 1972).

Plant Material. Free-hanging, aerial, mycorrhiza-free roots must be used. Roots that have reached the potting medium, touched the pot, or crawled over benches, become infected by mycorrhizal fungus which grows out of them and contaminates the culture medium.

Surface Sterilization. Roots are soaked in saturated calcium hypochlorite solution (10 g/140 ml water) for about 5 min.

Culture Vessels. Use 100-ml prescription bottles containing 10–20 ml solid medium which has been allowed to solidify on the under- (flat) surface; 125- or 250-ml Erlenmeyer flasks containing 25 or 50 ml medium, respectively, can also be used. For the subculture of larger roots, 1000-ml prescription bottles containing 200 ml medium should be used.

Table A-23. Modified Murashige-Skoog (1962) medium for the culture of *Epidendrum* leaf tips (Churchill, Ball, and Arditti, 1970)

Item number	Component	Amount per liter of culture medium (final concentration in culture medium)	Stock solution (a concentrate prepared for repeated and convenient use)	Volume of stock solution per liter of culture medium	Remarks
	Macroelements[a]				
1	Potassium phosphate, KH_2PO_4	170 mg	17 g/liter	10 ml	
2	Magnesium sulfate, $MgSO_4 \cdot 7H_2O$	370 mg	37 g/liter	10 ml	
3	Calcium chloride, $CaCl_2 \cdot 2H_2O$	440 mg	44 g/liter	10 ml	
4	Potassium nitrate, KNO_3[a]	1900 mg	85 g/liter[a]	20 ml[a]	or weigh[a]
5	Ammonium nitrate, NH_4NO_3[a]	1650 mg	82.5 g/liter[a]	20 ml[a]	or weigh[a]
6	*Iron chelate*[b]				
a	Disodium EDTA, NA_2-EDTA	74.6 mg	7.46 g/liter		
b	Ferrous sulfate, $FeSO_4 \cdot 7H_2O$	27.8 mg	2.78 g/liter		
7	*Microelements*[b]				
c	Boric acid, H_3BO_3	6.2 mg	620 mg/liter		
d	Manganese sulfate, $MnSO_4 \cdot 4H_2O$	22.3 mg	223 mg/liter		
e	Zinc chloride, $ZnCl_2$	3.93 mg	393 mg/liter	10 ml	one solution
f	Potassium iodide, KI	0.83 mg	83 mg/liter		
g	Sodium molybdate, $Na_2MoO_4 \cdot 2H_2O$	0.25 mg	25 mg/liter		
h	Copper sulfate, $CuSO_4 \cdot 5H_2O$	0.025 mg	2.5 mg/liter		
i	Cobalt chloride, $CoCl_2 \cdot 6H_2O$	0.025 mg	2.5 mg/liter		
8	*Amino acid*[c] Glycine	2 mg	2 g/liter 95% ethanol	1 ml[c]	
9	*Auxin*[d] 2,4-Dichlorophenoxyacetic acid	1 mg	50 mg/25 ml 95% ethanol	0.5 ml[d]	
10	*Cytokinin*[e] 6-Benzyl amino purine (Benzyl adenine)	0.5 mg	50 mg/50 ml 95% ethanol	0.5 ml[e]	
11	*Vitamin*[f] Thiamine (vitamin B_1)	0.4 mg	80 mg/100 ml 95% ethanol	0.5 ml[f]	
12	*Sugar*[g] Sucrose	30 g	no stock	no stock	weigh
13	Water, distilled[g]	to 1000 ml			
14	*Solidifier*[g] Agar	10–15 g	no stock	no stock	weigh

[a] Solutions containing ammonium and nitrate may become contaminated. Therefore, stock solutions should not be prepared. If made, they must be kept frozen between uses.

[b] Add the chelated iron (items a–b) and all microelements (items c–i) to the same one liter of distilled water; stir and/or heat until dissolved. Add 10 ml per liter of culture medium.

[c] Keep frozen between uses.

[d] If the auxin does not dissolve, add a few drops of HCl. Keep stock solution refrigerated.

[e] If the cytokinin does not dissolve, add a pellet or two of KOH. Keep the stock solution refrigerated.

[f] Keep refrigerated.

[g] Add items 1–10 to 700 ml of distilled water (item 13) and dissolve; adjust the pH to 5.5; add the sugar (item 12) and bring the volume up to 1000 ml with more distilled water (item 13). Sterilize by filtration and distribute into preautoclaved culture vessels. Alternately, dissolve items 1–7 and 12 in 1000 ml of distilled water (item 13) and autoclave; add items 8–11 with sterile pipettes under sterile conditions to the autoclaved salt solution and distribute into preautoclaved culture vessels. When solid medium is required, dissolve the sugar (item 12) and the agar (item 14) in 750 ml of distilled water (item 13) and autoclave. Add items 1–11 to 250 ml of distilled water (item 13) and adjust the pH to 5.5; sterilize by filtration; mix with the autoclaved solution while it is still hot and liquid; swirl to mix well and dispense into sterile culture vessels. Alternately, add items 1–7 to 800 ml of distilled water (item 13); adjust the pH to 5.5; add the sugar (item 12) and bring the volume up to 1000 ml with more distilled water (item 13). Dissolve the agar (item 14) and autoclave the solution. After autoclaving and while it is still hot and liquid, add items 8–11 with sterile pipettes under sterile conditions. Swirl to mix well and distribute into preautoclaved culture vessels.

Culture Conditions. Use the same conditions as for *Epidendrum* leaf tips (p. 246; Churchill, Ball, and Arditti, 1970, 1973), except that the root tips are grown on solid medium.

Culture Medium. Modified Ojima and Fujiwara (1962) medium is most suitable for root-tip cultures (Table A-24).

Table A-24. Modified Ojima and Fujiwara (1962) medium for the culture of *Epidendrum* root tips (Churchill, Ball, and Arditti, 1972)

Item number	Component	Amount per liter of medium (final concentration in culture medium)	Stock solution (a concentrate prepared for repeated and convenient use)	Volume of stock solution per liter of culture medium	Remarks
	Macroelements[a]				
1	Potassium nitrate, KNO_3[a]	20.2 mg	2.02 g/liter[a]	10 ml[a]	or weigh[a]
2	Calcium nitrate, $Ca(NO_3)_2 \cdot 4H_2O$[a]	136.7 mg	13.67 g/liter[a]	10 ml[a]	or weigh[a]
3	Potassium phosphate, KH_2PO_4	4.08 mg	408 mg/liter	10 ml	
4	Magnesium sulfate, $MgSO_4 \cdot 7H_2O$	48 mg	4.80 g/liter	10 ml	
5	Ferric sulfate, $Fe_2(SO_4)_3$	1 mg	1 g/liter	1 ml	
6	*Microelements*[b]				
a	Manganous chloride, $MnCl_2 \cdot 4H_2O$	1 mg	1 g/liter		
b	Zinc sulfate, $ZnSO_4 \cdot 7H_2O$	0.02 mg	20 mg/liter		
c	Potassium iodide, KI	0.02 mg	20 mg/liter	1 ml	one solution[b]
d	Boric acid, H_3BO_3	0.02 mg	20 mg/liter		
e	Ammonium molybdate, $(NH_4)_2MoO_4$	0.02 mg	20 mg/liter		
	Vitamins[c]				
7	Niacin (Nicotinic acid)[c]	0.5 mg	50 mg/100 ml 95% ethanol	1 ml	
8	Pyridoxine (vitamin B_6)[c]	0.5 mg	50 mg/100 ml 95% ethanol	1 ml	or combine[c]
9	Thiamine (vitamin B_1)[a]	0.1 mg	10 mg/100 ml 95% ethanol	1 ml	
	Complex additive				
10	Neopeptone	300 mg	no stock	no stock	weigh
	Sugar[d]				
11	Sucrose	20 g	no stock	no stock	weigh
12	Water, distilled[d]	to 1000 ml			
	Solidifier[d]				
13	Agar	10–15 g	no stock	no stock	weigh

[a] Solutions containing nitrate and ammonium may become contaminated on standing. Therefore, it is best to weigh items 1 and 2 every time. If stock solutions are prepared, they must be kept frozen.

[b] Add all microelements to the same one liter of distilled water; stir and/or heat until dissolved. Add 1 ml per liter of culture medium.

[c] The vitamins may be combined into one stock solution. Add 50 mg each of niacin and pyridoxine and 10 mg of thiamine to the same 100 ml of 95% ethanol and use 1 ml of this per liter of culture medium. Refrigerate between uses.

[d] Add items 1–10 to 800 ml of distilled water (item 12) and dissolve; adjust pH to 5.0 (it will change to 5.1, which is the desired pH); add the sugar (item 11) and bring the volume up to 1000 ml with more distilled water (item 12) For solid medium, dissolve the agar (item 13) by adding it to the gently boiling solution while stirring. When fully dissolved, distribute into culture vessels and autoclave.

Procedure. Root tips are placed on the medium and allowed to grow. After 2 months they elongate and can be subcultured by removing and transferring the tips to new medium. The procedure can be repeated 3 months later. Thereafter, transfers can be made every 6 months. Or the tips can be placed in a large bottle from the outset and not transferred.

Developmental Sequence. Roots simply grow in length, but their diameters and growth rate decrease with time. After one year, some roots may be 5–6 cm long while others reach 15 cm, but all become thinner than roots of equal length growing on plants. After two years in culture, the roots can still grow but lose their chlorophyll. Detipped roots do not grow.

General Comments. The culture medium apparently does not provide roots with sufficient amounts of some or all requirements. Neither is it capable of inducing callus formation. Roots on Murashige-Skoog, Heller's, and a special "meristem" medium (Ball, Arditti, and Churchill, 1971) liquid or solid, shaken or not, die. Some roots, like those of *Phalaenopsis*, swell tantalizingly, as if to form a callus, but die just the same. Perhaps someday a method for the production of callus cultures and plants from orchid root tips may be developed. Several orchids naturally produce buds and plants on their roots. For the time being, however, root-tip culture of orchids may be a subject for wishful thinking and a means for the production of roots to be used as experimental organs.

Laelia

Use the same procedures as for *Brassocattleya* (p. 216; Kako, 1973).

Laeliocattleya

Use the same procedures as for *Brassocattleya* (p. 216; Kako, 1973).

Lycaste

Use the same procedures as for *Cymbidium* (p. 233; Morel, 1960, 1963, 1964a, 1965b).

Miltonia

Use the same procedures as for *Cymbidium* (p. 233; Morel, 1960, 1963, 1964a, 1965b, 1970).

Neostylis

Use the same procedures as for *Ascofinetia* (p. 212; Intuwong and Sagawa, 1973).

Neottia nidus-avis

Renewal of apical growth occurs at the tips of *Neottia nidus-avis* roots maintained in the dark at 12° C or 15° C. This is followed by the formation of protocorm-like bodies, the development of buds, and the appearance of adventitious roots (Champagnat, 1971).

Odontioda

Development of excised meristem is relatively simple. A large callus consisting of numerous protocorm-like bodies is formed. Each of them leads to a plantlet (Morel, 1974). Procedures used for *Odontonia* should also apply to *Odontioda*.

Odontoglossum

Use the same procedures as for *Cymbidium* (p. 233; Morel, 1960, 1963, 1964a, 1965b, 1970).

Odontonia

Use the same procedures as for *Cymbidium* (p. 233; Morel, 1960, 1963, 1964a, 1965b, 1970).

Oncidium

Clonal propagation of *Oncidium* is possible through the culture of shoot tips and flower stalks.

Clonal Propagation of *Oncidium* by Means of Shoot-Tip Cultures

Not many details are available. However, the context in which this genus is mentioned (Bertsch, 1967) suggests that the procedures used for *Cymbidium* (p. 233; Morel, 1960, 1963, 1964a, 1965b, 1970) may also be employed for *Oncidium*. In addition, I have seen a number of impressive cultures in Dr. Yoneo Sagawa's laboratory at the University of Hawaii. I am assuming that they are using a procedure similar to those for *Cattleya* (p. 222; Scully, 1967) and *Cymbidium* (p. 233; Sagawa, Shoji, and Shoji, 1966).

Clonal Propagation of *Oncidium* by Means of Flower-Stalk-Tip Cultures

Propagation methods involving the culture of flower-stem parts are nondestructive. Therefore, several investigators have tried to develop culture methods for flower-stem parts of a number of species. One of these species is *Oncidium papilio* (Fast, 1973).

Plant Material. Flower stalks of *Oncidium papilio* with apical buds which are still dormant are used.

Surface Sterilization. Remove all dry sheaths and rinse sections under running water. Dip in alcohol, pass through a flame, immediately immerse in freshly filtered 5% (w/v) calcium hypochlorite, and soak for about 10 min while occasionally shaking.

Culture Vessels. Use 30×180 mm test tubes with 10 ml liquid medium, covered with cotton buns or two-hole rubber stoppers with cotton stuffed in their holes or 25- to 500-ml Erlenmeyer flasks stoppered in the same manner.

Culture Conditions. Maintain cultures under diffuse light at temperature of 20–24° C. When a rotating table is used, set it at 5 rpm.

Culture Media. Use a modified Knudson C (Table A-25) medium (liquid or solid) for callus induction. Use a modified Murashige-Skoog (Table A-26a) with half the amount of mineral components or a mixture of it with Knudson C full strength (1:1, v/v), both either liquid or solid (Tables A-25, A-26a), for propagation of the callus. For differentiation, use a solid half-strength Murashige-Skoog or the mixture of Murashige-Skoog and Knudson C media, either one with the addition of 5–10% (w/v) tomato or banana homogenate (Table A-25, A-26b).

Procedure. Remove the top 2 cm from a flower stalk, take off all dry sheaths, and wash under running water. After surface sterilization (see above), the section must be

Table A-25. Knudson C (1946) medium modified for the culture of *Oncidium* (Fast. 1973)[a]

Item number	Component	Amount per liter of culture medium (final concentration in culture medium)	Stock solution (a concentrate prepared for repeated and convenient use)	Volume of stock solution per liter of culture medium	Remarks
	Macroelements				
1	Ammonium sulfate, $(NH_4)_2SO_4$	1 g	100 g/liter	10 ml	or weigh
2	Calcium nitrate, $Ca(NO_3)_2 \cdot 4H_2O$	500 mg	50 g/liter	10 ml	
3	Potassium chloride, KCl	250 mg	25 g/liter	10 ml	
4	Potassium phosphate, monobasic, KH_2PO_4	250 mg	25 g/liter	10 ml	
5	Magnesium sulfate, $MgSO_4 \cdot 7H_2O$	250 mg	25 g/liter	10 ml	
6	Iron chelate, Fe-EDTA	25 mg	2.5 g/liter	10 ml	
7	*Microelements*				
a	Boric acid, H_3BO_3	1 mg	1 g/liter		
b	Zinc sulfate, $ZnSO_4 \cdot 7H_2O$	1 mg	1 g/liter		
c	Manganese sulfate, $MnSO_4 \cdot 4H_2O$	0.01 mg	10 mg/liter	1 ml	one solution
d	Cupric sulfate, $CuSO_4 \cdot 5H_2O$	0.03 mg	30 mg/liter		
e	Aluminum chloride, $AlCl_3$	0.03 mg	30 mg/liter		
f	Nickel chloride, $NiCl_2 \cdot 6H_2O$	0.03 mg	30 mg/liter		
g	Potassium iodide, KI	0.01 mg	10 mg/liter		

[a] Prepare in accordance with instructions for Table A-10 and include items 9–11.

Table A-26a and b. Modified Murashige-Skoog (1962) full-strength medium for the culture of *Oncidium* (Fast, 1973)

Item number	Component	Amount per liter of culture medium (final concentration in culture medium)	Stock solution (a concentrate prepared for repeated and convenient use)	Volume of stock solution per liter of culture medium	Remarks
	Macroelements[a]				
1	Ammonium sulfate, $(NH_4)_2SO_4$[a]	1.65 g	165 g/liter[a]	10 ml[a]	or weigh[a]
2	Potassium nitrate, KNO_3[a]	1.9 g	190 g/liter[a]	10 ml[a]	or weigh[a]
3	Potassium phosphate, monobasic KH_2PO_4	170 mg	17 g/liter	10 ml	
4	Magnesium sulfate, $MgSO_4 \cdot 7H_2O$	370 mg	37 g/liter	10 ml	
5	Calcium chloride, $CaCl_2 \cdot 2H_2O$	440 mg	44 g/liter	10 ml	
6	Iron chelate, Fe_2-EDTA	25 mg	25 g/liter	10 ml	
7	*Microelements*[b]				
a	Boric acid, H_3BO_3	1 mg	1 g/liter		
b	Zinc sulfate, $ZnSO_4 \cdot 7H_2O$	7 mg	7 g/liter		
c	Manganese sulfate, $MnSO_4 \cdot 4H_2O$	0.01 mg	10 mg/liter	1 ml	one solution[b]
d	Cupric sulfate, $CuSO_4 \cdot 5H_2O$	0.03 mg	30 mg/liter		
e	Aluminum chloride, $AlCl_3$	0.03 mg	30 mg/liter		
f	Nickel chloride, $NiCl_2 \cdot 6H_2O$	0.03 mg	30 mg/liter		
g	Potassium iodide, KI	0.01 mg	10 mg/liter		
	Vitamins[c,d,e]				
8	Niacin (nicotinic acid)	1 mg	100 mg/100 ml 95% ethanol	1 ml	
9	Thiamine (vitamin B_1)	0.5 mg	50 mg/100 ml 95% ethanol	1 ml	or combine[d]
10	Pyridoxine (vitamin B_6)	0.5 mg	50 mg/100 ml 95% ethanol	1 ml	
	Auxin[c,e,f]				
11	NAA	0.5 mg	50 mg/100 ml 95% ethanol	1 ml	
	Cytokinin[c,e,f]				or combine[f]
12	Kinetin	0.05 mg	5 mg/100 ml 95% ethanol	1 ml	
	Complex additives				
13	Peptone[c]	1 g	no stock	no stock	weigh
14	Tomato or banana pulp[g]	50–100 g	no stock	no stock	weigh
	Sugar[h]				
15	Sucrose	20 g	no stock	no stock	weigh
	Solidifier[h]				
16	Agar	10–12 g	no stock	no stock	weigh
17	Water, distilled[h]	to 1000 ml			

[a] Solutions containing nitrate and ammonium may become contaminated on standing. Therefore, it is best to weigh items 1 and 2 every time. If stock solutions are prepared, they must be kept frozen.

[b] Add all microelements to the same one liter of distilled water; stir and/or heat until dissolved. Add 1 ml per liter of culture medium.

[c] Add only to medium A-26a.

[d] All vitamins may be combined into the same 100 ml of 95% ethanol; use 1 ml per liter of culture medium. Refrigerate or freeze between uses.

[e] All vitamins and both hormones may be combined into the same 100 ml of 95% ethanol; use 1 ml per liter of culture medium. Refrigerate or freeze between uses.

[f] Both hormones may be combined into the same 100 ml of 95% ethanol; use 1 ml per liter of culture medium. Refrigerate or freeze between uses.

[g] Add only to solution A-26b.

[h] Mix items 1–7, 13, and 14 with 800 ml of distilled water (item 17); adjust the pH to 5.0–5.5; add the sugar (item 15) and bring the volume up to 1000 ml with more distilled water (item 17). To dissolve the agar (item 16), add it slowly, while stirring, to the gently boiling solution. When the agar is fully dissolved, autoclave the medium under standard conditions. Use agar only if a solid medium is desired. Combine vitamins (items 8–10), auxin (item 11), and cytokinin (item 12) and add after the medium has been autoclaved (and before it solidifies if agar has been included), using sterile glassware and under aseptic conditions. Mix well and distribute the medium into sterile culture vessels.

handled with sterile forceps. Under aseptic conditions, the very tip is cut off with a sterile scalpel and discarded, and the 2–3 mm section below is removed and placed with the cut surface on the agar nutrient medium when solid medium is utilized.

Developmental Sequence. Depending on the physiological condition of the bud, a callus and subsequently protocorm-like bodies will be formed 4–8 weeks after the start of culture. These bodies are separated and subcultured. This is repeated every 4 weeks depending on the vitality of the explant, the composition of the nutrient medium, and the season. Several thousand protocorms can be obtained 6 months after the start of propagation. Shoots and roots will form on a medium which contains tomato or banana extract. After 6 months, the new plantlets should be transferred once more onto the same medium in larger flasks (500-ml Erlenmeyer flasks). This allows growth of strong plants which are planted and treated like normal seedlings.

General Comments. Oncidium papilio is a very pretty orchid which can be propagated from seed or through tissue culture rather than collected from the forest and thereby brought to near extinction.

Ophrys

Explants (cubes, 5 mm on each side) of *Ophrys fuciflora* and other species taken in July during the rest period and maintained on a modified Murashige-Skoog (essentially as in Table A-1 but with 0.1 μg/liter naphthalene acetic acid and 0.1 μg/liter of kinetin) form callus cultures on which protocorm-like bodies develop (Champagnat and Morel, 1972; Morel, 1974).

Paphiopedilum

Success with shoot-tip cultures of *Paphiopedilum* has been very limited (Morel, 1974).

Phajus

Use the same procedures as for *Cymbidium* (p. 233; Morel, 1960, 1963, 1964a, 1965b, 1970).

Phalaenopsis

Like a number of other orchids (for a list, see Churchill, Ball, and Arditti, 1972), some *Phalaenopsis* species may naturally produce buds or shoots on their roots. These include *P. deliciosa* (Reichenbach, 1885), *P. schilleriana* (Anonymous, 1885), and *P. stuartiana* (Scully, 1971). However, attempts in our laboratory to produce plants or even callus cultures from *Phalaenopsis* roots have failed to date. Occasionally, root tips would swell as if to produce a callus, but these and all other *Phalaenopsis* root explants have invariably died (Arditti, unpublished). Roots of *Neottia nidus-avis* also form protocorms on which buds and adventitious roots are formed (Champagnat, 1971).

Several *Phalaenopsis* species produce plantlets on their flower stalks. This and the natural tendency of horticulturists to attempt propagation with or from buds are no doubt responsible for early efforts (reported in the older British orchid literature) to propagate *Phalaenopsis* by producing plantlets from nodes on flower stalks. The old method was to place the nodes just below the surface of peat or sphagnum moss, keep the medium moist, and hope. Occasionally, plantlets were produced.

It was natural that the development of media for orchid seed germination (Knudson, 1921, 1922, 1946) would lead to attempts to culture of *Phalaenopsis* flower-stalk buds *in vitro*. Despite reports of success rates of up to 89%, a method employing the Knudson C medium (Rotor, 1949) did not find wide application. One reason for the abandonment of this technique was the high percentage of contaimination in the hands of hobbyists and commercial growers (Intuwong *et al.*, 1972). A number of modifications or different procedures have been published since (Intuwong *et al.*, 1972; Kotomori and Murashige, 1965; Sagawa, 1961; Sagawa and Niimoto, 1960; Scully, 1965, 1966; Tse, Smith, and Hackett, 1971; Urata and Iwanaga, 1965).

Attempts to culture meristems from flower stalks and buds of *Phalaenopsis* have not been very successful. Mortality rates of explants during culture and following division are very high, largely because of the presence of phenolic compounds. These compounds become oxidized on the cut surface and the oxidation products are toxic (Morel, 1970). Nevertheless, protocorms can be obtained from meristems of flower-stalk buds (Intuwong and Sagawa, 1974; Morel, 1970).

Vegetative Propagation of *Phalaenopsis* by Flower-Stalk Cuttings

The first method for *in vitro* culture of buds from *Phalaenopsis* flower stalks (Rotor, 1949) has been modified a number of times. The most recent modification involves a two-stage sterilization with Clorox and culturing on a modified Vacin and Went (1949) medium (Intuwong *et al.*, 1972).

Plant Material. Use clean, healthy, vigorous flower stalks with buds in their nodes. Stalks on which only a few flowers have bloomed are best; old stalks should be avoided.

Surface Sterilization. Wipe stalks 2–3 times using cheesecloth wet with 95% ethyl alcohol (ethanol) or 10% Clorox (10 ml Clorox and 90 ml distilled water plus 2–3 drops of Tween 20). Following sectioning, soak the nodes 15 min in 10% Clorox. After removal of the bracts, soak the sections in 5% Clorox (5 ml Clorox and 95 ml distilled water plus 2–3 drops of Tween 20) for 10 min and dip in sterile distilled water for 3 min. If Tween 20 is not available, use 2–3 drops of a mild household detergent.

Culture Vessels. Use 10 × 100 mm vials containing 12 ml medium.

Culture Conditions. Maintain cultures under approximately 200 ft-candles of continuous illumination. Under the original conditions, the light source was probably General Electric Power Groove white fluorescent tubes, but Sylvania Gro Lux lamps could also be used. In addition, the cultures may be maintained under light conditions usually employed for seedlings. The temperature should be 23–29° C.

Culture Medium. A modified Vacin and Went (1949) medium is used (Table A-27).

Procedure. Remove flower stalks from a plant and wipe them using cheesecloth wet with 95% ethanol or 10% Clorox. With a sterile razor blade or scalpel, cut the stalk into 65-mm sections, leaving 25 mm above the node and 40 mm below it. Soak the sections in 10% Clorox for 15 min. Expose the bud by removing the bract which covers it with sterile forceps. Care must be taken to remove the entire bract from all sides of the stalk without injuring the bud. Then transfer the sections to 5% Clorox for 10 min and rinse with sterile distilled water for 3 min. Place the section on a sterile petri dish or glass slide. Cut away 12 mm from each end with a sterile razor blade (preferably the type which has one cutting edge and a blunt side covered with a sleeve; these are known as Valet-type blades) or scalpel. All tools must be dipped frequently in 95% ethanol or 10% Clorox to insure their sterility.

Table A-27. Modified Vacin and Went (1949) medium used for the culture of *Phalaenopsis* stalk cuttings (Intuwong, Kunisaki, and Sagawa, 1972)

Item number	Component	Amount per liter of culture medium (final concentration in culture medium)	Stock solution (a concentrate prepared for repeated and convenient use)	Volume of stock solution per liter of culture medium	Remarks
	Macroelements[a,b,c]				
1	Tricalcium phosphate, $Ca_3(PO_4)_2$[a]	200 mg	20 g/liter[a]	10 ml[a]	
2	Potassium nitrate, KNO_3[b]	525 mg	52.5 g/liter[b]	10 ml[b]	or weigh[b]
3	Potassium phosphate, KH_2PO_4	250 mg	25 g/liter	10 ml	
4	Magnesium sulfate, $MgSO_4 \cdot 7H_2O$	250 mg	25 g/liter	10 ml	
5	Ammonium sulfate, $(NH_4)_2SO_4$[b]	500 mg	50 g/liter[b]	10 ml[b]	or weigh[b]
6	Ferric tartrate, $Fe_2(C_4H_4O_6)_3$[c]	28 mg	2.8 g/liter[c]	10 ml[c]	
	Microelements				
7	Manganese sulfate, $MnSO_4 \cdot 2H_2O$	5.7 mg	5.7 g/liter	1 ml	
	Sugar				
8	Sucrose	20 g	no stock	no stock	weigh
9	Water, distilled[d]	to 1000 ml			
	Solidifier[d,e]				
10	Agar	9 g[e]	no stock	no stock	weigh

[a] If the salt does not dissolve completely, shake the solution well before dispensing to mix well; or better yet, weigh out each time.

[b] Solutions containing ammonium and nitrate may become contaminated. Therefore, stock solutions should not be prepared. If made, they must be kept frozen between uses.

[c] Ferric tartrate is relatively insoluble. Grinding it with a mortar and pestle before dissolving helps. The addition of a pellet or two of KOH to the solution will increase solubility, but a precipitate may form nevertheless. To insure equal distribution, shake stock solution well before dispensing.

[d] Dissolve items 1–7 in 900 ml of distilled water (item 9); adjust the pH to 4.8–5.0; add sugar (item 8) and bring the volume up to 1000 ml with more distilled water (item 9). Add the agar (item 10) slowly, while stirring, to the gently boiling solution. When fully dissolved, dispense into culture vessels and autoclave.

[e] If cultures are maintained at 29° C, the amount of agar should be increased to 12–15 g/liter.

Transfer the sections from the petri dish or glass slide to culture vials, inserting them at a slight angle to just below the bud. Place the vials under the required culture conditions.

Developmental Sequence. Shoot growth generally appears within a month. Most shoots are well rooted and ready for removal from the vial after 2 months. After that, the plantlets develop and should be treated like seedlings.

General Comments. If inflorescences appear instead of plantlets, allow the cultures to remain undisturbed and aseptically remove the terminal portion of the new flower stalk. As a result of this step, plantlets may be formed from the lowermost node of the new inflorescence.

The main advantage of this method is that the plant itself is not damaged or endangered. A disadvantage is the lack of callus formation. This limits propagation to the available flower-stalk buds. In our laboratory, some buds have produced two plantlets on occasion. Also, not all sections survive and some buds fail to grow. A great improvement of the procedure would be the induction of callus, and we are currently working on that.

A more recent method is described on p. 258.

Clonal Propagation of *Phalaenopsis* by Shoot-Tip Culture

Considerable difficulties have been encountered in the development of shoot-tip (or other tissue) culture methods for *Phalaenopsis*. A major problem is generated by the high content of phenolic compounds in shoot tips. Explants turn black quickly, oxidation products of the phenolics diffuse into the medium, and the tissues die (Morel, 1974). We also encountered the same problem, but like others (Morel, 1974) have been unable to find a satisfactory solution. Not so at the University of Hawaii, where a successful method for the culture of *Phalaenopsis* shoot tips was developed (Intuwong and Sagawa, 1974).

Plant Material. Phalaenopsis amabilis, *P.* xStar of Santa Crux, *P.* xSurfrider, *P.* xRuby Lips, and *P.* xArcadia × *P. cochlaearis* were used in the original work. Explants are removed from vegetative shoots with 6–7 leaves or from plantlets obtained from aseptic cultures of flower-stalk nodes. Leaf blades are removed and the shoot axis is then sterilized with 10% Clorox. After the leaf bases are removed, the material is sterilized again, this time with 5% Clorox. Explants, 2–3 mm³ in size, consisting of the apical meristem, 2–4 leaf primordia, and 2–3 axillary buds covered by scalelike leaves, are removed after the final sterilization and cultured.

Surface Sterilization. Sterilization following removal of the leaves is for 15 min with 10% (v/v) Clorox (10 ml Clorox:90 ml distilled water:1 drop Tween 20 wetting agent). After the leaf bases are removed, the shoot axes are sterilized for 10 min in 5% (v/v) Clorox (5 ml Clorox:95 ml distilled water). Then they are rinsed with sterile distilled water for 3 min. Explants are removed after the rinse.

Culture Vessels. Use 50-ml Erlenmeyer flasks containing 20 ml medium.

Culture Conditions. Cultures are maintained under continuous illumination of 200 ft-candles (General Electric Power Groove white fluorescent lamps were used in the original work) at 26° ± 2° C. Liquid cultures should be agitated at 160 rpm (a New Brunswick Model V shaker was used for the initial experiments).

Culture Medium. Solid or liquid Vacin and Went medium modified as for the culture of flower-stalk cuttings (Table A-27) and enriched with 15% (v/v) coconut water (used to replace an equal volume of distilled water) is employed. For solid medium 0.9% (w/v) agar is added (9 g agar per liter of medium). Sucrose is omitted from the solid medium onto which protocorm-like bodies are transferred after being in liquid for a month. The solid medium used to induce further proliferation is also free of sucrose.

Procedure. Explants are cultured in agitated liquid medium, changed every 10 days for a month, and then transferred onto a solid, sucrose-free medium. Frequent sub-cultures to new medium without sucrose result in the production of numerous pseudobulb-like bodies.

Yellowish protocorm-like bodies (PLB) are produced on explants of axillary and terminal buds within a month of culture. The same happens on inflorescence nodes. On transfer to solid, sucrose-free medium, the PLB turn green. If left undisturbed on solid medium, these bodies form plantlets within 3–5 months. However, if they are frequently subcultured onto new solid, sucrose-free medium, numerous new PLB are produced.

Developmental Sequence. At first the PLB are less than 0.5 mm in diameter, rough, and globular. On reaching a diameter of 0.5–1 mm, they become shiny, remain globular, and form many trichomes (rhizoids) on their lower half. When they reach a diameter of 1–3 mm, a dark green spot becomes apparent (the first leaf appears from this point later) and many trichomes are still present. An expanded leaf and a root near its base appear when the PLB are 4 mm long. They are still 4 mm in diameter when the leaf enlarges, the root elongates, and velamen develops. Three months are required for this developmental process.

General Comments. Numerous plants were produced by this technique at the University of Hawaii. It should, therefore, prove useful to orchid propagators everywhere.

Clonal Propagation of *Phalaenopsis* by Means of Flower-Stalk-Node Cultures

Lateral buds on *Phalaenopsis* flower stalks generally do not start to grow until the tip is removed. This is typical expression of apical dominance. To overcome it, we utilized the antiauxin *trans*-cinnamic (tCA) acid (Arditti, Ball, and Reisinger, 1975; Reisinger, Ball, and Arditti, 1976).

Plant Material. Use mature flower stalks. Best results are obtained with buds on nodes from the upper sections of stalks.

Surface Sterilization. Remove the scale which covers each bud. Wash the bud with distilled water and 2–3 drops of a mild nearly neutral household detergent. Rinse with distilled water and immerse in a 50% Clorox solution (Clorox:distilled water, 1:1, v/v) for 4–6 min. Dip momentarily in sterile distilled water to remove the Clorox and insert in culture medium.

Culture Vessels. A variety of containers can be used. They include Erlenmeyer flasks (125 ml or 250 ml), test tubes (150 mm or 250 mm × 25 mm), urine sample containers (175 ml), or prescription bottles (100 ml). Fill culture vessels with medium to approximately 25% of capacity.

Culture Conditions. Maintain cultures under approximately 150 ft-candles and 16-hour photoperiods. Sylvania Gro Lux fluorescent tubes were used in the original experiments, but other suitable light sources could be employed. The temperature should be 22–25° C.

Culture Medium. Employ the medium used for the culture of *Dendrobium* node sections (Table A-21), with the following modifications:
1. Replace the micronutrients (items 6a–6h) with those of the medium used for the differentiation of plants from leaf-tip callus (Table A-16, items 6a–6d).
2. Use 1.48 mg tCA per liter of medium for upper- and base-section nodes.
3. Use 14.8 mg tCA per liter of medium for mid-section nodes.
4. Add 13 mg isoleucine (an amino acid) per liter of medium. To prepare a stock solution dissolve 650 mg isoleucine in 10 ml of 95% ethyl alcohol (ethanol), add a few drops of KOH to help solubilization, and adjust the final volume to 25 ml with 95% ethanol. Store in a refrigerator and use 0.5 ml per liter of medium.
5. In mixing the medium add the isoleucine together with items 1–10 in Table A-21.

General Comments. At least in our hands this method has been more successful than other procedures for the culture of *Phalaenopsis* flower-stalk nodes.

Pleione

Details of the procedure are not given (Morel, 1971a). However, it would appear that the methods used for *Cymbidium* (p. 233; Morel, 1960, 1963, 1964a, 1965b, 1970) can also be employed for this genus.

Rhynchostylis gigantea

Monopodial orchids have been more difficult to propagate through tissue culture, especially of their shoot tips, than the sympodial ones. The reason for this, at least in part, is probably that they have different or more complex requirements. Thus, "after reviewing the previous . . . work on tissue and organ culture, . . . an . . . attempt

Table A-28. Medium for the culture of shoot-tip and bud explants from *Rhynchostylis gigantea* (Vajrabhaya and Vajrabhaya, 1970)

Item number	Component	Amount per liter of culture medium (final concentration in culture medium)	Stock solution (a concentrate prepared for repeated and convenient use)	Volume of stock solution per liter of culture medium	Remarks
	Macroelements[a]				
1	Calcium nitrate, Ca(NO$_3$)$_2$·4H$_2$O[a]	500 mg	50 g/liter[a]	10 ml[a]	or weigh[a]
2	Ammonium sulfate, (NH$_4$)$_2$SO$_4$[a]	500 mg	50 g/liter[a]	10 ml[a]	or weigh[a]
3	Potassium chloride, KCl	250 mg	25 g/liter	10 ml	
4	Magnesium sulfate, MgSO$_4$·7H$_2$O	250 mg	25 g/liter	10 ml	
5	Potassium phosphate, KH$_2$PO$_4$	250 mg	25 g/liter	10 ml	
6	*Microelements*[b]				
a	Chelated iron, Fe-EDTA	50 mg	50 g/liter		
b	Manganese chloride, MnCl$_2$·4H$_2$O	2 mg	2 g/liter		
c	Boric acid, H$_3$BO$_3$	1 mg	1 g/liter		
d	Zinc sulfate, ZnSO$_4$·7H$_2$O	0.1 mg	100 mg/liter	1 ml	one solution[b]
e	Sodium molybdate, Na$_2$MoO$_4$·2H$_2$O	0.02 mg	20 mg/liter		
f	Cobaltous chloride, CoCl$_2$·6H$_2$O	0.02 mg	20 mg/liter		
g	Cupric chloride, CuCl$_2$·2H$_2$O	0.01 mg	10 mg/liter		
	Vitamins[c]				
7	Niacin (nicotinic acid)[c]	1.25 mg	125 mg/100 ml 95% ethanol	1 ml[c]	
8	Calcium pantothenate[c]	0.25 mg	100 mg/100 ml 95% ethanol	0.25 ml[c]	
9	Thiamine (vitamin B$_1$)[c]	0.25 mg	100 mg/100 ml 95% ethanol	0.25 ml[c]	or combine[c]
10	Pyridoxine (vitamin B$_6$)[c]	0.25 mg	100 mg/100 ml 95% ethanol	0.25 ml[c]	
	Auxin[d]				
11	Naphthaleneacetic acid (NAA)	0.1 mg	10 mg/100 ml 95% ethanol[d]	1 ml	
	Amino acid[e]				
12	Glycine	7.5 mg	750 mg/liter[e]	10 ml	
	Complex additives				
13	Tryptone	500 mg	no stock	no stock	weigh
14	Coconut water	100 ml	no stock	no stock	fresh
	Sugar[f]				
15	Sucrose	20 g	no stock	no stock	weigh
16	Water, distilled[f]	to 1000 ml			
	Solidifier[f]				
17	Agar	6 g	no stock	no stock	weigh

[a] Solutions containing nitrate and ammonium tend to become contaminated on standing. Therefore, it is better to weigh components 1 and 2 every time. If stock solutions are prepared, they must be kept frozen.

[b] Add all microelements to the same one liter and use 1 ml of this solution.

[c] The vitamins may be combined into one stock solution. Add 125 mg of niacin and 25 mg of each of the other three vitamins to the same 100 ml of 95% ethanol and use 1 ml of this per liter of medium. Refrigerate between uses.

[d] If the auxin does not dissolve, add a few drops of HCl. Refrigerate.

[e] Keep frozen between uses.

[f] Mix 1–6, 13, and 14 with 700 ml of distilled water (item 16); adjust the pH to 5.2–5.5; add sugar (item 15) and bring the volume up to 1000 ml with more distilled water (item 16). Allow the solution to come to a gentle boil and add the agar (item 17) slowly, while stirring. When it has dissolved fully, autoclave the medium under standard conditions. The vitamins (items 7–10), auxin (item 11), and glycine (item 12) are added after autoclaving while the medium is still liquid. Mix well and distribute into sterile culture vessels.

was made to formulate a new medium for culturing tissues of monopodial-type orchids." The attempt was successful to a limited extent and "even though it cannot be applied easily in the commercial multiplication of this type of orchid at the present time, it may provide a clue for further developments in culturing orchid tissues" (Vajrabhaya and Vajrabhaya, 1970).

Plant Material. In the original experiment, seedlings of *Rhynchostylis gigantea* collected from the wild were utilized. Buds from leaf-covered stems and shoot tips were used as the source of explants.

Surface Sterilization. Use the procedure employed for *Cymbidium* (p. 234; Sagawa et al., 1966).

Culture Vessels. Employ 21 × 173 mm test tubes, containing medium to a height of 35 mm, placed in an upright position.

Culture Conditions. Maintain cultures under diffuse light of an intensity ranging between 2000 and 3000 lux for 14-hr photoperiods. In the original experiments, Philips TL 40/33 and TL 40/54 fluorescent tubes were used in a ratio of 1:1. It would seem reasonable to assume that Sylvania Gro Lux (or equivalent) or a combination of cool white fluorescent tubes and incandescent bulbs would be equally suitable. The temperature should be 24–27° C.

Culture Medium. A semisolid medium formulated especially for this species is used (Table A-28). The medium is also suitable for *Dendrobium* and *Cattleya*.

Procedure. The apical meristem is excised like that of *Cymbidium* (p. 234; Sagawa et al., 1966). Only 5–6 explants can be secured from any one seedling of the size used in the original experiments. Explants are placed on the culture medium. During the first week of culture, most of them enlarge and some portions turn green. From the second through fourth weeks, a few produce new tissues, but some of these die. At the end of 2 months, only one explant in 30 survived in the original experiment. The survivors formed calli of up to 10 mm in diameter. Growth was slow, but no abnormalities were detected after five subcultures. If not subcultured, the calli will produce plantlets.

General Comments. Disadvantages of this method are the low rate of success and the need to destroy an entire plant or growth. However, considering the difficulties encountered with the culture of monopodial orchids, the procedure represents a significant advance in the clonal propagation of desirable clones.

Schomburgkia superbiens

Use the same procedures as for *Cattleya* (p. 226; Scully, 1967).

Spathoglottis

The existence of a culture method is mentioned in an article on *Phalaenopsis* (Intuwong and Sagawa, 1974).

Vanda

In Hawaii and other areas, *Vanda* blossoms are of commercial importance for the production of leis, corsages, and other decorative uses, or as cut flowers for export. In addition, many clones are much sought-after by hobby growers. Thus the need for a fast method of clonal propagation was felt keenly. The genus proved difficult for a while (Morel, 1964a, 1965a,b), but several methods have been developed recently. One procedure utilizes Murashige-Skoog medium (Tables A-1, A-22), but the explants grow slowly, forming a callus (Morel, 1970). Later, protocorm-like bodies are formed. Details are also available about procedures to induce polyploidy in plantlets raised from tissue cultures (Kunisaki, Kim, and Sagawa, 1972; Sagawa and Sehgal, 1967; Sanguthai and Sagawa, 1973; Teo, Kunisaki, and Sagawa, 1973).

Shoot-Tip Culture of Terete-Leaf *Vanda*

If we are to accept the proposition that all plant cells can be made to grow and even dedifferentiate or differentiate *in vitro*, then it is also necessary to assume that success is predicated on the formulation of suitable culture media and on appropriate light and temperature conditions. This, indeed, has proven to be the case with *Vanda* shoot tips. As with many difficult problems, the solution was radical and required imagination: the sugar had to be removed from some media (Kunisaki, Kim, and Sagawa, 1972).

Plant Material. Stems of *Vanda* (xMiss Joaquim in the original experiments) are removed at the node of the fifth visible leaf. Tissue above this node is still soft and succulent, and axillary buds are easy to excise.

Surface Sterilization. Before removal of the sheaths, 10% Clorox is used for 10 min and afterward 5% for 5 min.

Culture Vessels. Use the same vessels as for *Cymbidium* (p. 234; Sagawa *et al.*, 1966).

Culture Conditions. Liquid cultures are placed on a rotator (a New Brunswick Model V shaker operated at 160 rpm was used in the original research). Solid ones are maintained on a shelf or bench. Both are kept under 200 ft-candles continuous illumination provided by General Electric Power Groove white fluorescent lamps (Sylvania Gro Lux could also prove satisfactory). The temperature should be $26 \pm 3°C$.

Culture Media. Initially, the explants are placed on solid Vacin and Went medium (Table A-27), modified by replacing 150 ml of the distilled water (item 9) with an equal volume of coconut water (CW) and using 8 g agar (item 10) instead of 9 g (VW + 15% CW + 20 g Su + 8 g agar). Best proliferation is obtained in liquid Vacin and Went medium containing 15% CW [150 ml, replacing an equal volume of distilled water (item 9)], but no sugar (i.e., item 8 in Table A-27 is omitted; VW + 15% CW − Su). Differentiation (plantlet formation) is obtained on VW medium (Table A-27) plus 15% coconut water and 10–20 g sugar (i.e., item 8 in Table A-27 is either used unchanged or cut in half; VW + 15% CW + 10 g Su or VW + 15% CW + 20 g Su, both containing agar).

Procedure. Remove leaf portions beyond the sheath and cut stems at internodes into smaller sections. Surface-sterilize these sections in 10% Clorox for 10 min. Remove the sheaths, sterilize with 5% Clorox (v/v) for 3 min, and place on culture medium. After 45 days on solid modified VW (VW + 15% CW + 20 g Su + 8 g agar) approximately 63% of the explants will form semispherical structures. At this stage, the leaves and apex should be removed from each swollen bud, otherwise proliferation will not occur and only one plantlet will be formed. Proliferation will begin approximately 60 days after the second excision. For rapid and vigorous proliferation, the tissue must now be transferred to the liquid VW + 15% CW − Su. When plantlets are desired, the proliferating bodies are transferred onto solid VW + 15% CW + 10 g Su or VW + 15% CW + 20 g Su.

Developmental Sequence. Initial growth and proliferation occur on the first medium; increased proliferation takes place on the second; plantlets differentiate on the third.

General Comments. This is a rapid method for clonal propagation of terete *Vanda* which does require the sacrifice of a shoot, two excisions, and several tissue transfers. Because of that, it may seem a bit complicated. However, with limited practice, it should be an easy procedure to master.

Stem Culture of Terete-Leaf *Vanda*

Until 1967, *Vanda* clones were not being propagated fast enough to suit the need of Hawaiian growers. In the search for faster methods, a successful attempt was made to develop methods for aseptic stem propagation of *Vanda* xMiss Joaquim (Sagawa and Sehgal, 1967).

Plant Material. Clean stems cut into 45–50-mm sections are used.

Surface Sterilization. Use 10% (v/v) Clorox for 20–30 min (10 ml Clorox and 90 ml distilled water).

Culture Vessels. Employ 25 × 100 mm vials containing culture medium to a height of 30–35 mm. As plants become larger, transfer to 125- or 250-ml Erlenmeyer flasks containing 25 or 50 ml medium, respectively.

Culture Conditions. Maintain cultures under conditions appropriate for orchid seed germination (Arditti, 1967).

Culture Medium. Vacin and Went (1949) medium (Tables A-17, A-27) modified by the use of 8 g agar instead of the usual amount (item 10 in Table A-17 or A-27).

Procedure. Sections should be 45–50 mm long with 12–15 mm above and 35–40 mm below the node. Using a sterile razor blade, remove the leaf, exposing the bud. Surface-sterilize with 10% Clorox for 20–30 min. On a sterile surface, using a sterilized razor blade or scalpel, remove 3–4 mm from each end (these are usually discolored portions) Then insert the sections into the medium at a slight angle with approximately 10 mm of the portion below the bud in the agar. Place vials under the appropriate culture conditions. Generally, treat sections and the resulting plantlets like seedlings.

Developmental Sequence. Shoot growth may occur first, but within 2–3 months cuttings are well rooted and ready for planting in a greenhouse.

General Comments. Up to 80% of vegetative stem cuttings produce plantlets with this method. Sections from flower stalks may swell, but the results are not as good.

Propagation of Strap-Leaf Vanda by Shoot-Tip Culture

Even as late as 1973, limited literature was available on shoot-tip or other tissue-culture methods for the clonal propagation of monopodial orchids. Because of that, publication of a new method for the propagation of strap-leaf *Vanda* (*V. insignis* × *V. tessellata*) was of considerable interest (Teo, Kunisaki, and Sagawa, 1973).

Plant Material. Apical and axillary buds from seedlings of strap-leaf *Vanda* which had 8–12 leaves were used in the original experiments.

Surface Sterilization. Follow the instructions for *Cymbidium* (p. 234; Sagawa *et al.*, 1966).

Culture Vessels. Use those recommended for *Cymbidium* (p. 234).

Culture Conditions. Maintain cultures at 26 ± 3° C under continous illumination of approximately 200 ft-candles. In the original experiment, the light sources were General Electric Power Groove fluorescent lamps, but others (Sylvania Gro Lux, for example) should also prove satisfactory. Liquid cultures should be agitated (a New Brunswick Model V shaker operated at 160 rpm was used by Teo *et al.*, 1973).

Culture Media. Liquid Vacin and Went (1949) medium (Table A-27), modified by the addition of 15% coconut water (150 ml CW instead of an equal volume of distilled water, item 9 in Table A-27), is used for the initial culture (VW + CW). To promote proliferation, the tissues should be subcultured into liquid VW + CW, but minus sugar (item 8 in Table A-27), *i.e.*, VW + CW − Su. For differentiation into plantlets, protocorm-like bodies (PLB) are transferred onto solid unmodified VW (Table A-17).

Procedure. Excise the buds and sterilize them according to the procedure used for *Cymbidium* (p. 234; Sagawa *et al.*, 1966). Place the explants in liquid VW + CW. After a month, excise the leaf primordia which cover the explants. When growth and proliferation start, transfer the tissues to liquid VW + CW − Su. PLB will form and separate from each other due to the agitation. These should be transferred to solid VW for differentiation into plantlets.

Developmental Sequence. Approximately 25% of all cultures can be expected to proliferate. The explants swell initially and then become spherical owing to the development of leaf primordia. If these are not removed, there will be no further proliferation. If they are excised, the tissues proliferate very well on VW + CW − Su, forming PLB which are separated by the agitation. Some tissues in proliferating cultures produce PLB continuously. Others continue to proliferate, but also form plantlets. A third group may form clumps of plantlets with only leaves. On transfer to solid VW, plantlets differentiate from PLB.

General Comments. When buds are visible (i.e., not covered by leaf sheaths), culture contamination rates may be high. This is probably because debris accumulate in the leaf axils, facilated by the strap leaves. To minimize contamination, it is best to obtain explants from buds which are still tightly enclosed within sheaths. Owing to the need to perform a second excision and to transfer the tissues at least twice, the procedure may require some practice.

In vitro Culture of *Vanda* Miss Joaquim

One of the most common and popular *Vanda* hybrids is cv Miss Joaquim (*V. teres* × *V. hookeriana*). It is not surprising, therefore, that a number of workers have used it in efforts to develop tissue-culture methods for *Vanda*. One method was developed at the Botany Department of the University of Singapore (Goh, 1970).

Plant Material. Shoot tips, axillary buds, and roots excised from 15-month-old seedlings are used.

Surface Sterilization. Since the tissue are obtained from seedlings growing under sterile conditions, surface decontamination should not be needed. When necessary, tissues can be sterilized for 5 min with 5% (w/v) calcium hypochlorite (5 g calcium hypochlorite mixed with enough distilled water to bring the total volume up to 100 ml) and rinsed with sterile distilled water before being placed into culture.

Culture Vessels. Use 100- or 125-ml Erlenmeyer flasks containing 20 ml or 25 ml culture medium, respectively.

Table A-29. White's (1943) medium for the culture of *Vanda* explants

Item number	Component	Amount per liter of culture medium (final concentration in culture medium)	Stock solution (a concentrate prepared for repeated and convenient use)	Volume of stock solution per liter of culture medium	Remarks
	Macroelements[a]				
1	Calcium nitrate, $Ca(NO_3)_2$[a]	200 mg	20 g/liter[a]	10 ml[a]	or weigh[a]
2	Potassium nitrate, KNO_3[a]	80 mg	8 g/liter[a]	10 ml[a]	or weigh[a]
3	Sodium phosphate, $NaH_2PO_4 \cdot H_2O$	16.5 mg	1.65 g/liter	10 ml	
4	Potassium chloride, KCl	65 mg	6.5 g/liter	10 ml	
5	Sodium sulfate, Na_2SO_4	200 mg	20 g/liter	10 ml	
6	Magnesium sulfate, $MgSO_4$	360 mg	36 g/liter	10 ml	
	Iron[b]				
7	Ferric sulfate, $Fe_2(SO_4)_3$	2.5 mg	250 mg/liter[b]	10 ml[b]	
8	*Microelements*[c]				
a	Manganese sulfate, $MnSO_4$	4.5 mg	4.5 g/liter		
b	Zinc sulfate, $ZnSO_4$	1.5 mg	1.5 g/liter	1 ml	one solution[c]
c	Boric acid, H_3BO_3	1.5 mg	1.5 g/liter		
d	Potassium iodide, KI	0.75 mg	750 mg/liter		
	Amino acid[d]				
9	Glycine	3 mg	300 mg/100 ml 95% ethanol[d]	1 ml	
	Vitamins				
10	Niacin (nicotinic acid)[e]	0.5 mg	10 mg/100 ml 95% ethanol[e]	1 ml	
11	Pyridoxine (vitamin B_6)[e]	0.1 mg	10 mg/100 ml 95% ethanol[e]	1 ml	or combine[e]
12	Thiamine (vitamin B_1)[e]	0.1 mg	10 mg/100 ml 95% ethanol[e]	1 ml	
	Sugar[f]				
13	Sucrose	20 g	no stock	no stock	
14	Water, distilled[f]	to 1000 ml			
	Solidifier[f]				
15	Agar	7.5 g	no stock	no stock	

[a] Solutions of nitrogenous salts or organic substances may become contaminated. Therefore, stock solutions should not be prepared. If made, they must be kept frozen between uses.

[b] If a precipitate forms, shake well before dispensing.

[c] Add all microelements to the same one liter, stir and/or heat until dissolved. Add 1 ml to the culture medium.

[d] Keep refrigerated or frozen between uses.

[e] If desired, all three vitamins can be dissolved in the same 100 ml and 1 ml of this solution used per liter of culture medium. Keep refrigerated or frozen between uses.

[f] Dissolve items 1–8 in 750 ml of distilled water (item 14); adjust the pH to 5.5; add the sugar (item 13); bring the volume up to 1000 ml with more distilled water (item 14); autoclave; under sterile conditions, add glycine (item 9) and the vitamins (items 10–12); mix well and distribute into autoclaved culture vessels. If a solid medium is required, bring the final 1000 ml to a gentle boil, add the agar slowly while stirring, and autoclave. Before the sterile solution is solidified, add the glycine (item 9) and vitamins (items 10–12) under aseptic conditions. Then mix well and dispense into autoclaved culture vessels.

Culture Conditions. Shoot cultures should be maintained under 12-hr photoperiods (light intensity and type of illumination were not given) at 27° C. Root tips were kept in the dark during the initial experiments.

Culture Medium. White's (White, 1943) medium (Table A-29) enriched with 20% (v/v) coconut water (200 ml coconut water substituted for an equal volume of distilled water) was used for culturing the seedlings which served as explant sources. The shoot and root tips as well as the axillary buds should be cultured on White's medium (Table A-29) enriched with 2 mg 2,4-D per liter. Excised roots can also be cultured on White's medium containing 10% tomato juice (v/v; 100 ml of tomato juice used to replace an equal volume of distilled water, item 14 in Table A-29) or 100 ppm (100 mg/liter) indoleacetic acid.

Procedure. Explants are placed into culture and allowed to develop. Plantlets, when formed, are removed and cultured individually.

Developmental Sequence. Rapid cell division takes place in shoot-tip explants, forming new growth centers. Some of them become organized into growing apices from which young shoots develop within about 3 months. When excised and subcultured, these shoots produce one or more plantlets.

Axillary buds give rise to side shoots when cultured on a solid medium. No roots are produced, however; therefore, plantlets are not formed.

Roots elongate in culture and turn white. Their anatomical features are the same as those of normal roots.

General Comments. Shoot-tip explants can be used for the clonal propagation of *Vanda* xMiss Joaquim. On an appropriate medium, roots should develop on the shoots which arise from axillary buds. Perhaps the medium used to induce root formation on *Dendrobium* shoots could be used (Table A-22). Sometime in the future, a way may be found to induce callus or plantlet formation from root tissues.

Vandofinetia

A culture method is mentioned in an article on *Phalaenopsis* (Intuwong and Sagawa, 1974).

Vascostylis

Use the same procedure as for *Ascofinetia* (p. 212; Intuwong and Sagawa, 1973).

Vuylstekeara

Use Knudson C or Knop's medium and generally the same procedures as for *Cymbidium* (p. 233; Morel, 1960, 1963, 1964a, 1965b, 1970).

Zygopetalum

Details are not given beyond the statement that methods used for *Cymbidium* were extended to *Zygopetalum* (Bertsch, 1967). Hence, it would seem that the procedures used for *Cymbidium* (p. 233; Morel, 1960, 1963, 1964a, 1965b, 1970) would also apply to *Zygopetalum*.

Discussion

Present methods for the tissue culture of orchids can be used as a means of fast clonal propagation, as a research tool, and as a basis for the development of other procedures.

Use of Orchid Tissue Culture in Basic Research

In most instances, there is a lag period between fundamental discoveries and their practical application. This has also been true for orchids because the initial reports of "meristem" (i.e., shoot-tip) cultures (Morel, 1960) appeared fifteen years after shoot tips from other plants were cultured for the first time (Ball, 1946). The method was quickly applied to several genera and "mericlones" soon became an important part of orchidology. On the other hand, utilization of orchid tissue cultures for basic research has sadly lagged behind their commerical application. One reason for this may simply be the fact that only a few investigators are familiar enough with orchids and still fewer work with them. Hence, it may be well to point out areas where orchid tissue cultures can be valuable.

Roots. Orchid roots may be ageotropic, or sometimes even negatively geotropic. These phenomena were observed, studied, and reported many years ago (Tischler, 1905) and cited more recently (Wilkins, 1966; for a short review, see Churchill, Ball, and Arditti, 1972). Unfortunately, they have not been studied in the light of recent knowledge or theories. Negative geotropism can often be seen in seedling roots of *Phalaenopsis*, *Cymbidium*, *Epidendrum*, and *Cattleya* growing *in vitro*. At least in *Cymbidium*, the color of the substrate may be of importance since roots tend to grow into black media (Werckmeister, 1970, 1971).

In nature, one can often observe aerial roots which grow sideways and eventually bend down from their own weight. Others point upward and remain that way for their entire life span and after death. An imposing example of this is provided by *Grammatophyllum speciosum*. Some plants of this species reach a giant size, and large specimens have been estimated to weigh a ton or more. Their aerial roots are hard, point upward, have rigid, sharp, thorny laterals, and form large, debris-accumulating, nestlike masses. The laterals, first noticeable 4–5 cm below (in a normally growing root, the position will be above) the tip as small bumps, always grow at a right angle to the main axis, reach 2–3 cm in length, and point sideways or upward, but never downward. Older laterals may also have short (1–2 mm) thornlike side branches.

When the roots die, they become very hard and sharp, and cause pain if they penetrate the skin. Many large plants of *G. speciosum* grow on the trees along a beautiful avenue at Hortus Botanicus Bogoriensis (Kebun Raya), Bogor, and all of their roots behave in the same way. The view is both fascinating and spectacular. It also suggests that orchid roots *in vitro* may be used profitably in geotropism research.

Roots of *Vanda*, *Epidendrum*, *Brassia*, and *Oncidium* lack statholiths (Tischler, 1905), thereby offering a unique opportunity to study the role of these organelles in geotropism of roots *in vitro*. When *Phalaenopsis* seedlings are grown under Gro Lux lamps, their roots point up. *Cymbidium* roots grown in agar darkened by charcoal point down. These observations suggest that such roots in culture could be used for studies of light and geotropism.

Some orchid roots, *Taeniophyllum*, *Microcoelia*, *Polyrrhiza*, *Dendrophylax*, *Sarcochilus*, and *Campylocentrum*, are green and perform many of the functions of leaves and stems (for a short review, see Churchill, Ball, and Arditti, 1972). In *Taeniophyllum* (a species common on some trees at Kebun Raya), stems are very short with internodes 1–1.5 mm long. The leaves are reduced to tiny brownish scales which cover the stem apex (Holttum, 1964) but apparently cannot photosynthesize. Roots are green or whitish-green and probably perform not only their regular functions but also those of stems and leaves. When cultured, separately or as part of a whole plant, these roots could be used to study a variety of problems. Even roots of orchids with normal stems and leaves are green (*Epidendrum* and *Cattleya*, for example) and are capable of photosynthesis (Erickson, 1957). In culture, they could prove to be a valuable system for certain studies.

The velamen (a spongelike tissue) of orchid roots is of considerable developmental, physiological, and ecological interest. Anthocyanin production takes place in the roots of some orchid species. Phytoalexins can be extracted from *Cymbidium* roots which contain mycorrhiza (Arditti and Flick, unpublished). Orchid seedlings grown in flasks can become infected by mycorrhizal fungi, which suggests that seedlings, plantlets, or excised roots in culture can be used to study the establishment of mycorrhiza.

Mineral uptake, thigmotropism, chemotropism, statoliths or their abscence, and the ability of roots to attach themselves to surfaces can also be studied with orchid roots *in vitro*. The same is true for other questions. Unfortunately, however, orchid roots seem to be neglected and those of more mundane, and perhaps less suitable, plants are generally used.

Flowers. Orchid seedlings and mature plants have been reported to bloom *in vitro* (for a review, see Arditti, 1967a). Flower-stalk nodes of *Phalaenopsis* may produce a new flower stem when placed in culture (Intuwong *et al.*, 1972). Recently, the bud of a flower-stalk node of *Arachnis* x Maggie Oei developed when placed in liquid, stationary Knudson C medium (Tables A-9, A-16; Knudson, 1946) by an Indonesian worker at Kebun Raya. Flowers of *Dendrobium* have been maintained and pollinated in specially designed culture vessels (Ito, 1961; Urata and Iwanaga, 1965). Fruits which matured under these conditions contained viable seeds.

Obviously, orchid plants, buds, blooms, and fruits cultured *in vitro* can be used for studies of flowering, flower physiology, fruit development, and embryology. Perhaps the techniques may need adjustments to particular problems, but they are available.

Differentiation. Orchid explants in culture form calli which often consist of protocorm-like bodies. These in turn form plantlets. Sometimes explants form shoots only, but never roots exclusively. Development of calli, plantlets, shoots, and roots can be affected by the media employed (Bivins and Hackett, 1969; Fonnesbech, 1972a,b). Plant hormones and their analogs or anatagonists can be used to induce or regulate development and control metabolism *in vitro*. There are many other opportunities, most of which have been neglected to date.

Culture Conditions

Basic and practical information can be obtained by comparing and tabulating the conditions employed for the orchids cultured to date (Table A-30, items 73–77). These include light intensity (item 73), photoperiods (item 74), temperature (item 75), agitation (item 76), pH (item 77), and state of the medium (liquid vs. solid, item 71). On the basis of such comparisons, it may be possible to predict the requirements of certain genera or species or modes of development (i.e., proliferation vs. differentiation).

State of the Medium. Both liquid and solid media (Table A-30, item 71) are used for the culture of orchid tissues. *Cymbidium* and *Cattleya* can be cultured on either, but results are better and proliferation (i.e., increase) is faster on liquid media. Growth of *Cymbidium* explants is over 100% greater in agitated liquid media than on solid ones (Wimber, 1965). Leaf-tip cultures are also more successful in agitated (actually, "oscillated") liquid solutions. With *Epidendrum* leaf tips, results are almost entirely negative when solid media are used. However, once a callus is formed, it proliferates well on solid Murashige-Skoog or Linsmaier-Skoog media. *Cattleya* leaf tips form proliferating calli on liquid media and plantlets on agar. When solid media are used, the amount of agar can be important since some tissue seems to survive and grow best on softer substrates.

Agitation. Liquid media are generally agitated, but the speed and manner of agitation vary with no apparent pattern (Table A-30, item 76). Some workers prefer wheels rotating in a vertical plane. Others use gyrorotatory or horizontally oscillating shakers. Reported shaker speeds vary from a slow $\frac{1}{5}$ rpm (Jasper, 1966a,b) to a fast 160–200 rpm (Scully, 1967). We have found that leaf tips survive best at 60 horizontal oscillations per minute and die at faster speeds on gyrorotatory shakers.

The reasons for the better results and/or increased proliferation in agitated liquid cultures are not entirely clear. It is possible that the shaking impedes polarity development, thereby inhibiting root and/or shoot development (Scully, 1967; Wimber, 1963, 1965). Other possibilities are improved aeration, increased surface area, and equal distribution or dilution of metabolites which could be toxic. But proliferation

Table A-30. Composition of media used for tissue culture of orchids

No.	Component	Anacamptis pyramidalis (Morel, 1970) Table A-1	Arundina bambusifolia (Mitra, 1971) Shoot tips, 6–8 mm; stem disks Table A-3	Shoot (stem) tips, 1–2 mm Table A-4	Ascofinetia, Neostylis, Vascostylis (Intuwong and Sagawa, 1973) Table A-6	Brassocattleya, Cattleya, Laelia, Laeliocattleya (Kako, 1973) Table A-1 (modif.) Starting	Callus form.
1	Nitrogen, total (mmoles)	60.01	4.83–5.66	2.94	12.75	60.01	60.01
2	urea, NH_2CONH_2 (mmoles)		0.42–0.83				
3	ammonium, NH_4^+ (mmoles)	20.61	2	0.63	7.56	20.61	20.61
4	nitrate, NO_3^- (mmoles)	39.40	2	2.31	5.19	39.40	39.40
5	ammonium/nitrate ratio	0.52	1	0.27	1.46	0.52	0.52
6	Phosphorus, phosphate, PO_4^{---} (mmoles)	1.25	2.76	1.50	3.14	1.25	1.25
7	Potassium, K^+ (mmoles)	20.05	1.98	2.45	7.03	1.25	1.25
8	Sulfur, sulfate, SO_4^{--} (mmoles)	1.70	1.43	1.07	4.83	1.70	1.70
9	Calcium, Ca^{++} (mmoles)	2.99	0.85	0.82	1.95	2.99	2.99
10	Magnesium, Mg^{++} (mmoles)	1.50	0.97	0.97	1.01	1.50	1.50
11	Iron, chelated with EDTA (mmoles)	0.10		0.01		0.1	0.1
12	ferric, Fe^{+++} (mmoles)		0.02		0.19		
13	ferrous, Fe^{++} (mmoles)	0.10		0.01		0.1	0.1
14	Macroelements, total (mmoles)	87.72	17.26–19.51	9.76	31.76	68.80	68.80
15	Microelements, total (mmoles)	6.24	0.019	0.889	0.034	6.25	6.25
16	Aluminium, Al^{+++} (μmoles)						
17	Borate, BO_3^{---} (μmoles)	100	9.7	9.7		100	100
18	Chloride, Cl^- (μmoles)	6000	4.04	874		6010	6010
19	Cobalt, Co^{+++} (μmoles)	0.11	1.36	1.36		0.11	0.11
20	Copper, Cu^{++} (μmoles)	0.10	0.28	0.28		0.11	0.10
21	Iodine, I^- (μmoles)	5.00	0.18	0.18		5	5
22	Manganese, Mn^{++} (μmoles)	99.99	2.02	2.02	33.63	99.99	99.99
23	Molybdenum, molybdic acid, MoO_3 (μmoles)						
24	molybdate, MoO_4^{--} (μmoles)	0.10	0.21	0.21		1.03	1.03
25	Nickel, Ni^{++} (μmoles)						
26	Sodium, Na^+ (μmoles)	0.20	0.42	0.42		2.06	2.06
27	Zinc, Zn^{++} (μmoles)	28.83	0.28	0.28		28.83	28.83
28	Minerals, total including urea (mmoles)	93.96	17.27–19.53	10.74	31.79	75.05	75.05
29	Hormones, total (μmoles)	17.61				12.44	91.71
30	Auxins, total (μmoles)	5.71				0.54	45.24
31	IAA—indoleacetic acid (μmoles)	5.71					
32	IBA—indolebutyric acid (μmoles)						
33	2,4-D—2,4-dichlorophenoxyacetic acid (μmoles)						45.24
34	NAA—naphthaleneacetic acid (μmoles)					0.54	
35	IAA/IBA or IBA/NAA ratio						
36	Antiauxin, *trans*-cinnamic acid (mmoles)						
37	Cytokinins, total (μmoles)	11.90				11.90	46.47
38	BA-benzyl adenine (μmoles)						
39	Ki-kinetin (μmoles)	11.90				11.90	46.47
40	Gibberellic acid, GA_3 (μmoles)						
41	Auxin/cytokinin ratio	0.48				22.04	0.97
42	Auxin/gibberellin ratio						
43	Cytokinin/gibberellin ratio						
44	Auxin/cytokinin/gibberellin ratio						
45	Polyols, total (μmoles)						
46	inositol (μmoles)						
47	Amino acids, total (μmoles)	266.42				266.42	266.42
48	asparagine (μmoles)						
49	glutamic acid (μmoles)						
50	glycine (μmoles)	266.42				266.42	266.42
51	asparagine/glutamic acid ratio						
52	Vitamins, total (μmoles)	0.29				0.29	0.29
53	Bi—biotin (μmoles)						
54	FA—folic acid (μmoles)						
55	Nc—niacin (μmoles)						
56	Pa—pantothenate, calcium (μmoles)						
57	Py—pyridoxine (μmoles)						
58	Th—thiamine (μmoles)	0.29				0.29	0.29
59	Nc/Py/Th/Bi/FA/Pa ratio (Nc = 1)						
60	Nc/Py/Th ratio (Nc = 1)						
61	Nucleotides and nucleic acids, total (mmoles)						
62	Cyt-cytidylic acid (mmoles)						
63	Gua-guanylic acid (mmoles)						
64	Cyt/Gua ratio						
65	Organic acids, total (μmoles)		304.3		285		
66	citric acid (μmoles)						
67	tartaric acid (μmoles)		304.3		285		
68	Sugar, sucrose (mmoles)	87.64	58.43	58.43	58.43	87.64	87.64
69	All components, total (mmoles)	181.91	76–78	69.17	91.51	162.99	163.97
70	Concentration ranking of medium (least conc. = 1)	26	8 or 9	5	14	23	24
71	Agar, grams (omit from liquid media)	10–15	9	9	9	none	10–15
72	Complex and other additives	ccnt wtr	pptn, RNA, yst extr, csn, ccnt wtr		bnana, ccnt, potato extr		
73	Light intensity	100–200 f-c	3000 lux	3000 lux	200 f-c	100–200 f-c	100–200 f-c
74	Photoperiod (hours)	12	12	12	continuous	continuous	continuous
75	Temperature (°C)	22	26 ± 1	26 ± 1	26 ± 3	25	25
76	Agitation	none	none	none	160 RPM	none	none
77	pH	5.2–5.5	5.2–5.5	5.2–5.5	5.5	5.2–5.5	5.2–5.5

		Cattleya							
		Shoot meristem (Lindemann, Gunckel, and Davidson, 1970)			Bud meristem (Morel, 1971a)	Lateral bud meristem (Reinert and Mohr, 1967)		Veg. shoot explants (Scully, 1967) and for *Epidendrum, Schomburgkia*	Leaf bases (Champagnat, Morel, and Mounetou, 1970)
		Starting	Maintenance	Rooting	Tables A-7, 8, 10 (comb. & modif.)	Initial	Di		
No.	Component	Table A-7	Table A-8	Table A-9		Table A-11	Table A-11	Table A-12	Table A-13
1	Nitrogen, total (mmoles)	19.38	19.38	16.02	31.88	18.46	18.46	12.75	19.38
2	urea, NH_2CONH_2 (mmoles)								
3	ammonium, NH_4^+ (mmoles)	15.14	15.14	7.56	21.39	5.00	5.00	7.56	15.14
4	nitrate, NO_3^- (mmoles)	4.24	4.24	8.46	10.49	13.46	13.46	5.19	4.24
5	ammonium/nitrate ratio	3.57	3.57	0.89	2.04	0.37	0.37	1.46	3.57
6	Phosphorus, phosphate, PO_4^{---} (mmoles)	0.99	0.99	1.83	1.84	1.84	1.84	3.14	0.92
7	Potassium, K^+ (mmoles)	15.07	15.07	1.83	5.19	8.55	8.55	7.03	14.33
8	Sulfur, sulfate, SO_4^{--} (mmoles)	8.06	8.06	4.90	7.69	1.69	1.69	4.83	8.08
9	Calcium, Ca^{++} (mmoles)	2.12	2.12	4.23	2.12	4.23	4.23	1.95	2.12
10	Magnesium, Mg^{++} (mmoles)	0.49	0.49	1.01	1.01	1.62	1.62	1.01	0.51
11	Iron, chelated with EDTA (mmoles)					0.07	0.07		
12	ferric, Fe^{+++} (mmoles)	0.02	0.02			0.07	0.07	0.19	0.004
13	ferrous, Fe^{++} (mmoles)			0.09	0.09				
14	Macroelements, total (mmoles)	46.13	46.13	29.91	50.83	36.46	36.46	31.76	41.37
15	Microelements, total (mmoles)	14.16	14.16	0.036	3.38	6.74	6.74	0.034	13.47
16	Aluminium, Al^{+++} (μmoles)	0.13	0.13						0.13
17	Borate, BO_3^{---} (μmoles)	16.40	16.40	0.91		0.49	0.49		
18	Chloride, Cl^- (μmoles)	14084	14084		3354.14	6706.28	6706.28		1342.11
19	Cobalt, Co^{+++} (μmoles)								
20	Copper, Cu^{++} (μmoles)	0.08	0.08	0.23		0.006	0.006		1.2
21	Iodine, I^- (μmoles)	59.63	59.63						0.06
22	Manganese, Mn^{++} (μmoles)	3.05	3.05	33.63	33.63	33.63	33.63	33.63	0.05
23	Molybdenum, molybdic acid, MoO_4 (μmoles)			0.11					
24	molybdate, MoO_4^{--} (μmoles)								
25	Nickel, Ni^{++} (μmoles)	0.13	0.13						0.13
26	Sodium, Na^+ (μmoles)								
27	Zinc, Zn^{++} (μmoles)	0.20	0.20	1.15		0.11	0.11		3.47
28	Minerals, total including urea (mmoles)	60.29	60.29	29.95	54.21	43.20	43.20	31.79	54.78
29	Hormones, total (μmoles)	1.47	2		1.54	18.01	22.66		4.65
30	Auxins, total (μmoles)	0.54	1		0.54	18.01	18.01		
31	IAA—indoleacetic acid (μmoles)								
32	IBA—indolebutyric acid (μmoles)					8.61	8.61		
33	2,4-D—2,4-dichlorophenoxyacetic acid (μmoles)								
34	NAA—naphthaleneacetic acid (μmoles)	0.54	1		0.54	9.40	9.40		
35	IAA/IBA or IBA/NAA ratio					0.92	0.92		
36	Antiauxin, *trans*-cinnamic acid (mmoles)								
37	Cytokinins, total (μmoles)	0.93	1				4.65		4.65
38	BA-benzyl adenine (μmoles)								
39	Ki-kinetin (μmoles)	0.93	1		1		4.65		4.65
40	Gibberellic acid, GA (μmoles)		1						
41	Auxin/cytokinin ratio	0.58	1		0.54		3.87		
42	Auxin/gibberellin ratio		1						
43	Cytokinin/gibberellin ratio		1						
44	Auxin/cytokinin/gibberellin ratio		1/1/1						
45	Polyols, total (μmoles)		100			555.06	555.06		
46	inositol (μmoles)		100			555.06	555.06		
47	Amino acids, total (μmoles)		187.83		187.83	26.64	26.64		
48	asparagine (μmoles)		87.92		87.92				
49	glutamic acid (μmoles)		99.91		99.91				
50	glycine (μmoles)					26.64	26.64		
51	asparagine/glutamic acid ratio		0.88		0.88				
52	Vitamins, total (μmoles)		23.1			6.79	6.79		
53	Bi—biotin (μmoles)		0.1						
54	FA—folic acid (μmoles)		10						
55	Nc—niacin (μmoles)		10			4.06	4.06		
56	Pa—pantothenate, calcium (μmoles)		1						
57	Py—pyridoxine (μmoles)		1			2.43	2.43		
58	Th—thiamine (μmoles)		1			0.3	0.3		
59	Nc/Py/Th/Bi/FA/Pa ratio (Nc = 1)		1/0.1/0.1/ 0.01/1/0.01						
60	Nc/Py/Th ratio (Nc = 1)		1/0.1/0.1			1/0.6/0.074	1/0.6/0.074		
61	Nucleotides and nucleic acids, total (mmoles)		1						
62	Cyt-cytidylic acid (mmoles)		0.5						
63	Gua-guanylic acid (mmoles)		0.5						
64	Cyt/Gua ratio		1						
65	Organic acids, total (μmoles)	16.12	16.12					285	
66	citric acid (μmoles)	16.12	16.12						
67	tartaric acid (μmoles)							285	
68	Sugar, sucrose (mmoles)	1.46	58.43	58.43	58.43	58.43	58.43	58.43	58.43
69	All components, total (mmoles)	61.77	120.04	88.38	112.83	101.68	102.24	90.51	113.21
70	Concentration ranking of medium (least conc. = 1)	3	21	10	18	15	16	13	19
71	Agar, grams (omit from liquid media)	none	none	12–15	15–20	6	6	9	
72	Complex and other additives	ccnt wtr	ccnt wtr, csn hydr	ccnt wtr, csn hydr	ccnt wtr			ccnt wtr	
73	Light intensity			like sdlgs	dark	200 f-c	200 f-c	100–180 f-c	as for sdlgs
74	Photoperiod (hours)			like sdlgs	none	16	16	continuous	as for sdlgs
75	Temperature (°C)			like sdlgs	25–30	24–28	24–28	26 $\pm$ 4	as for sdlgs
76	Agitation	roller tube	roller tube	none	clinostat, 2 RPM	wheel, 1 RPM		160 RPM	
77	pH	5.2–5.5	5.2	5.3	5.2–5.5	5.0	5.0	5.0–5.2	5.3

No.	Component	Cattleya — Leaf tips (Churchill, Arditti, and Ball, 1971) — Initial (Table A-14)	Maintenance (Table A-15)	Diff. (Table A-16)	Cattleya — Shoot tip (Morel, 1960, 1964a) Cal. Lyc., Milt., Onc., Odont Oda., Phj., Pln Z., Vuyl. (Tables A-9, 10, 16)	Cattleya — Shoot meristem (Sagawa, Shoji, and Shoji, 1966) (Table A-17)	Cymbidium — Shoot tip cultures (Wimber, 1963) (Table A-18)	Cymbidium — Propagation in vitro (Fonnesbech, 1972a,b) (Table A-19)
1	Nitrogen, total (mmoles)	7.06	60.01	16.02	31.88	12.75	12.75	7.92
2	urea, NH_2CONH_2 (mmoles)							
3	ammonium, NH_4^+ (mmoles)		20.61	7.56	21.39	7.56	7.56	4.54
4	nitrate, NO_3^- (mmoles)	7.06	39.40	8.46	10.49	5.19	5.19	3.38
5	ammonium/nitrate ratio		0.52	0.89	2.04	1.46	1.46	1.34
6	Phosphorus, phosphate, PO_4^{---} (mmoles)	1.05	1.25	1.83	1.84	3.14	3.00	3.11
7	Potassium, K^+ (mmoles)	10.06	20.06	1.83	5.19	7.03	6.69	4.38
8	Sulfur, sulfate, SO_4^{--} (mmoles)	1.01	1.71	4.90	8.70	4.83	4.78	3.50
9	Calcium, Ca^{++} (mmoles)	0.51	2.99	4.23	2.12	1.95	1.50	1.69
10	Magnesium, Mg^{++} (mmoles)	1.01	1.50	1.01	1.01	1.01	1.01	1.01
11	Iron, chelated with EDTA (mmoles)		0.10					0.1
12	ferric, Fe^{+++} (mmoles)	0.004				0.19	0.24	
13	ferrous, Fe^{++} (mmoles)		0.10	0.09	0.09			0.1
14	Macroelements, total (mmoles)	20.70	87.72	29.91	50.83	31.76	29.97	21.71
15	Microelements, total (mmoles)	9.27	6.22	0.036	3.83	0.034		0.63
16	Aluminium, Al^{+++} (μmoles)	0.13						
17	Borate, BO_3^{---} (μmoles)	16.17	100.26	0.91				161.7
18	Chloride, Cl^- (μmoles)	1148.11	5985.54		3350.14			
19	Cobalt, Co^{+++} (μmoles)		0.11					
20	Copper, Cu^{++} (μmoles)	1.2	0.10	0.23				0.1
21	Iodine, I^- (μmoles)	0.06	5.00					
22	Manganese, Mn^{++} (μmoles)	0.05	99.99	33.63	33.63	33.63		112.11
23	Molybdenum, molybdic acid, MoO_3 (μmoles)			0.11				
24	molybdate, MoO_4^{---} (μmoles)		0.10					1
25	Nickel, Ni^{++} (μmoles)	0.13						
26	Sodium, Na^+ (μmoles)	8101.34	0.20					2
27	Zinc, Zn^{++} (μmoles)	3.47	31.30	1.15				347.8
28	Minerals, total including urea (mmoles)	29.97	93.94	29.95	54.21	31.79	29.97	22.34
29	Hormones, total (μmoles)	7.31	11.89		1.54			11
30	Auxins, total (μmoles)	4.53	11.42		0.54			10
31	IAA—indoleacetic acid (μmoles)		11.42					
32	IBA—indolebutyric acid (μmoles)							
33	2,4-D—2,4-dichlorophenoxyacetic acid (μmoles)							
34	NAA—naphthaleneacetic acid (μmoles)	4.53			0.54			10
35	IAA/IBA or IBA/NAA ratio							
36	Antiauxin, trans-cinnamic acid (mmoles)							
37	Cytokinins, total (μmoles)	2.78	0.43		1			1
38	BA-benzyl adenine (μmoles)	2.78						
39	Ki-kinetin (μmoles)		0.47		1			1
40	Gibberellic acid, GA_3 (μmoles)							
41	Auxin/cytokinin ratio	1.63	24.30		0.54			10
42	Auxin/gibberellin ratio							
43	Cytokinin/gibberellin ratio							
44	Auxin/cytokinin/gibberellin ratio							
45	Polyols, total (μmoles)		555.06					555.06
46	inositol (μmoles)		555.06					555.06
47	Amino acids, total (μmoles)				187.83			26.64
48	asparagine (μmoles)				88.12			
49	glutamic acid (μmoles)				99.71			
50	glycine (μmoles)							26.64
51	asparagine/glutamic acid ratio				0.90			
52	Vitamins, total (μmoles)	2.97	1.19					12.03
53	Bi—biotin (μmoles)							
54	FA—folic acid (μmoles)							
55	Nc—niacin (μmoles)							
56	Pa—pantothenate, calcium (μmoles)							8.12
57	Py—pyridoxine (μmoles)							
58	Th—thiamine (μmoles)	2.97	1.19					2.43
59	Nc/Py/Th/Bi/FA/Pa ratio (Nc = 1)							1.48
60	Nc/Py/Th ratio (Nc = 1)							1/0.3/0.8
61	Nucleotides and nucleic acids, total (mmoles)							
62	Cyt-cytidylic acid (mmoles)							
63	Gua-guanylic acid (mmoles)							
64	Cyt/Gua ratio							
65	Organic acids, total (μmoles)					285	0.36	
66	citric acid (μmoles)							
67	tartaric acid (μmoles)					285	0.36	
68	Sugar, sucrose (mmoles)	87.64	87.64	58.43	58.43	58.43	58.43	87.64—116.88
69	All components, total (mmoles)	117.62	182.15	88.38	112.83	90.51	88.76	110.6—139.8
70	Concentration ranking of medium (least conc. = 1)	20	27	10	18	13	11	1% or 22
71	Agar, grams (omit from liquid media)	10	10	12—15	15—20	16		8
72	Complex and other additives			ripe banana			tryptone	csmino acids, trpt, ccnt wtr
73	Light intensity	150 f-c	150 f-c	150 f-c	100—180 f-c	120 f-c	100 f-c	3.3 W/m²
74	Photoperiod (hours)	18	18	18	12	continuous	continuous	
75	Temperature (°C)	22—25	22—25	22—25	22	22—25	22	22—25
76	Agitation	60 oscil					rotation	vertical wheel
77	pH	5.3.	5.5.	5.3	5.3	5.0—5.5	5.2—5.5	5.5

No.	Component	Dendrobium — Shoot tips (Sagawa and Shoji, 1967) Table A-17 (modif.)	Dendrobium — Node cultures (Mosich, Ball, and Arditti, 1973, 1974) Initial Table A-21	Dendrobium — Node cultures Rooting Table A-22	Dendrobium — Flower stalk cuttings (Singh and Sagawa, 1972) Table A-27	Epidendrum — Leaf tips (Churchill, Ball, and Arditti, 1970, 1973) Initial Table A-23	Epidendrum — Leaf tips Maintenance Table A-15	Epidendrum — Leaf tips Diff. Table A-16	Epidendrum — Root tips (Churchill, Ball, and Arditti, 1972) Table A-24
1	Nitrogen, total (mmoles)	12.15	5.46	60.01	12.15	60.01	60.01	16.02	2.72
2	urea, NH_2CONH_2 (mmoles)								
3	ammonium, NH_4^+ (mmoles)	7.56		20.61	7.56	20.61	20.61	7.56	
4	nitrate, NO_3^- (mmoles)	5.19	5.46	39.40	5.19	39.40	39.40	8.46	2.72
5	ammonium/nitrate ratio	1.46		0.52	1.46	0.52	0.52	0.89	
6	Phosphorus, phosphate, PO_4^{---} (mmoles)	3.14	2.54	1.25	3.14	1.25	1.25	1.83	0.03
7	Potassium, K^+ (mmoles)	7.03	3.58	20.05	7.03	20.05	20.06	1.83	0.23
8	Sulfur, sulfate, SO_4^{--} (mmoles)	4.83	0.51	1.70	4.85	1.70	1.71	4.90	0.214
9	Calcium, Ca^{++} (mmoles)	1.95	2.11	2.99	1.95	2.99	2.99	4.23	0.58
10	Magnesium, Mg^{++} (mmoles)	1.01	0.51	1.50	1.01	1.50	1.50	1.01	0.195
11	Iron, chelated with EDTA (mmoles)		0.002	0.1		0.1	0.1		
12	ferric, Fe^{+++} (mmoles)	0.19	0.03		0.19	0.1	0.1	0.09	0.0125
13	ferrous, Fe^{++} (mmoles)			0.1					
14	Macroelements, total (mmoles)	31.76	14.74	87.72	31.76	87.72	87.72	29.91	3.982
15	Microelements, total (mmoles)	0.034	0.006	6.24	0.034	6.24	6.22	0.036	0.016
16	Aluminium, Al^{+++} (µmoles)								
17	Borate, BO_3^{---} (µmoles)		0.91	100.26		100.26	100.26	0.91	0.32
18	Chloride, Cl^- (µmoles)		3.21	6000		6000	5985.54		10.10
19	Cobalt, Co^{+++} (µmoles)		0.11	0.11		0.11	0.11		
20	Copper, Cu^{++} (µmoles)		0.32	0.1		0.1	0.1	0.23	
21	Iodine, I^- (µmoles)			5		5	5		0.12
22	Manganese, Mn^{++} (µmoles)	33.63	0.18	99.99	33.63	99.99	99.99	99.99	5.05
23	Molybdenum, molybdic acid, MoO_3 (mmoles)							0.11	
24	molybdate, MoO_4^{--} (µmoles)		0.18	0.1		0.1	0.1		
25	Nickel, Ni^{++} (µmoles)			0.2					
26	Sodium, Na^+ (µmoles)		0.2				0.2		
27	Zinc, Zn^{++} (µmoles)		0.11	28.83		28.83	31.30	1.15	0.07
28	Minerals, total including urea (mmoles)	31.79	14.75	93.96	31.79	93.96	93.94	29.95	3.998
29	Hormones, total (µmoles)			0.57		7.31	11.89		
30	Auxins, total (µmoles)			0.57		4.53	11.42		
31	IAA—indoleacetic acid (µmoles)			0.57			11.42		
32	IBA—indolebutyric acid (µmoles)								
33	2,4-D—2,4-dichlorophenoxyacetic acid (µmoles)								
34	NAA—naphthaleneacetic acid (µmoles)								
35	IAA/IBA or IBA/NAA ratio								
36	Antiauxin, *trans*-cinnamic acid (mmoles)		0.01–1.0						
37	Cytokinins, total (µmoles)					2.78	0.47		
38	BA-benzyl adenine (µmoles)					2.78			
39	Ki-kinetin (µmoles)						0.47		
40	Gibberellic acid, GA (µmoles)								
41	Auxin/cytokinin ratio					1.63	24.30		
42	Auxin/gibberellin ratio								
43	Cytokinin/gibberellin ratio								
44	Auxin/cytokinin/gibberellin ratio								
45	Polyols, total (µmoles)			555.06			555.06		
46	inositol (µmoles)			555.06			555.06		
47	Amino acids, total (µmoles)					26.64			
48	asparagine (µmoles)								
49	glutamic acid (µmoles)								
50	glycine (µmoles)					26.64			
51	asparagine/glutamic acid ratio								
52	Vitamins, total (µmoles)			1.19		1.19	1.19		6.79
53	Bi—biotin (µmoles)								
54	FA—folic acid (µmoles)								
55	Nc—niacin (µmoles)								4.06
56	Pa—pantothenate, calcium (µmoles)								2.43
57	Py—pyridoxine (µmoles)								
58	Th—thiamine (µmoles)			1.19		1.19	1.19		0.30
59	Nc/Py/Th/Bi/FA/Pa ratio (Nc = 1)								
60	Nc/Py/Th ratio (Nc = 1)								1/0.6/0.074
61	Nucleotides and nucleic acids, total (mmoles)								
62	Cyt-cytidylic acid (mmoles)								
63	Gua-guanylic acid (mmoles)								
64	Cyt/Gua ratio								
65	Organic acids, total (µmoles)	285	0.03		285				
66	citric acid (µmoles)		0.03						
67	tartaric acid (µmoles)	285			285				
68	Sugar, sucrose (mmoles)	58.43	58.43	87.64	58.43	87.64	87.64	58.43	58.43
69	All components, total (mmoles)	90.51	73.2–74.2	182.15	90.51	181.63	182.15	88.38	62.44
70	Concentration ranking of medium (least conc. = 1)	13	6 or 7	27	13	25	27	10	4
71	Agar, grams (omit from liquid media)	8	13	13	9	10–15	10	12–15	10–15
72	Complex and other additives	ccnt wtr						ripe banana	peptone
73	Light intensity	200 f-c	150 f-c	150 f-c	200 f-c	150 f-c	150 f-c	150 f-c	150 f-c
74	Photoperiod (hours)	continuous	16	16	continuous	18	16–18	16–18	16–18
75	Temperature (°C)	23–29	22–25	22–25	23–29	22–25	22–25	22–25	22–25
76	Agitation	160 RPM				60 oscil			
77	pH	5.3	5.5	5.5–5.8	4.8–5.0	5.5	5.5	5.3	5.1

Table A-30 continued

No.	Component	Phalenopsis flower stalk cuttings (Intuwong, Kunisaki, and Sagawa, 1972)	Rhynchostylis gigantea (Vajrabhaya and Vajrabhaya, 1970)	Vanda: Shoot tips of terete and strap-leaf types (Kunisaki, Kim, and Sagawa, 1972; Teo, Kunisaki, and Sagawa, 1973) Initial	Proliferation	Diff.	Stem cultures (Sagawa, and Seghal, 1967)
		Table A-27	Table A-28	Table A-27	Table A-27	Table A-27	Tables A-17, 27
1	Nitrogen, total (mmoles)	12.15	11.80	12.15	12.15	12.15	12.15
2	urea, NH_2CONH_2 (mmoles)						
3	ammonium, NH_4^+ (mmoles)	7.56	7.56	7.56	7.56	7.56	7.56
4	nitrate, NO_3^{--} (mmoles)	5.19	4.24	5.19	5.19	5.19	5.19
5	ammonium/nitrate ratio	1.46	1.78	1.46	1.46	1.46	1.46
6	Phosphorus, phosphate, PO_4^{---} (mmoles)	3.14	1.84	3.14	3.14	3.14	3.14
7	Potassium, K^+ (mmoles)	7.03	5.19	7.03	7.03	7.03	7.03
8	Sulfur, sulfate, SO_4^{--} (mmoles)	4.85	4.79	4.85	4.85	4.85	4.85
9	Calcium, Ca^{++} (mmoles)	1.95.	2.12	1.95	1.95	1.95	1.95
10	Magnesium, Mg^{++} (mmoles)	1.01	1.01	1.01	1.01	1.01	1.01
11	Iron, chelated with EDTA (mmoles)		0.1				
12	ferric, Fe^{+++} (mmoles)	0.19		0.19	0.19	0.19	0.19
13	ferrous, Fe^{++} (mmoles)						
14	Macroelements, total (mmoles)	31 76	26.85	31.76	31.76	31.76	31.76
15	Microelements, total (mmoles)	0.034	3.40	0.034	0.034	0.034	0.034
16	Aluminium, Al^{+++} (μmoles)						
17	Borate, BO_3^{---} (μmoles)		16.17				
18	Chloride, Cl^- (μmoles)		3374				
19	Cobalt, Co^{+++} (μmoles)		0.084				
20	Copper, Cu^{++} (μmoles)		0.059				
21	Iodine, I^- (μmoles)						
22	Manganese, Mn^{++} (μmoles)	33.63	10.11	33.63	33.63	33.63	33.63
23	Molybdenum, molybdic acid, MoO_3 (μmoles)						
24	molybdate, MoO_4^{--} (μmoles)		0.083				
25	Nickel, Ni^{++} (μmoles)						
26	Sodium, Na^+ (μmoles)		0.166				
27	Zinc, Zn^{++} (μmoles)		0.35				
28	Minerals, total including urea (mmoles)	31.79	30.25	31.79	31.79	31.79	31.79
29	Hormones, total (μmoles)		0.54				
30	Auxins, total (μmoles)		0.54				
31	IAA—indoleacetic acid (μmoles)						
32	IBA—indolebutyric acid (μmoles)						
33	2,4-D—2,4-dichlorophenoxyacetic acid (μmoles)						
34	NAA—naphthaleneacetic acid (μmoles)						
35	IAA/IBA or IBA/NAA ratio		0.54				
36	Antiauxin, trans-cinnamic acid (mmoles)						
37	Cytokinins, total (μmoles)						
38	BA-benzyl adenine (μmoles)						
39	Ki-kinetin (μmoles)						
40	Gibberellic acid, GA_3 (μmoles)						
41	Auxin/cytokinin ratio						
42	Auxin/gibberellin ratio						
43	Cytokinin/gibberellin ratio						
44	Auxin/cytokinin/gibberellin ratio						
45	Polyols, total (μmoles)						
46	inositol (μmoles)						
47	Amino acids, total (μmoles)		99.91				
48	asparagine (μmoles)						
49	glutamic acid (μmoles)						
50	glycine (μmoles)		99.91				
51	asparagine/glutamic acid ratio						
52	Vitamins, total (μmoles)		12.64				
53	Bi—biotin (μmoles)						
54	FA—folic acid (μmoles)						
55	Nc—niacin (μmoles)		10.15				
56	Pa—pantothenate, calcium (μmoles)		0.53				
57	Py—pyridoxine (μmoles)		1.22				
58	Th—thiamine (μmoles)		0.74				
59	Nc/Py/Th/Bi/FA/Pa ratio (Nc = 1)						
60	Nc/Py/Th ratio (Nc = 1)						
61	Nucleotides and nucleic acids, total (mmoles)						
62	Cyt-cytidylic acid (mmoles)						
63	Gua-guanylic acid (mmoles)						
64	Cyt/Gua ratio						
65	Organic acids, total (μmoles)	285		285	285	285	285
66	citric acid (μmoles)						
67	tartaric acid (μmoles)	285		285	285	285	285
68	Sugar, sucrose (μmoles)	58.43	58.43	58.43		29.2–58.43	58.43
69	All components, total (mmoles)	90.51	88.79	90.51	32.08	61.3–90.5	90.51
70	Concentration ranking of medium (least conc. = 1)	13	12	13	1	2 or 13	13
71	Agar, grams (omit from liquid media)	9	6	8		8	8
72	Complex and other additives		ccnt wtr, tr'pt	ccnt wtr	ccnt wtr	ccnt wtr	
73	Light intensity	200 f-c	2000–3000 lux	200 f-c	200 f-c	200 f-c	200 f-c
74	Photoperiod (hours)	continuous	14	continuous	continuous	continuous	continuous
75	Temperature (°C)	23–29	24–27	23–29	23–29	23–29	23–29
76	Agitation				160 RPM		
77	pH	4.8–5.0	5.2–5.5	4.8–5.0	4.8–5.0	4.8–5.0	4.8–5.0

has also been reported to increase in a stationary liquid medium (Kako, 1973). Therefore, in trying to culture a new species or genus, it may be best to try stationary and agitated liquid media as well as solid ones.

Illumination. Considerable differences exist in the light intensities used for orchid tissue cultures. The range is from darkness through less than 100 ft-candles to as much as 2000 (Table A-30, item 73). In this respect, it is important to keep in mind that the foot-candle is a unit which measures brightness of light relative to the human eye, not energy levels. Therefore, different amounts of energy may be provided by sources of similar foot-candle intensity or vise versa; it all depends on the light source. And the light sources used do vary a great deal. Watts per area—W/m², for example (Fonnesbech, 1972a)—is one good way to measure and express light intensity.

General Electric Power Groove white lamps (Teo, Kunisaki, and Sagawa, 1973) Sylvania Gro Lux tubes plus incandescent bulbs (Churchill, Ball, and Arditti, 1973), Atlas Super Gro, Osram-L-Fluora 77 (Fonnesbech, 1972a), and Philips fluorescent lights (Vajrabhaya and Vajrabhaya, 1970) have all been used. Data on controlled comparisons are not available. However, since different species have been cultured under various light sources in several laboratories, it seems safe to assume that light quality or intensity is not of overiding or critical importance as long as they are kept within certain broad limits.

Photoperiods (Table A-30, item 74) also vary from none at all (i.e., complete darkness; Morel, 1971a) to continuous illumination (Wimber, 1963). Altogether, it it seems that a broad spectrum exists for photoperiods as it does for light intensity.

Light periods of 12–18 hr and intensities of 100–200 ft-candles, about 150 μW/cm² or 2000–3000 lux, seem to be suitable for most species. In other words, orchid tissues grow well under illumination which is also suitable for seed germination and seedling development (Arditti, 1967a).

pH. Most media used for orchid tissue culture are in the pH range of 5.0–5.5. Only one has a pH of 4.8–5.0 (Table A-30, item 77). Since acidity may change with autoclaving, some media are adjusted to pH 5.6–5.9 before sterilization. On the whole, it seems that the pH requirements of all orchids cultured to date are similar. In general, the pH of tissue-culture media is similar to that used for orchid seed germination (Arditti, 1967a).

Temperature. All reports (Table A-30, item 75) are that cultures are maintained at 22–29° C (24 ± 2° to 26 ± 3°). The extremes for germinating seeds are 6–40° C, with the optimum in the same range as that for tissue cultures (Arditti, 1967a).

Seed Germination and Tissue Culture. The available data (Table A-30, items 71–75, 77) suggest that the conditions for tissue culture are very similar to those used for seed germination (Arditti, 1967a). Therefore, in developing procedures for tissue culture of additional species, it may be advisable to start with the conditions used for seed germination of the same orchid.

Media Components

Some media used for orchid tissue culture contain many components; others are simpler. In either case, concentrations and chemical forms of the components vary considerably. Therefore, comparisons can be made only after all concentrations are converted into molarities, millimoles (mmoles), or micromoles (μmoles). In addition, media contain components of defined chemical nature (salts, vitamins, hormones, amino acids, organic acids, nucleotides, nucleic acids and chelating agents), as well as complex, not entirely defined ones (peptone, tryptone, casein hydrolysate, yeast and/or potato extract, and green or ripe banana). The latter cannot be converted into molarities and the reasons for their effects are not entirely clear; thus comparisons with respect to them are possible only on a presence or absence basis (Table A-30, item 72). A general problem with all comparisons is, of course, the existence of very few controlled comparative studies where only one component is varied at a time.

Some workers obtain best results with one medium and keep using it for more than one species and various tissues. In other instances, several media are tested for each species or tissue and the one giving the best (or only positive) results is reported; others are not always listed. Still, the knowledge of which media work best with certain taxonomic groups (Table A-31) may be of importance during the development of culture media for additional genera and species.

Nitrogen. Several nitrogen sources and combinations seem to be satisfactory in general and for particular genera (Table A-30, items 1–5). Total nitrogen content varies from a low of 2.72 moles to a high of 60.01 mmoles (Table A-30, item 1). Nearly a ninefold variation exists between the media used for a single genus—*Cattleya*. Concentrations in media used for shoot-tip cultures vary between 12.75 and 31.88 mmoles. Ammonium:nitrate ratios (Table A-30, item 5) vary by a factor of nearly 10 (0.37–3.57) in all media, but also in those used for the *Cattleya* alliance.

Germinating seeds may require, or have a preference for, organic or ammonia nitrogen (Arditti, 1967a), but this does not appear to be the case with explants. Only one medium contains urea (Table A-30, item 2) and some include only nitrate (Table A-30, item 4). Thus, no correlations can be made from the available data. It is possible that the optimum covers a wide range of sources, concentrations, and ratios. Or it may be that the requirements for, and effects of, nitrogen sources depend on, and/or are related to, other media components. Indeed, *Vanda* tissues, which are sensitive to nitrogen content, can withstand higher concentrations in the presence of kinetin (Payawal and de Guzman, 1972).

Phosphorus. Phosphate content (Table A-30, item 6) in media used for tissues other than roots (which grow in the very low concentration of 0.03 mmoles) varies from 0.92 to 3.14 mmoles (nearly a factor of four) for all orchids cultured or for a single genus—*Cattleya*. Concentrations of 1.84, 3.00, and 3.14 mmoles are all satisfactory for *Cymbidium* explants. As with nitrogen, comparisons and correlations do not appear possible.

Table A-31. Tissue culture media for orchids arranged taxonomically

	Media (Table number)	
Group	Used	Similar
Tribe Ophrydoideae		
Subtribe Platanthereae, *Anacamptis*	A-1	
Tribe Polychondroideae		
Subtribe Sobralieae, *Arundina*	A-3, A-4	
Tribe Kerosphaeroideae		
Series A, Acranthae		
Subtribe Coelogyneae, *Pleione*	Components from A-9, A-10, A-16	
Subtribe Laelieae, *xBrassocattleya, Cattleya, Epidendrum, Laelia, Schomburgkia*	A-1, A-7, A-8, A-12, A-16, A-22	A-24, A-17
Subtribe Dendrobieae, *Dendrobium*	A-17	A-6, A-12, A-24
Series B, Pleuranthae	A-21	A-1, A-22
Subseries A, Sympodiales		
Subtribe Phajeae, *Calanthe, Phajus*	Components from A-9, A-10, A-16	
Subtribe Cymbidieae, *Cymbidium*		
Subtribe Zygopetaleae, *Lycaste, Zygopetalum*	A-25, A-26	
Subtribe Oncidieae, *Miltonia, Oncidium, Odontoglossum, xOdontonia, xVuylstekeara*[a]		
Subseries B, Monopodiales		
Subtribe Sarcantheae		
Section Sarcochilinae, *Phalaenopsis*	A-24	A-6, A-12, A-17
Rhynchostylis	A-25	
Section Vandinae, *Vanda*	A-24, A-17	A-6, A-12
Section Vandinae × Saccolabiinae, *xAscofinetia*[a]		
Section Vandinae × Sarcochilinae, *xVascostylis*[a]	A-6	A-12, A-17, A-24
Section Saccolabiinae × Sarcochilinae, *xNeostylis*[a]		

[a] Hybrid genera:
xAscofinetia-Neofinetia × *Ascocentrum*
xBrassocattleya-Brassavola × *Cattleya*
xNeostylis-Neofinetia × *Rhynchostylis*
xOdontonia-Odontoglossum × *Miltonia*
xVascostylis-xAscocenda (Ascocentrum × *Vanda)* × *Rhynchostylis*
xVuylstekeara-Cochlioda × *Miltonia* × *Odontoglossum* (Miltonioda; Odontonia)

Potassium, Sulfur, Calcium, Magnesium, and Total Macroelements. Large variations exist (Table A-30, items 7–14) and correlations do not appear possible. The apparent uniformity of requirements of *Vanda, Ascofinetia, Neostylis, Vascostylis,* and *Phalaenopsis* (all Pleuranthae, Monopodiales, Sarcantheae) may well be due to preference by Dr. Sagawa's laboratory. The same medium or very similar media are used in that laboratory for *Cattleya, Epidendrum,* and *Schomburgkia* (Acranthae, Laelieae), *Dendrobium* (Acranthae, Dendrobieae), and *Cymbidium* (Pleuranthae, Sympodiales, Cymbidieae). The reason for this preference is very logical: this medium works. In contrast with these similarities stand the different requirements of *Cattleya* and *Epidendrum* (both Acranthae, Laelieae) leaf tips (Table A-30, A-31). Several media were tried in both cases but each species formed callus cultures on a different solution. *Cattleya* leaf tips did not proliferate and formed a single plantlets on a solid medium similar to the Knudson

C (Tables A-9, A-16), Vacin and Went (Tables A-6, A-12, A-17, A-27) and Wimber (Table A-18) media (Ball, Arditti, and Churchill, 1971; Churchill, Ball, and Arditti, 1970, 1972, 1973).

Iron. As with media used for seed germination (Arditti, 1967a), ferric tartrate or citrate is employed in some tissue-culture solutions to overcome solubility problems (in formulations prepared before the advent of chelating agents). Inorganic ferric or ferrous salts (sulfate and chloride) are used in other media. More recently, the tendency has been to add chelated iron (Fonnesbech, 1972a; Vajrabhaya and Vajrabhaya, 1970) or to combine an inorganic salt with EDTA (Table A-30, items 11–13). Therefore, comparisons, if they are to be meaningful, must be between citric- and tartaric-acid salts, iron citrate or tartrate vs. the inorganic forms, chlorides against sulfates, and ferrous against ferric ions. Fortunately, this is possible for a single genus (*Cattleya*) and suggests that, at least in the media used, the form in which iron is supplied does not seem to make much difference. Ferric citrate, tartrate, or chloride (as well as two forms of sulfate with or without chelating agents) and ferrous sulfate are both suitable for *Cymbidium.* The monopodial Sarcantheae (*Phalaenopsis, Rhynchostylis, Vanda,* and the intergeneric hybrids) grow equally well on ferric tartrate or chelated iron (Table A-30, items 11, 12, 67). Citric and tartaric acid themselves seem to have no effect in the concentrations used (Table A-30, items 65–67).

What happens to the iron in tissue-culture media is not exactly clear. It is possible that some of it may become insoluble, forming ferrous phosphate, $Fe(PO_4)_2$, as in seed-germination media (Arditti, 1967a), but sufficient amounts probably remain available. Or enough iron may be released owing to solubility equilibria as a result of uptake by the tissue. This process may be slow, but orchid metabolism and tissue growth are not very fast either.

Microelements. Some media contain no purposefully added microelements, while others are enriched with few or several of them (Table A-30, items 15–27). Variations exist in media used for one or a number of genera and groups (Table A-30, items 15–27; Table A-31). As a result, an argument could be advanced that like seeds (Arditti, 1967a), orchid explants do not really require microelements. To say the least, this is highly unlikely and most improbable. The most plausible explanation is the one advanced for seed media, i.e., that enough impurities are available in the agar, other salts, and the glass of culture vessels to satisfy the needs of explants.

Total Mineral Content. Macroelements (Table A-30, items 1–14), microelements (Table A-30, items 15–27), and total elements (Table A-30, item 28) for tissues other than roots range from 10.74 to 93.96 mmoles (nearly a factor of nine). Considerable variations exist between media used for the same or different genera (Tables A-30, A-31). The few similarities could be due to preferences by investigators, although the fact that some media are better than others may indicate that their composition is more appropriate.

Content in the medium used for root culture is a very low, 3.998 mmoles, but still higher than the 0.667 mmoles found in effluates of orchid-supporting tree trunks (Arditti, 1967a; Curtis, 1946).

Auxins. Not all media include auxins (Table A-30, items 30–35). Those that do contain indoleacetic (IAA), indolebutyric (IBA), 2,4-dichlorophenoxyacetic (2,4-D), or naphthaleneacetic (NAA) acid. A few media contain combinations of two auxins (Table A-30, item 35). Concentrations vary considerably (Table A-30, item 30) and auxins are used in initial, maintenance, or differentiation media. Most of the auxin-containing media are used for the culture of Laeliaea and Sympodiales (Tables A-30, A-31). In the case of *Dendrobium*, auxin is added only to the rooting medium (Tables A-21, A-30, A-31). IAA when used alone has no effect on *Cymbidium* tissues. NAA is toxic at 1 mM concentration, but 10 μmoles/liter produce optimal fresh weight and vigorous protocorm-like bodies (Fonnesbech, 1972a). When 2,4-D is used at 1 μmole/liter, weight increases are high but the protocorm-like bodies are abnormal. Both NAA and 2,4-D are inhibitory at higher concentrations (Fonnesbech, 1972a). Optimal concentrations of NAA or 2,4-D for *Cattleya* are 0.1 ppm (Ichihashi and Kako, 1973). *Vanda* tissues form roots on 1.25 ppm NAA (Payawal and de Guzman, 1972). Care should be exercised with 2,4-D since it may cause mutations.

Antiauxins. On the assumption that *Dendrobium* buds are inhibited by high auxin content owing to apical dominance, *trans*-cinnamic acid (tCA), an antiauxin, was added to initial culture media (Tables A-21; A-30, item 36; A-31). Depending on bud age, different concentrations are required, but there is no growth in the absence of tCA. The high antiauxin concentration apparently inhibits root formation, since only shoots develop. To induce root initiation, the shoots must be transferred to an auxin-containing rooting medium (Tables A-22, A-30, A-31).

Cytokinins. Only some media contain cytokinins (Table A-30, items 37–39). These media are used for the culture of Laelieae, Dendrobieae (both Acranthea), and all sympodial Pleuranthae (Table A-20). In liquid media, kinetin promotes callus formation and increases in fresh weight. On solid media, 100 μmoles/liter kinetin induce formation of numerous small shoots without affecting the fresh weight. Benzyl adenine acts like kinetin but at lower concentrations (Fonnesbech, 1972a). At 100 μmoles/liter, kinetin is slightly inhibitory and strongly so at 1 mmole. Root and shoot growth in *Cymbidium* are inhibited by all kinetin concentrations (Fonnesbech, 1972a). Benzyl adenine induces root growth (at 1 μmole) from the protocorm-like body itself rather than from shoot bases (Fonnesbech, 1972a). In *Vanda* cultures, 1–4 ppm kinetin enhance protocorm formation (Payawal and de Guzman, 1972).

Auxin:kinetin ratios vary considerably (Table A-30, item 41), and there are interactions between the two. Maximal fresh weights are obtained with a ratio of 10:1. However, the increases were not significantly better than those obtained with 1 or 10 μmoles NAA alone (Fonnesbech, 1972a). The two hormones together inhibit leaf and shoot growth initiated by GA_3 (Fonnesbech, 1972a). NAA and kinetin inhibit each other's effect in *Vanda* cultures (Payawal and de Guzman, 1972).

Gibberellic Acid. One medium contains GA_3 (Table A-30, item 40) in a 1:1:1 ratio with naphthaleneacetic acid and kinetin (Table A-30, items 42–44) and as only one third of all hormones present (Table A-30, item 29). GA_3 is used in a medium employed for *Cattleya* culture (Tables A-8, A-30), and since explants from this genus can be grown on gibberellic acid–free medium, it would be interesting to determine if this hormone is really required.

In *Cymbidium* cultures, GA_3 inhibits weight gains and reduces the number of protocorm-like bodies, but increases shoot growth (Fonnesbech, 1972a).

Polyol. Inositol, considered to be part of the Vitamin B_1 complex and one of the active principles in coconut water, is present in some media (Table A-30, items 45, 46), but there does not seem to be a real requirement for it. In *Cymbidium* cultures, 100 mg/liter improved growth over media lacking it, but the increase was not significant (Fonnesbech, 1972a).

Amino Acids. Glycine and glutamic acid are used most often (Table A-30, items 47–51), but asparagine is also included in some media (Table A-30, item 48). The total concentration of amino acids is generally low (Table A-30, item 47), and they provide only a small proportion of the total nitrogen (Table A-30, item 1 vs. item 47). Therefore, it is reasonable to assume that they satisfy specific requirements which are not very certain anyway. For example, not all culture media for *Cattleya* shoot tips contain amino acids. *Rhynchostylis* (Sarcantheae, Sarcochilinae), *Anacamptis* (Platanthreae), and all sympodial orchids are cultured on amino acids–containing media (Tables A-30, A-31).

Casamino acids (casein hydrolysate) and tryptone increase the growth of *Cymbidium* tissues, but their effect can be simulated to some extent with 300 mg/liter of glutamine (Fonnesbech, 1972b). In these cultures, asparagine was without effect and arginine was inhibitory. In contrast, arginine stimulates the growth of unripe *Cattleya* seeds and those of *Vanda*, whereas asparagine enhances the growth of *Cymbidium* seedlings (Arditti, 1967a).

Vitamins. Thiamine is used most often, but other vitamins have also been employed (Table A-30, items 52–60). In seedlings, the pyrimidine moiety of thiamine is sufficient alone and may be provided by the mycorrhizal fungus (Arditti, 1967a; Hijner and Arditti, 1973). In *Cymbidium* cultures, vitamins seem to be unnecessary despite a slight improvement in growth when niacin is present (Fonnesbech, 1972b). This vitamin may also be provided by mycorrhizal fungi (Hijner and Arditti, 1973), can be deficient in some orchids (Arditti, 1967b), and seems to be the only one of value in seed germination and seedling cultures (Arditti, 1967a; Noggle and Wynd, 1943).

Purines and Pyrimidines. Adenine sulfate, guanosine-2′,3′-monophosphate, cytidine-5′-monophosphate, and uridine-5′-monophosphate are without effect in *Cymbidium* cultures (Fonnesbech, 1972b).

Nucleotides and Nucleic Acids. Only one medium (used for the culture of *Cattleya* explants) contains cytidylic, guanylic, and ribonucleic acids (Table A-30, items 61–64). Since *Cattleya* tissues grow well on media which do not contain these additives, it is possible that requirements for them are not absolute. A medium used for *Arundina* also contains RNA (Mitra, 1971).

Sugar. Sucrose is generally used (Table A-30, item 68). Concentrations are mostly 84.64 mmoles or 58.43 mmoles per liter. Only 1.46 mmoles are used in one *Cattleya* medium (Table A-7). *Vanda* tissues proliferate best in a sugar-free medium which contains coconut water (Table A-27). In fact, sucrose appears to be toxic in this case, for reasons which are not entirely clear. It would be interesting to determine whether other sugars (glucose or fructose, for example) or cold (filter) sterilized sucrose (11% of sucrose is hydrolyzed to glucose and fructose during autoclaving) would also be toxic, or if the toxicity is due to an osmotic effect.

Cymbidium is reported to grow better on sucrose than on maltose, glucose, fructose, or mannose (Fonnesbech, 1972b). Some seedlings grow well on mannose (Ernst, 1967b), and in other cases. fructose, glucose, maltose, and sucrose seem to be equally effective (Arditti, 1967a; Arditti, Healey, and Ernst, 1972; Arditti, and Healey, 1971). Thus it would seem that the subject is in need of further investigation, especially since sucrose is partially hydrolyzed during autoclaving and tissues or seedlings are, in fact, growing on a mixture of sucrose, glucose, and fructose.

Complex Additives. It is difficult to determine the reason for the effects of each complex additive (Table A-30, item 72; Table A-32). Many have been tested with seeds and seedlings (Arditti, 1967a, 1968a; Ernst, 1967a) and tissue cultures, but there is little consistency in the results. Even coconut water may be inhibitory or without significant effect (Fonnesbech, 1972b). Malt extract has no effect and that of yeast is inhibitory to *Cymbidium* cultures, as is the liquid endosperm of *Aesculus hippocastanum* (Fonnesbech, 1972b). Growth of *Cattleya*, *Dendrobium*, and *Vanda* are stimulated by 0.1–0.2% peptone (Morel, 1974).

Total Concentration of Media. Considerable differences exist in the total concentration of culture media (Table A-30, item 69). The most dilute media are used for *Vanda*. *Cattleya* shoot tips grow equally well on dilute or concentrated media. Leaf tips of *Cattleya* and *Epidendrum* and the resulting calli are cultured on the most concentrated solutions. When placed on a dilute medium, *Cattleya* leaf tips form a single protocorm-like body and later a plantlet, but do not proliferate (Churchill, Ball, and Arditti, 1973). There is no growth or callus formation from *Epidendrum* leaf tips placed on the same medium.

General Comments. The available information is clearly insufficient (Tables A-30, A-31), mainly because there are not enough comparative reports. What can be stated is that (1) culture medium requirements of orchids vary, (2) several media can be

Table A-32. Typical analyses of complex additives and agar used in orchid culture media[a]

	Complex additives				Agar		
	Casamino acids	Peptone	Tryptone	Yeast extract	Bacto	Noble	Purified
Percent:							
Ash	3.64	3.53	7.28	10.1	4.50	2.60	1.75
Ether soluble extract		0.37	0.30				
Total nitrogen	11.15	16.16	13.14	9.1	0.17	0.10	0.14
Primary proteose nitrogen		0.60	0.20				
Secondary proteose nitrogen		0.68	1.63				
Peptone nitrogen		15.38	11.29				
Ammonia nitrogen		0.04	0.02				
Free amino nitrogen		3.20	4.73				
Amide nitrogen		0.49	1.11				
Mono-amino nitrogen		9.42	7.31				
Di-amino nitrogen		4.07	3.45				
Arginine	3.8	8.0	3.3	0.7			
Aspartic acid	0.49	5.9	6.4	5.1			
Cystine		0.22	0.19				
Glutamic acid	5.1	11.0	18.9	6.5			
Glycine	1.1	23.0	2.4	2.4			
Histidine	2.3	0.96	2.0	0.9			
Isoleucine	4.6	2.0	4.8	21.9			
Leucine	9.9	3.5	3.5	3.6			
Lysine	6.7	4.3	6.8	4.0			
Methionine	2.2	0.83	2.4	0.7			
Phenylalanine	4.0	2.3	4.1	2.2			
Threonine	3.3	1.6	3.1	3.4			
Tryptophane	0.8	0.42	1.45	0.8			
Tyrosine	1.3	2.3	7.1	0.6			
Valine	7.2	3.2	6.3	3.4			
Organic sulphur		0.33	0.53				
Inorganic sulphur		0.29	0.04				
Sulfate					2.54	1.90	1.32
Phosphorus	0.35	0.079	0.75	0.8			
Barium					0.01	0.01	0.01
Iron	0.0006	0.0023	0.0071				
SiO_2	0.053	0.042	0.090				
Silica					0.19	0.26	0.09
Potassium	0.88	0.22	0.30				
Sodium	0.77	1.08	2.69	0.3			
Magnesium	0.0032	0.056	0.045				
Calcium	0.0025	0.058	0.096		0.13	0.23	0.27
Chlorine		0.27	0.29				
Chloride	11.2	0.27	0.29	0.1	0.43	0.18	0.13
Parts per million:							
Manganese	7.6	8.6	13.2	7.8			
Lead	4.0	15.00	6.00	16.0			
Arsenic	0.50	0.09	0.07	0.1			
Copper	10.00	17.00	16.00	19.0			
Zinc	8.00	18.00	30.00	88.00			
μg/g:							
Pyridoxine	0.73	2.5	2.6	20.0			
Biotin	0.102	0.32	0.36	1.4			
Thiamine	0.12	0.50	0.33	3.2			
Niacin	2.7	35.00	11.00	273.0			
Riboflavin	0.03	4.00	0.18	13.0			
Reaction, pH		7.00[b]	7.2[b]				

[a] Courtesy of Difco Laboratories, Detroit, Mich.
[b] Measured in 1% solution of distilled water after autoclaving 15 min at 121°C.

suitable for one genus, and (3) more than one genus can be cultured on a specific medium. This is really not stating very much. Still, it is the best under the circumstances.

CONCLUSION

Tissue culture is still something of an art. Selection of media is often based as much on intuition as on theoretical considerations, although in some instances, like the use of antiauxins, it is possible to make educated guesses based on previous experience. Success is often a matter of luck, or at least is not always based on hard work, perseverance, a fertile mind, manual dexterity, good intentions, and the other attributes which according to popular belief (or legend) help lead to the conquest of adversity and the overcoming of difficulties. Those who wish to develop procedures for additional orchids would be wise to start their quest (or odyssey) with a medium and conditions found suitable for a related species or genus.

ACKNOWLEDGMENTS

Our research in this area is supported in part by grants from the American Orchid Society, Emma D. Menninger, the Stanley Smith Horticultural Trust, the National Science Foundation, the Office of Naval Research (contract NR-108-796), and the California Federation of Women's Clubs. I thank Yoneo Sagawa, University of Hawaii, for his hospitality; Elaine D. Etingoff for putting the appendix together and typing it from bits of flimsy paper mailed from Indonesia; Michael S. Strauss, C. M. Hanegraa, and Brigitta H. Flick for being generally helpful; and the Rod McClelan Orchid Co., Dos Pueblos Orchid Co., and the Universal Orchid Co. for donating plants.

This appendix was written during my sabbatical leave at Kebun Raya (Hortus Botanicus Bogoriensis), Bogor, Indonesia. Research at these famous Botanical Gardens has contributed many advances to orchidology through the years. Melchior Treub, an orchid embryologist of note; G. Tischler, who looked for statoliths; J. J. Smith, a famous systematist; F. A. F. C. Went, who studied the flowering stimulus of *Dendrobium crumenatum*; Hans Burgeff, of orchid mycorrhiza fame; and Hans Fitting, the great German plant physiologist who introduced the word "hormone" into plant physiology following his investigation of post-pollination in *Phalaenopsis*—all worked at Kebun Raya. It was appropriate that I should write about orchids at a place where so many great orchidologists have worked. I thank Dr. Didin S. Sastrapradja, Director, and Saleh Idris, M.Sc., Assistant Director, for providing me with the conditions and comforts necessary for writing, as well as a laboratory where I could work.

Notes to Appendix

The following information may be of assistance to those not experienced in the preparation of culture media.

Agar. Agar may vary depending on the source or batch. The differences may be in purity, mineral content, organic substances, or the amount required to solidify a medium. Bacto Agar (Difco Laboratories, Detroit, Mich.) is a commonly used brand in the United States. However, we have used other brands with equal success. Agar purchased in food stores (in Bogor, Indonesia, and also near Irvine and in Los Angeles, Calif.) may be suitable or even preferable in some instances. In general, it may be wise to test agar from a new source before using it in critical cases.

Auxins. See Hormones, below.

Banana. Banana homogenate can enhance the growth of orchid seedlings or plant-lets. No information is available on the reason(s) for this effect. Depending on the medium, the homogenate may be of fruits which are green, ripe, or intermediate. Growth enhancement may vary with the variety of banana used, but the differences are not large enough to justify concern. We generally use bananas (bought at the nearest food store) which are ripe or nearly so, but not ones which are very soft, overripe, and with large black patches on the skin.

A simple way to prepare the homogenate is to place the required weight of fruit tissue in a blender with an equal volume of distilled water. Homogenize until the tissue is completely disrupted. Add the homogenate to the medium and adjust the final volume as required with distilled water. Then check the pH and adjust it if necessary.

Banana-containing media can be autoclaved without loss of activity. They are slightly darker in color than media which do not contain banana. If the tissue is not sufficiently homogenized, it may settle to the bottom of the culture vessels. Should a precipitate form after autoclaving, its distribution may be improved by swirling the flasks when the agar has cooled but not yet solidified.

Casamino Acids. Casamino acids are acid hydrolized casein. Hydrolysis is continued until all nitrogenous substances in the casein are converted to amino acids or other relatively simple substances. The result is a complex mixture of a composition which may vary. Therefore, only "typical analyses" are available (Table A-32). Casamino acids can be autoclaved unless otherwise specified.

Clorox. Clorox is a product available in the United States. A variety of similar products are marketed under different brand names in various countries. They usually contain 5.25% sodium hypochlorite and are used as liquid bleaching agents.

Coconut Water. Coconut water (sometimes called coconut milk) is a liquid endo-sperm. It can enhance the growth of cells, tissues, or organs *in vitro*. Its exact compo-sition has not been determined, and the same is true regarding the reason(s) for its effect(s). Water from green coconut is preferable, but we have had reasonable success with liquid removed from relatively mature nuts purchased in local food stores. Unless otherwise specified, coconut water can be autoclaved.

Cytokinins. Cytokinins (kinetin, benzyl adenine, etc.) are soluble in dimethyl-sulfoxide (however, see Hormones, below).

Gibberellins. See Hormones, below.

Hormones. Hormones (auxins, cytokinins, gibberellins) are sparingly soluble or insoluble in water, and this may present a problem which can be solved in several ways. One possibility is to use their soluble salts (potassium salts of auxins, for example). Another is to dissolve them in ethyl alcohol (ethanol plus a few drops of dilute acid, if necessary—hydrochloric acid, for instance) or base (potassium hydroxide is suitable). We prefer ethanolic solutions because they also solve the problem of sterilizing these substances.

Many organic molecules, including plant hormones, are destroyed by autoclaving. Therefore, they must be sterilized by filtration, a process which is somewhat complicated and may require relatively sophisticated or expensive equipment. A simpler approach is to dissolve these in ethyl alcohol (at least 70% in distilled water), which is a good sterilant as well as a suitable solvent. Stock solutions prepared in this manner must be concentrated enough to allow for the addition of each hormone in 1 ml or less per liter of medium. Media are prepared as usual, but the hormones are omitted. They are added to the hot solution following autoclaving and mixed by swirling. The complete medium is then distributed into autoclaved culture vessels.

Iron. Iron presents a problem because it tends to precipitate in media. The addition of organic acids (citric, for example) alleviates the problem but does not solve it. These acids are used in media formulated before the advent of chelating agents such as EDTA. In this appendix, all media are presented as originally reported since I did not wish to modify them without prior testing. Therefore, the use of EDTA is not included in several tables. Those who wish to do so may modify these media by using an equal (i.e., equimolar) amount of iron as a chelate, which can be prepared by mixing sodium EDTA with $FeSO_4$ as listed in other tables, or by purchasing one of several chelated iron preparations now available on the market.

Neopeptone. Neopeptone is an enzymatically digested protein preparation. Its exact composition and reason(s) for positive activity are not known. The typical analysis of neopeptone differs from that of peptone (see below) and may vary with batches or manufacturers.

Peptone. Peptone is a water-soluble protein hydrolysate with a high amino acid content. Its composition may vary and only typical analyses are available (Table A-32). Differences may exist between peptones from various sources or batches.

Solutions. Solutions should always be prepared carefully using a sensitive balance and accurate volumetric glassware. Some of the substances used in culture media are very active and even what may appear to be a negligible error could prove to be significant.

Sterilization. Sterilization of tissues (actually surface decontamination), media, and working areas is very important since it eliminates organisms which contaminate cultures. Work areas can be sterilized by swabbing with alcohol or a hypochlorite solution (in the U.S., Clorox, Purex, or other commercial preparations of sodium hypochlorite are used). In addition, a sterilizing (UV) lamp can be employed.

Care must be taken in decontaminating tissues because the agent used may kill them. Since tissues may differ in their sensitivity, it is best to use recommended or proven procedures.

Media can be sterilized by autoclaving (in an autoclave or pressure cooker), but as pointed out above (see Hormones), some substances may be destroyed in the process. Therefore, media should not be sterilized by autoclaving unless it is known that this will not affect them deleteriously. Filter sterilization (or stock solutions in alcohol as indicated for hormones, above) should be used for substances or media that are damaged by autoclaving.

Stock Solutions. Weighing components of a medium can be time-consuming and subject to errors. Therefore, more concentrated solutions of some media components are prepared in many laboratories. These are called stock solutions. For example, if the recipe calls for 1 gram per liter(g/l) of magnesium sulfate, a stock solution containing 10 g/l can be prepared. Then, in making the medium, 100 ml (one tenth of a liter and therefore one tenth of the magnesium sulfate) of the stock solution is used. This is faster than weighing 1 g every time and also more accurate.

Storage. Storage of stock solutions should be under appropriate conditions. Solutions of some inorganic salts become contaminated with time. Therefore, it is best to prepare them fresh every few months or when they are no longer completely clear. Storage in a refrigerator or freezer can prolong the life of such solutions.

Solutions of organic substances in water must be kept frozen. Alcoholic solutions should be refrigerated. Since some organic substances may be affected by light, it is wise to keep these stock solutions in the dark. Autoclaved media should not be stored for excessively long periods.

Vitamins. Vitamins should generally be handled like hormones (even if their mode of action is different) when preparing stock solutions or sterilizing media (see above).

Yeast Extract. Yeast extract contains vitamins and other substances which may be required by tissues. It is the water extract of autolyzed yeast and may vary depending on the mode of preparation or batch.

Literature Cited

In a section bearing the same heading as this one, I wrote a few years ago (Arditti, 1967) that numerous articles are available on the subject of orchid seed germination. Some of them are excellent, others exceedingly poor. The same is true about articles on tissue culture and "meristeming" of orchids. Despite this I have made an effort to list all articles on the subject to ensure as complete a list of references as possible. Still, I may have inadvertently omitted some papers (in English or other languages) simply because they escaped my attention. I apologize for such omissions and hope to list them in an updated list in a future volume.

Anonymous. 1885. Buds out of place. Gard. Chron., Ser. 2, 25:249.

——. 1967. Mass multiplication for orchids. New Scientist 35:551.

Arditti, J. 1967a. Factors affecting the germination of orchid seeds. Bot. Rev. 33:1–97.

——. 1967b. Niacin biosynthesis in germinating xLaeliocattleya orchid embryos and young seedlings. Amer. J. Bot. 54:291–298.

——. 1968a. Germination and growth of orchids on banana fruit tissue and some of its extracts. Amer. Orchid Soc. Bull. 39:112–116.

——. 1968b. A flasking tool for orchids. Amer. Orchid Soc. Bull. 39:715–716.

——. 1972a. Professor Lewis Knudson und die asymbiotische Keimung von Orchideensamen: das fünfzigjährige Jubiläum. Die Orchidee 23:243–248.

——. 1972b. Professor Lewis Knudson and the asymbiotic germination of orchid seeds: the fiftieth anniversary. Amer. Orchid Soc. Bull. 41:899–904.

——. 1974. Seed germination and tissue culture of orchids. Proc. Sym. on Modern Methods in Propagation, Hybridizing and Culture of Orchids, Prague, p. 1–32.

Arditti, J., E. A. Ball, and M.-E. Churchill. 1971. Propagación clonal de orquideas utilizando apices de hojas. Orquideologia (Colombia) 6:113–117, 129–133, 135.

——. 1972. Propagación clonal de orquideas utilizando apices de hojas. Orquidea (Mexico) 2:290–300.

Arditti, J., E. A. Ball, and D. M. Reisinger. 1975. Cultivo de yemas del escapo floral: un metodo para la propagacion vegetativa de phalaenopsis. Orquidea (Mexico) 5:242–254.

Arditti, J., and A. S. Dunn. 1969. Experimental plant physiology. Holt, Rinehart and Winston, New York.

Arditti, J., P. L. Healey, and R. Ernst. 1972. The role of mycorrhiza in nutrient uptake of orchids. II. Extracellular hydrolysis of oligosaccharides by asymbiotic seedlings. Amer. Orchid Soc. Bull. 41:503–510.

Arditti, J., S. K. Mosich, and E. A. Ball. 1973. Dendrobium node cultures: a new means of clonal propagation. Aust. Orchid Rev. 38:175–179.

Ball, E. A. 1946. Development in sterile culture of stem tips and subadjacent regions on Tropaeolum and Lupinus albus. Amer. J. Bot. 33:301–318.

Ball, E. A., J. Arditti, and M.-E. Churchill. 1971. Clonal propagation of orchids from leaf tips. Orchid Rev. 79:281–288.

Bergman, F. J. 1972a. Shoot tip multiplication of orchid clones, Part I. The status of "meristem" propagation through 1971. Amer. Hort. 51(2):20–23.

——. 1972b. Shoot tip multiplication of orchid clones, Part II. The status of "meristem" propagation through 1971. Amer. Hort. 51(3):41–44.

Bernard, N. 1899. Sur la germination du Neottia nidus-avis. C. R. Acad. Sci. Paris 128:1253–1255.

——. 1908. La culture des orchidées dans ses rapports avec la symbiose. Soc. Roy. Agric. et Bot. Gand 16. Also in J. Soc. Nat. Hort. France, 4th Ser., 24:180–185.

Bertsch, W. 1967. A new frontier: orchid propagation by meristem tissue culture. Amer. Orchid Soc. Bull. 36:32–38.

Bivins, J. L., and W. P. Hackett. 1969. The effect of medium and wounding techniques on aseptic culture of Cymbidium orchids from shoot apices. Plant Propagator 15:9–14.

Blowers, J. 1967. Mericlones at Vacherot and Lecoufle, France. Amer. Orchid Soc. Bull. 36:579–581.

Champagnat, M. 1971. Recherches sur la multiplication végétative de Neottia nidus-avis Rich. Ann. Sci. Nat., Bot. et Biol. Veg., Ser. 12, 12:209–247.

Champagnat, M., and G. Morel. 1969. Multiplication végétative des Cattleya à partir de bourgeons cultivées in vitro. Soc. Bot. Fr., Mémoires 116:111–132.

——. 1972. La culture in vitro des tissus de tubercules d'Ophrys. C. R. Acad. Sci. Paris 274:3379–3380.

Champagnat, M., G. Morel, P. Chabut, and A. M. Cognet. 1966. Recherches morphologiques et histologiques sur la multiplication végétative de quelques orquidées du genre Cymbidium. Rev. Gen. Bot. 73:706–746.

Champagnat, M., G. Morel, and G. Gambade. 1968. Particularités morphologiques et pourvoir de regénération du Cymbidium virescens cultivé in vitro. Soc. Bot. Fr., Mémoires 115:236–244.

Champagnat, M., G. Morel, and B. Mounetou. 1970. La multiplication végétative des Cattleya à partir de jeunes feuilles cultivées aseptiquement in vitro. Ann. Sci. Nat. Bot., Ser. 12, 11:97–113.

Churchill, M.-E., J. Arditti, and E. A. Ball. 1971. Clonal propagation of orchids from leaf tips. Amer. Orchid Soc. Bull. 40:109–113.

——. 1972. Propagacao clonal de orquideas à partir de apices de folha. Bol. Soc. Campineira de Orchideas 2:23–28.

Churchill, M.-E., E. A. Ball, and J. Arditti. 1970. Production of orchid plants from seedling leaf tips. Orchid Dig.:271–273.

——. 1972. Tissue culture of orchids. II. Methods for root tips. Amer. Orchid Soc. Bull. 41:726–730.

——. 1973. Tissue culture of orchids. I. Methods for leaf tips. New Phytol. 72:161–166.

Churchill, M.-E., B. H. Flick, E. A. Ball, and J. Arditti. 1971. Vermehrung von Orchideen durch Blattspitzen. Die Orchidee 22:147–151.

——. 1973. Kultur von Orchideengewebe. II. Methoden für Wurzelspitzen. Die Orchidee 24:98–101.

Curtis, J. T. 1946. Nutrient supply of epiphytic orchids in the mountains of Haiti. Ecology 27:264–266.

Erickson, L. C. 1957. Respiration and photosynthesis in Cattleya roots. Amer. Orchid Soc. Bull. 26:401–402.

Ernst, R. 1967a. Effects of select organic nutrient additives on growth in vitro of Phalaenopsis seedlings. Amer. Orchid Soc. Bull. 36:694–704.

——. 1967b. Effects of carbohydrate selection on the growth rate of freshly-germinated Phalaenopsis and Dendrobium seed. Amer. Orchid Soc. Bull. 36:1068–1073.

Ernst, R., J. Arditti, and P. L. Healey. 1971. Carbohydrate physiology of orchid seedlings. II. Hydrolysis and effects of oligosaccharides. Amer. J. Bot. 58:827–835.

Fast, G. 1973. Die Vermehrung von Oncidium papilio durch Triebspitzen-Kultur und Besprechung einiger Nährmedien. Die Orchidee 24:240–246.

Fonnesbech, M. 1972a. Growth hormones and propagation of Cymbidium in vitro. Physiol. Plant. 27:310–316.

——. 1972b. Organic nutrients in the media for propagation of Cymbidium in vitro. Physiol. Plant. 27:360–364.

Fréson, R., and N. Vanseveren. 1968. La propagation des orchidées par la méthode de culture des méristèmes "in vitro." Assoc. Nat. Professeurs Biol. de Belgique 14:86–94.

Gautheret, R.-J. 1959. La culture des tissus végétaux. Masson, Paris.

Goh, C. J. 1970. Tissue culture of Vanda Miss Joaquim. J. Singapore Nat. Acad. Sci. 2:31–33.

——. 1973. Meristem culture of Aranda Deborah. Malayan Orchid Rev. 11:10–14.

Gripp, P. 1966. Cymbidium propagation. Amer. Orchid Soc. Bull. 35:4–7.

Hahn, J. 1970. Die Vermehrung der Orchideen durch Meristemkultur. Zierpflanzenbau 10:508–516.

Harrison, C. R. 1968. A simple method for flasking orchid seeds. Amer. Orchid Soc. Bull. 39:715–716.

Harrison, C. R., and J. Arditti. 1970. Growing orchids from seed. Orchid Dig. 39:199–204.

Hijner, J. A., and J. Arditti. 1973. Orchid myocorrhiza: vitamin production and requirements by the symbionts. Amer. J. Bot. 60:829–835.

Holttum, R. E. 1964. Orchids of Malaya. 3d ed. Gov. Printing Press, Singapore.

Ichihashi, S., and S. Kako. 1973. Studies on clonal propagation of Cattleya through tissue culture methods. I. Factors affecting survival and growth of shoot meristem of Cattleya in vitro. J. Japan. Soc. Hort. Sci. 42:364–370.

Ilsley, P. 1965. Meristem tissue propagation techniques and potentials. Orchid Rev. 73:371–376.

——. 1966. Meristem tissue propagation techniques and potentials. Orchid Rev. 74:69.

Intuwong, O., J. T. Kunisaki, and Y. Sagawa. 1972. Vegetative propagation of Phalaenopsis by flower stem cuttings. Na Okika O Hawaii–Hawaii Orchid J. 1:13–18.

Intuwong, O., and Y. Sagawa. 1973. Clonal propagation of Sarcanthine orchids by aseptic culture of inflorescences. Amer. Orchid Soc. Bull. 42:209–215.

——. 1974. Clonal propagation of Phalaenopsis by shoot-tip culture. Amer. Orchid Soc. Bull. 43:893–895.

Ito, I. 1961. In vitro culture of ovary and seed in orchids. Mimeo. Olericulture Lab., Fac. Agric., Kyoto Prefectual Univ., Kyoto, Japan.

Jasper, B. 1966a. A method for meristem culture. Amer. Orchid Soc. Bull. 35:10–11.

——. 1966b. Mericlone propagation. Mimeo. Privately published.

Jessel, W. H., Jr. 1966. More on the meristem. Amer. Orchid Soc. Bull. 35:35–36.

Kako, S. 1973. Clonal propagation of Cattleya through shoot meristem culture. Japan Agric. Res. Quart. 7:109–115.

Kim, K.-K., J. T. Kunisaki, and Y. Sagawa. 1970. Shoot tip culture of Dendrobium. Amer. Orchid Soc. Bull. 39:1077–1080.

Knudson, L. 1921. La germinacion no simbiotica de las semillas de orquideas. Bol. Real Soc. Espanola Hist. Nat. 21:250–260.

——. 1922. Non-symbiotic germination of orchid seeds. Bot. Gaz. 73:1–25.

——. 1946. A new nutriet for the germination of orchid seeds. Amer. Orchid Soc. Bull. 15:214–217.

Kock, W. E. 1967. The meristem revolution and orchid patents. Amer. Orchid Soc. Bull. 36:125–126.

Kotomori, S., and T. Murashige. 1965. Some aspects of aseptic propagation of orchids. Amer. Orchid Soc. Bull. 34:484–489.

Kukulczanka, K. 1969. Sadzonki goździków wolne od wiruów. Owoce, Warsaw, Kwiaty 7:12–14.

——. 1970. Rozmnażanie storczyków z tkanek merystematycznych. Ogrodnictwo 1:18–22.

Kunisaki, J. T., K.-K. Kim, and Y. Sagawa. 1972. Shoot tip culture of Vanda. Amer. Orchid Soc. Bull. 41:435–439.

Leffring, L. 1968. Vermeerdering van orchideeën door midel van meristemcultuur. Med. Dir. Tuin. 31:392–395.

Lindemann, E. G. P. 1967a. Growth requirements for meristem culture of Cattleya. Diss. Abstr., Sect. B28:2284–2285.

——. 1967b. Growth requirements for meristem culture of Cattleya. Ph. D. diss., Rutgers Univ., University Microfilms, Ann Arbor, Mich.

Lindemann, E. G. P., J. E. Gunckel, and O. W. Davison. 1970. Meristem culture of Cattleya. Amer. Orchid Soc. Bull. 39:1002–1004.

Linsmaier, E. M., And F. Skoog. 1965. Organic growth factor requirements of tobacco tissue culture. Physiol Plant. 18:100–127.

Lis, E. 1970. Rozmnażanie storczyków metoda kultur merystemów pedowych. Postępy Nauk Rolniczych. 6:77–83

Marston, M. E. 1969. Vegetative propagation in vitro, p. 393–394. In W. J. Whittington (ed.), Root growth. Butterworth, London.

Marston, M. E., and P. Voraurai. 1967. Multiplication of orchid clones by shoot meristem culture. A review of the literature. Univ. Nottingham, Dept. Hort., Misc. Pub. No. 17:1–8.

Matsui, T., K. Kawai, and Y. Samata. 1970. Effects of N^6-benzylaminopurine and α-naphthalenacetic acid on the organogenesis of Cymbidium. Fac. Agric. Bull., Tamaga Univ. (Tokyo) 10:9–106.

Mitra, G. C. 1971. Studies on seeds, shoot tips and stem discs of an orchid grown in aseptic culture. Indian J. Exp. Biol. 9:79–85.

Morel, G. 1960. Producing virus-free cymbidiums. Amer. Orchid Soc. Bull. 29:495–497.

——. 1963. La culture in vitro du méristème apical de certaines Orchidées. C.R. Acad. Sci. Paris 256:4955–4957.

——. 1964a. Tissue culture—a new means of clonal propagation of orchids. Amer. Orchid Soc. Bull. 33:473–478.

——. 1964b. La culture in vitro du méristème apical. Rev. Cytol. Biol. Vég. 27:304–314.

——. 1965a. Clonal propagation of orchids by meristem culture. Cymbidium Soc. News 20:3–11.

——. 1965b. Eine neue Methode erbgleicher Vermehrung: die Kultur von Triebspitzen-Meristemen. Die Orchidee 16:165–176.

——. 1970. Neues auf dem Gebiet der Meristem-Forschung. Die Orchidee 20:433–443.

——. 1971a. Les "Pleiones." Culture-multiplication. L'Orchidophile 6:8–94.

——. 1971b. The principles of clonal propagation of orchids. Proc. 6th World Orchid Conf., Sydney (1969), p. 101–106.

——. 1974. Clonal multiplication of orchids, p. 169–222. In C. L. Withner (ed.), The orchids: scientific studies. Wiley-Interscience, New York.

Morel, G., and M. Champagnat. 1969. Diffèrent modes d' évolution de l'apex au cours de la formation de protocormes, C. R.2ème Congres Européen de L'Orchidée, Paris, p. 20–26.

Mosich, S. K., E. A. Ball, and J. Arditti. 1973. Propagacion clonal de Dendrobium por medio del cultivo de nodos. Orquidea (Mexico) 3:244–260.

——. 1974. Clonal propagation of Dendrobium by means of node cultures. Amer. Orchid Soc. Bull. 43:1055–1061.

Mosich, S. K., E. A. Ball, B. H. Flick, and J. Arditti. 1974. Klonvermehrung von Dendrobium durch die Kultivierung von Stammnodien. Die Orchidee 25:129–134.

Murashige, T. 1974. Plant propagation through tissue culture. Ann. Rev. Plant Physiol. 25:135–166.

Murashige, T., and F. Skoog. 1962. A revised medium for rapid growth and bioassays with tobacco tissue cultures. Physiol. Plant. 15:472–497.

Noggle, G. R., and F. L. Wynd. 1943. Effects of vitamins on germination and growth of orchids. Bot. Gaz. 104:455–459.

Ojima, K., and A. Fujiwara. 1962. Studies on the growth promoting substance of the excised wheat root. III. Effects of tryptophan and some related substances. Tohoku J. Agric. Res. 13:69–98.

Payawal, P. C., and E. V. de Guzman. 1972. Growth and organ formation in orchid tissue culture as influenced by growth regulators and the mineral composition of the media. Kalikasan, Philip. J. Biol. 1:155–166.

Penningsfeld, F. 1973. Meristem cultivation of orchids, a special form of hydroponics. Proc. International Working Group on Soilless Culture, Wageningen, p. 99–105.

Penningsfeld, F., and G. Fast. 1968. Untersuchungen zur Meristemkultur von Orchideen in Weihenstephan. Der Erwerbsgärtner–Die Deutsche Gartenbauwirtschaft 43:no pagination.

Raalte, D. van. 1967. Meristeemcultuur bij orchideeën. Vakblad Bloemist. 22:65.

Raghavan, V., and J. G. Torrey. 1964. Inorganic and nitrogen nutrition of the seedlings of the orchid Cattleya. Amer. J. Bot. 51:264–274.

Reichenbach, H. G., Fil. 1885. On the proliferous roots of orchids. The report on the orchid conference. J. Roy. Hort. Soc. 7:18.

Reinert, R. A., and H. C. Mohr. 1967. Propagation of Cattleya by tissue culture of lateral bud meristems. Proc. Amer. Soc. Hort. Sci. 91:664–671.

Reisinger, D. M., E. A. Ball, and J. Arditti. 1976. Clonal propagation of Phalaenopsis by means of flower-stalk node cultures. Orchid Rev. 84:45–52.

Rotor, G., Jr. 1949. A method for vegetative propagation of Phalaenopsis species and hybrids. Amer. Orchid Soc. Bull. 18:738–739.

Rudolph, M. J., E. A. Ball, and J. Arditti. 1972. Tissue culture of orchids. III. Does orthochlorophenoxyacetic acid select for or induce anthocyanin production? Amer. Orchid Soc. Bull. 41:1074–1078.

Rutkowski, E. 1967a. Reflections of a meristemmer. Amer. Orchid. Soc. Bull. 36:390–406.

——. 1967b. Letter. Amer. Orchid Soc. Bull. 36:38.

——. 1971. How meristems multiply. Amer. Orchid Soc. Bull. 40:616–622.

Sagawa, Y. 1961. Vegetative propagation of Phalaenopsis stem cuttings. Amer. Orchid Soc. Bull. 18: 808–809.

Sagawa, Y., and D. Niimoto. 1960. Vegetative propagation of Phalaenopsis. Florida Orchidist 3:22.

Sagawa, Y., and O. P. Sehgal. 1967. Aseptic stem propagation of Vanda xMiss Joaquim. Bull. Pacific Orchid Soc. Hawaii 25:17–18.

Sagawa, Y., and T. Shoji. 1967. Clonal propagation of dendrobiums through meristem culture. Amer. Orchid Soc. Bull. 36:856–859.

Sagawa, Y., T. Shoji, and T. Shoji. 1966. Clonal propagation of cymbidiums through shoot meristem culture. Amer. Orchid Soc. Bull. 35:118–122.

Sanguthai, O., S. Sanguthai, and H. Kamemoto. 1973. Chromosome doubling of a Dendrobium hybrid with colchicine in meristem culture. Na Okika O Hawaii–Hawaii Orchid J. 2(2):12–16.

Sanguthai, S., and Y. Sagawa. 1973. Induction of polyploidy in Vanda by colchicine treatment. Na Okika O Hawaii-Hawaii Orchid J. 2(2):17–19.

Scully, R. M., Jr. 1965. Stem propagation of Phalaenopsis. Bull. Pacific Orchid Soc. Hawaii 23:13–16.

——. 1966. Stem propagation of Phalaenopsis. Amer. Orchid Soc. Bull. 35:40–42.

——. 1967. Aspects of meristem culture in the Cattleya alliance. Amer. Orchid Soc. Bull. 36:103–108.

——. 1971. Master growers' series. February is Phalaenopsis time in Florida. Amer. Orchid Soc. Bull. 40:103–108.

Shechter, Y., and J. Arditti. 1972. The discovery of asymbiotic orchid seed germination. Orchid Rev. 80:147–152.

Singh, H., and Y. Sagawa. 1972. Vegetative propagation of Dendrobium by flower stalk cuttings. Na Okika O Hawaii–Hawaii Orchid J. 1:19.

Spoerl, E. 1948. Amino acids as sources of nitrogen for orchid embryos. Amer. J. Bot. 35:88–95.

Steward, F. C., and M. O. Mapes. 1971. Morphogenesis in aseptic cell cultures of Cymbidium. Bot. Gaz. 132:65–70.

Stokes, M. J. 1974. The in-vitro propagation of Dactylorchis fuchsii (Druce). Vermeul. Orchid Rev. 82: 62–65.

Taylor, R. L. 1967. The foliar embryos of Malaxis paludosa. Can. J. Bot. 45:1553–1556.

Teo, C. K. H., J. T. Kunisaki, and Y. Sagawa. 1973. Clonal propagation of strap-leafed Vanda by shoot-tip culture. Amer. Orchid Soc. Bull. 42:402–405.

Thompson, R. P. 1971. Excision of a Cymbidium meristem: photographed in color. Amer. Orchid Soc. Bull. 40:580–584.

Tischler, G. 1905. Über das Vorkommen von Statolithen bei wenig oder gar nicht geotropischen Wurzeln. Flora 94:1–69.

Tse, A. T.-Y., R. J. Smith, and W. P. Hackett. 1971. Adventitious shoot formation on Phalaenopsis nodes. Amer. Orchid Soc. Bull. 40:807–810.

Ueda, H., and H. Torikata. 1968. Organogenesis in meristem cultures of *Cymbidium*. I. Studies on the effects of growth substances added to culture media under continuous illumination. J. Japan. Soc. Hort. Sci. 37:240–248.

———. 1969a. Organogenesis in the meristem tissue cultures of cymbidiums. II. Effects of growth substances on the organogenesis in dark culture. J. Japan. Soc. Hort. Sci. 38:188–193.

———. 1969b. Organogenesis in meristem cultures of cymbidiums. III. Histological studies on the shoot formation at the rhizome tips of *Cymbidium goeringii* Reichb. f. culture *in vitro*. J. Japan. Soc. Hort. Sci. 38:262–266.

———. 1972. Effects of light and culture medium on adventitious root formation by Cymbidium in aseptic culture. Amer. Orchid Soc. Bull. 41:322–327.

Urata, U., and E. T. Iwanaga. 1965. The use of Ito-type vials for vegetative propagation of Phalaenopsis. Amer. Orchid Soc. Bull. 34:410–413.

Vacherot, M. 1966. Meristem tissue culture propagation of orchids. Proc. 5th World Orchid Conf., Long Beach, p. 23–26.

Vacin, E., and F. W. Went. 1949. Some pH changes in nutrient solutions. Bot. Gaz. 110:605–613.

Vajrabhaya, M., and T. Vajrabhaya. 1970. Tissue culture of Rhynchostylis gigantea, a monopodial orchid. Amer. Orchid Soc. Bull. 39:907–910.

———. 1974. Variation in Dendrobium arising in meristem, p. 231–242. Proc. 7th World Orchid Conf., Medellin, Colombia (1972), p. 231–242.

Werckmeister, P. 1970. Über die Lichtinduktion der geotropen Orientierung von Luft- und Bodenwurzeln in Gewebekulturen von Cymbidium. Ber. Dtsch. Bot. Ges. 83:19–26.

———. 1971. Light induction of geotropism and the control of proliferation and growth of Cymbidium in tissue culture. Bot. Gaz. 132:346–350.

White, P. R. 1943. A handbook of plant tissue culture. Jaques Cattell Press, Lancaster, Pa.

Wilfret, G. J. 1966. Formation of protocorm-like bodies on excised Cymbidium shoot tips. Amer. Orchid Soc. Bull. 35:823–827.

Wilkins, M. B. 1966. Geotropism. Ann. Rev. Plant Physiol. 17:379–408.

Wimber, D. E. 1963. Clonal multiplication of cymbidiums through tissue culture of the shoot meristem. Amer. Orchid Soc. Bull. 32:105–107.

———. 1965. Additional observations on clonal multiplication of cymbidiums through cultures of shoot meristem. Cymbidium Soc. News 20:7–10.

Additional Literature

The following uncited books and papers may be of interest. Some were published or came to my attention after the manuscript was typed. Others were added because they contain general information.

Butenko, R. G. 1964. Kul'tura izolirovannyhk ckaneri i fiziologia morfogeneze rastenii. Acad. Sci. U.S.S.R. K.A. Timiryasev Plant Physiol. Inst. Nanka, Moscow.

———. 1968. Plant tissue culture and plant morphogenesis. Published for the National Science Foundation by the Israel Program for Scientific Translation, Jerusalem.

Gautheret, R. J. 1959. La culture des tissus végétaux, techniques et realisations. Masson, Paris.

Homes, J. 1968. Aspects particuliers de la structure du velamen ches plantules de *Cymbidium* Sw. cultivées in vitro. Bull. Soc. Roy. Bot. Belgique 101:257–263.

Koch, L. 1974. Neues Verfahren zur Vermehrung von Orchideen-Protokormen. Der Erwerbsgärtner 29:732–734.

Lucke, E. 1974. Tendenzen der Orchideenvermehrung. Der Erwerbsgärtner 29:729–732.

Mullin, M. 1970. Tissue culture of monocotyledonous plants. Aust. J. Biol. Sci. 23:473–477.

Raalte, D. van. 1967. Meristemcultuur bij orchideeën. Vakblad voor de Bloemisteriÿ. 22:65.

Reisinger, D. M., E. A. Ball, and J. Arditti. 1976. Clonal propagation of Phalaenopsis by means of flower-stalk node cultures. Orchid Rev. (England) 84:45–52.

Stewart, J., and J. Button. 1975. Tissue culture studies in Paphiopedilum. Amer. Orchid Soc. Bull. 44:591–599.

——. 1976. Rapid vegetative multiplication of Epidendrum O'brienianum in vitro and in the greenhouse. Amer. Orchid Soc. Bull. 45:922–930.

Stokes, M. J., E. Thomas, and D. P. Holdgate. 1975. Notes on the aseptic propagation of members of the tribe Cyrpipedieae. Orchid Rev. (England) 83:136–137.

Street, H. E. (ed.). 1973. Plant tissue and cell culture. Univ. Calif. Press, Berkeley.

Tanaka, M., A. Hasagawa, and M. Goi. 1975. Studies on the clonal propagation of monopodial orchids by tissue culture. I. Formation of protocorm-like bodies from leaf tissue in *Phalaenopsis* and *Vanda*. J. Japan. Soc. Hort. Sci. 44:47–58.

Tran-Thanh-Van, M. 1974. Growth and flowering of Cymbidium buds normally inhibited by apical dominance. J. Amer. Soc. Hort. Sci. 99:450–453.

Ueda, H., and H. Torikata. 1970. Organogenesis in the meristem cultures of cymbidiums. IV. Study on cytokinin activity in the extracts. J. Japan. Soc. Hort. Sci. 39:104–107.

——. 1970. Organogenesis in the meristem cultures of cymbidiums. V. Anatomical and histochemical studies on phagocytosis in the mycorrhizome of *Cymbidium goeringii* Reichb. f. J. Japan. Soc. Hort. Sci. 39:50–54.

——. 1972. Effects of light and culture medium on adventitious root formation by cymbidiums in aseptic culture. Amer. Orchid Soc. Bull. 41:322–327.

Vanseveren, N. 1970. Note sure quelques aspects morphologiques et histologiques de plantules de *Cattleya* Lindl. à croisance anormale, obtenues par propagation méristématique *in vitro*. Bull. Soc. Roy. Bot. Belgique 103:11–17.

Vanseveren, N., and R. Freson. 1969. La multiplication des Orchidées par la mèthode de culture in vitro des méristèmes de tige. Bull. Nat. Belges 50:444–460.

Voraurai, P. 1968. Shoot tip culture of a Dendrobium hybrid. Doctoral thesis, Univ. of Nottingham, Great Britain.

INDEX OF PERSONS

Where only one name is given in the text or in footnotes or literature cited, initials or last names have been added by the indexers for identification. Initials were not added for individuals usually referred to in the botanical literature by their last names only (*i.e.*, Fuchs, Kircher, etc.).

This index was prepared in part by E. D. Etingoff.

INDEX OF PLANT NAMES

This index includes common, scientific, and regional names as well as other taxonomic designations. Scientific names (*Cattleya labiata*, for example) are italicized. All others appear in Roman type. Taxonomic groupings above the generic level are in capital letters. Boldface numerals denote illustrations.

SUBJECT INDEX

Boldface numerals indicate an illustration; italic numerals refer to chemical structures.

ORCHID BIOLOGY

Designed by R. E. Rosenbaum.
Composed by Syntax International Pte. Ltd.
in 11 point Monophoto Baskerville 169 and Helvetica 765,
with display lines in Baskerville and Helvetica.
Printed offset by Vail-Ballou Press, Inc.
on Warren's Patina Coated Matte, 70 pound basis.
Bound by Vail-Ballou Press in Joanna book cloth,
with stamping in All Purpose foils, and with Multicolor Laurel endpapers.
Color plates printed by Simpson/Milligan Printing Co., Inc.

Library of Congress Cataloging in Publication Data
(For library cataloging purposes only)

Main entry under title:
Orchid biology.

   Includes bibliographies and indexes.
   1. Orchids. I. Arditti, Joseph.
QK495.064053   1977   584'.15   76-25648
ISBN 0-8014-1040-1